Other Useful Constants

Name	Symbol	Value
Planck's constant	h	4.136×10^{-15} ev sec
Boltzmann's constant	k	8.617×10^{-5} ev/K°
Coulomb constant	$e^2/4\pi\epsilon_0$	14.42 ev Å
Electron rest energy	mc^2	0.5110 Mev
Proton rest energy	M_Pc^2	938.3 Mev
Energy equivalent of 1 amu	Mc^2	931.5 Mev
Electron magnetic moment	$\mu = e\hbar/2m$	0.9273×10^{-23} joule m^2/weber
Bohr radius	$a = 4\pi\epsilon_0\hbar^2/me^2$	0.5292×10^{-10} m
Electron Compton wavelength	$\lambda_c = h/mc$	2.426×10^{-12} m
Fine-structure constant	$\alpha = e^2/4\pi\epsilon_0\hbar c$	1/137.0
Classical electron radius	$r_e = e^2/4\pi\epsilon_0mc^2$	2.818×10^{-15} m
Rydberg constant	R_∞	1.097×10^{-7} m

Conversion Factors

$1 \text{ ev} = 1.602 \times 10^{-19}$ joule

$1 \text{ Å} = 10^{-10}$ m

$1 \text{ amu} = 1.661 \times 10^{-27}$ kg $\leftrightarrow 931.5$ Mev

Fundamentals

of Optics and

Modern Physics

McGraw-Hill Series

in Fundamentals

of Physics

INTRODUCTORY PROGRAM

E. U. Condon, Editor

FUNDAMENTALS OF MECHANICS AND HEAT
by Hugh D. Young

FUNDAMENTALS OF ELECTRICITY AND MAGNETISM
by Arthur F. Kip

FUNDAMENTALS OF OPTICS AND MODERN PHYSICS
by Hugh D. Young

FUNDAMENTALS OF OPTICS
in preparation

CONCEPTS OF MODERN PHYSICS, *revised edition*
by Arthur Beiser

Fundamentals of Optics and Modern Physics

HUGH D. YOUNG

Associate Professor of Physics
Carnegie-Mellon University

McGraw-Hill Book Company

NEW YORK   ST. LOUIS   SAN FRANCISCO   TORONTO   LONDON   SYDNEY

THIS VOLUME IN the Introductory Program of the McGraw-Hill Series in Fundamentals of Physics is devoted to a brief account of optics and to a fuller account of the basic ideas of quantum mechanics as applied to atomic and molecular structure, nuclear physics, solid-state physics, and the study of particles at high energy. The volume is designed to be used by itself or, more specifically, as the text for a third semester course following the study of Professor Hugh Young's *Fundamentals of Mechanics and Heat* and Professor Arthur Kip's *Fundamentals of Electricity and Magnetism.* A student who has learned well the contents of these three volumes will have received a sound introduction to classical physics. He will also have been introduced to the vast triumphs of the past half century with its radical development of quantum mechanics and knowledge of atomic, molecular, and nuclear structure, as well as to the special electronic properties of matter in the solid state. These latter topics are all too often simply left out of the traditional one-year course in college physics. It is true that many textbooks devote one or two closing chapters to this vast range of exciting triumphs of modern physics, but these chapters are usually tacked on to a program that already contains more material than can be properly digested in one year. The result is that the material often is skipped or too cursorily dealt with to give the student any appreciation of the nature of the accomplishments of physicists in the present century.

This situation is bad in two ways. If the student goes into other professional specialties and studies no more than general introductory physics, he is left unequipped to comprehend in the slightest degree what modern physics is doing and what it has already done for its sister sciences, especially chemistry. If he has already decided to specialize in physics, he will not want to postpone his chance to be introduced to modern quantum physics until the intermediate and advanced courses.

The teaching of undergraduate chemistry has been, in general, more responsive than the teaching of physics to the need for introducing quantum concepts of atomic structure at the outset. Generally, physics teachers have been so conservative in holding on to old methods that there is a real danger that today's students may be led

v

to think that Niels Bohr was a great chemist rather than, along with Albert Einstein, one of the greatest physicists of this century. The present volume will be useful to those who recognize the need to bring more modern physics into the introductory college course.

E. U. CONDON
Professor of Physics and
Fellow of the Joint Institute for Laboratory Astrophysics
University of Colorado, Boulder, Colorado

THE PRINCIPAL OBJECTIVE of this book is to present in elementary form some of the most important physical theory that has been developed during the current century. Contemporary concepts of atomic and nuclear physics and the structure of matter are presented against a background of classical mechanics, electrodynamics, and optics, and at each stage in the presentation the empirical basis and physical motivation of new developments are exhibited clearly. Analytical techniques such as calculus and vector analysis are used freely wherever they are needed, and a strong attempt is made to exhibit the spirit of scientific inquiry and the empirical basis of natural science.

Specifically, this book is intended for the conclusion of a series of courses with a total length of one to two years, starting in the freshman or sophomore college year, and with a concurrent course in calculus. For the beginning of the sequence, the other volumes in the McGraw-Hill Series in Fundamentals of Physics are particularly suitable because of their uniformity of level and viewpoint, but there are several other suitable combinations.

As the table of Contents shows, the subject of optics is regarded as a natural and useful bridge between classical mechanics and electrodynamics and contemporary quantum theory. The classical theory of optics is a natural outgrowth of classical electrodynamics; in turn, optical phenomena have provided much of the important motivation for the development of quantum mechanics and its many applications, especially to an understanding of the macroscopic behavior of matter on the basis of its microscopic structure, one of the unifying themes of this book.

The table of Contents indicates the scope of the book, but we also wish to point out the following features:

1. The book assumes that the student has taken a thorough course in classical mechanics, electromagnetism, and elementary thermodynamics, including Maxwell's equations in integral form. However, applications of these equations are spelled out in considerable detail, since for most students they will be new and somewhat unfamiliar. Calculus and vector algebra, including line and surface integrals, are used freely where needed, but no knowledge

of the vector differential operations (grad, div, and curl) is assumed. As is customary, vector quantities are denoted by bold-face symbols; in addition, boldface **+**, **−**, **Σ**, and **=** signs are used in vector equations to denote vector operations and equality.

2. The book attempts to exhibit the inductive and empirical nature of physics along with its deductive aspects. Care has been taken to distinguish clearly between principles that are generalizations from experience and those that are derived and to indicate the experimental basis of the former. The relative status of each principle in the whole logical structure is thus made clear. The author has made every effort to avoid the two extremes of a dry recitation of experimental results or of a tightly knit body of theory without reference to empirical observations.

3. Throughout the book the importance of *models* is stressed. We rarely deal directly with physical reality but rather with simplified models designed to retain the essential features of a physical situation and eliminate the unessential ones, to facilitate analysis. The student is constantly reminded of the process of constructing models as idealizations of reality as well as of the limitations of analytical results imposed by the limitations of validity of the models.

4. The texture of the book is not entirely even; some sections are more difficult reading than others. This variation is deliberate; some topics are intrinsically more subtle or demanding than others, and in addition not all students have equal abilities. Almost always the most difficult sections are arranged in such a way that they can be omitted without undue interruption of continuity. In addition, several important topics which are likely to cause difficulty, such as the concept of waves, wave pulses, and group velocity, are introduced several different times with a "spiral" approach, in order to help the student attain successively higher levels of sophistication in these important but sometimes elusive concepts. In the latter chapters of the book, some topics which are conceptually most subtle are softened somewhat by including less than the usual amount of analytical detail.

5. The mks system of units is used exclusively. There seems little doubt that it will eventually be used universally in scientific work. In addition, the author feels strongly that the burden of mastering several systems of units simultaneously should not be added to that of mastering new physical concepts.

6. A large collection of over 300 problems is included. A few of

them are simple substitution exercises, designed to illustrate definitions, but most require some thought and insight on the part of the student. Many of the problems are literal or algebraic rather than numerical; some are too difficult for all except the best students, and there is plenty of material for "honors" sections. Many problems ask only for an order of magnitude or for a discussion; the author feels strongly that such questions are often at least as instructive as more specific problems having a definite numerical answer. For some problems the student will need to look up additional information in the *Handbook of Chemistry and Physics* or a similar reference; familiarity with such standard reference works is highly recommended.

This book grew out of the author's experience with the sophomore physics course for engineering and science students at Carnegie Institute of Technology, where it is used for the last semester of a four-semester sequence, three credit hours each semester. The sequence begins with mechanics, thermodynamics, electricity, and magnetism. A concurrent calculus course is taken all four semesters. This book is also suitable for the conclusion of a two- or three-semester sequence with four or five credit hours each semester; when used for such a course it may be desirable to shorten it somewhat. Several sections and a few entire chapters may be omitted without interrupting the continuity. These include Chapters 4 and 9 to 13 and Sections 2-4 to 2-7, 3-5, 3-6, and 7-7. By omitting selected combinations of these chapters or sections, courses with a variety of length and emphasis can be constructed.

Although this book is intended primarily as a high-level introductory text, it may also be used for an intermediate-level course following a first general physics course given without calculus. A thorough and detailed exposition of principles and a plentiful supply of challenging problems make it useful for such intermediate courses.

HUGH D. YOUNG

Acknowledgments

This book has benefited greatly from the advice of a number of people. The following have reviewed part or all of a preliminary form of the manuscript: Prof. Stanley Ballard, Dr. Arthur Beiser, Prof. Owen Chamberlain, Prof. Edward Condon, Prof. Arthur Kip, Prof. Hans Mark, and Dr. William Wolfe. Their critical comments and suggestions have been invaluable. The author is also grateful to his colleagues at Carnegie Institute of Technology, whose suggestions have greatly increased the book's usefulness as a teaching tool, and to the two generations of sophomores at Carnegie who mercilessly but constructively pointed out errors and obscure passages in the preliminary editions. Particular thanks are due to the various members of the secretarial staff at Carnegie who aided in the preparation of several successive versions of the manuscript. Finally and most important, the author acknowledges his great debt to his wife Alice for her unending patience, confidence, and moral support throughout the writing of this text.

Contents

"TO BOTH the intellect and the emotions the study of physics is exciting, satisfying, and even beautiful, and it is the author's intention to convey these qualities to the student." This remark appears at the beginning of the first volume of the Fundamentals of Physics Series, but it is even more appropriate for the present volume. The subject matter of this book includes some of the most exciting areas of physics, concentrating particularly on the physics that has developed in the twentieth century, some of it even during the lifetime of the reader. These recent years have witnessed many revolutionary changes in our conception of the physical world in which we live and remarkable progress in our understanding of it.

Optics forms a natural starting point for our studies, for a variety of reasons. Some branches of optics, especially those concerned with wave phenomena, are a natural outgrowth of classical electrodynamics and provide a beautiful illustration of the great power of Maxwell's electromagnetic field equations in unifying various branches of physical science. Conversely, however, the shortcomings and insufficiencies of this so-called *classical* branch of optics, especially with problems involving the interaction of matter and radiation, provided the original motivation for the development of quantum mechanics, one of the central themes in this book.

Since the language of waves and wave phenomena occupies a central position in both classical optics and contemporary quantum mechanics, we begin with a general discussion of waves, using as a prototype problem the propagation of waves in a simple mechanical system. The wave concept, together with Maxwell's electromagnetic field equations, provides the basis for an understanding of a wide variety of optical phenomena such as interference, diffraction, and polarization. We then discuss these, along with the simpler but more specialized subject of geometrical optics.

With Chap. 5 we begin an investigation of the inadequacies of classical optics, and in the process of analyzing them we develop the basic ideas of quantum mechanics, which form the core subject matter for the remainder of the book. A number of phenomena are introduced, concerning the structure of atoms and the interaction of radiation with matter, which cannot be understood on the basis of classical newtonian mechanics (even with relativistic modifications) and classical electromagnetism as formulated in Maxwell's equations. We discuss in some detail the basic modifications in the formal structure of these disciplines, which are needed for the foundation of quantum mechanics.

The next several chapters are devoted to applications of quantum mechanics to various systems whose understanding is central to a thorough analysis of the structure and properties of matter. Beginning with the simplest atom, hydrogen, we progress to more complicated atoms, molecules, matter in the solid state, and finally the structure of nuclei and of elementary particles.

The careful reader will notice several central themes running throughout this book. Among them are the use of idealized *models* to simplify complex situations, the general concept of waves and of wave propagation, the relationship of the *microscopic* structure of matter to its *macroscopic* properties, and such fundamental concepts as mass, energy, momentum, force, and the associated conservation principles. In these common themes is found much of the great power and beauty of physical science.

The author has tried throughout to exhibit his personal conviction that physics *is* beautiful, exciting, and satisfying. It is his hope that the reader will enjoy understanding new principles and grasping their power and usefulness and will feel the satisfaction and personal achievement that come from struggling with and solving challenging problems.

THE WAVE CONCEPT lies at the heart of much of contemporary physics, including electrodynamics, optics, and quantum theory. Several general principles and concepts of wave phenomena are reviewed, and mathematical language for describing waves is introduced, with particular reference to waves on a stretched string. The dynamical basis of waves on a string is discussed, and then sinusoidal waves are introduced as an important example of periodic waves. Finally, we discuss the principle of superposition, along with some mathematical techniques useful in calculations involving superposition.

1-1 Properties of Waves

The study of wave propagation forms an important and interesting chapter in physical science, cutting across the boundaries that have traditionally divided physics into domains such as mechanics, electromagnetism, optics, and atomic physics. The concepts of waves and of wave propagation have played a central and overwhelmingly important role throughout the development of physical theory and have had the happy effect of bringing unity to the most diverse branches of physical science. Thus it is entirely appropriate that this book, whose purpose is to present in elementary form some of the most important physical theory developed during the current century, should begin with a discussion of waves.

The first three chapters are concerned chiefly with optics, especially with phenomena requiring the use of wave concepts for their understanding. Although originally the term *optics* was used only for phenomena involving visible light, it is now used in a more general sense to include electromagnetic wave phenomena covering a wide range of frequencies and wavelengths, of which visible light forms a small but important part. Thus the study of optics is really the study of electromagnetic waves. In developing this topic, we first introduce some general wave concepts in the more familiar realm of mechanical waves and then review the important principles of electrodynamics from which an understanding of electromagnetic waves emerges.

A wave is a disturbance from an equilibrium state that moves or *propagates* with time from one region of space to another. Examples of wave motion are numerous, both in everyday experience and in the various physical sciences. The classical example is that of waves on the surface of a pond. Dropping a stone into the water produces a disturbance which spreads out horizontally in all directions along the surface. An even more commonplace example is sound; a source of sound produces a fluctuation in pressure in the surrounding atmosphere, and this disturbance is propagated to distant points.

In both these examples the wave motion consists of successive displacements of various portions of a mechanical medium, but it is important to understand that the matter constituting the medium is not itself transported to distant points. In the case of water waves, the individual water molecules have predominantly an up-and-down motion with respect to their equilibrium position (a smooth water surface). Similarly, travel of sound from a violin to a listener in a concert hall is a propagation of air pressure variations, not an actual transport of air molecules.

Some kinds of waves occur without a mechanical medium. One of the most important of these is an electromagnetic wave, in which the disturbance from equilibrium is the presence of time-varying electric and magnetic fields in a certain region of space, inducing corresponding electromagnetic disturbances at distant points. Although the physical nature of electromagnetic waves is quite different from that of mechanical waves, they share a number of common features and may be described with the same general language. Light, radio waves, x-rays, and γ rays are all examples of electromagnetic waves.

Further removed from ordinary experience is the wavelike nature of fundamental particles. As in the case of electromagnetic waves, no material medium is involved, but it is appropriate in some respects to represent a fundamental particle, such as an electron, as a disturbance from an equilibrium (vacuum) state which propagates from one region of space to another as the particle moves. The concept of the wave nature of particles is one of the cornerstones of present-day quantum mechanics, and it will be discussed in detail in Chaps. 5 through 7.

As frequently happens in the formulation of physical principles, the most familiar phenomena are not always the simplest ones to analyze in detail. It is often instructive and useful to select a particularly simple situation to exhibit basic ideas, uncluttered by undue mathematical complexity. We select as our prototype of wave motion the propagation of waves on a stretched string. We tie one end of a long string to a fixed object and then, keeping the tension constant, impart a motion to the other end, as shown in Fig. 1-1.

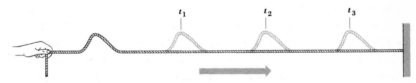

Fig. 1-1   *Wave pulse on a stretched string, produced by giving one end a transverse "flipping" motion. The pulse is shown at several successive times; it moves with a definite speed and without change of shape.*

Observation of the resulting motion reveals several striking features. First, the disturbance, which we may call a *wave pulse*, maintains its shape as it travels along the string. Second, experiment shows that the pulse moves with a definite speed, independent of its shape or size. Third, the displacements of individual points on the string are found to be perpendicular, or *transverse*, to the equilibrium position of the string and to the direction of propagation of the wave; any such wave is called a *transverse wave*.

A thorough understanding of wave motion of a stretched string must include not only the above observations of the general characteristics of the motion but also the basis of these characteristics in the general principles relating forces and motions, namely, Newton's laws of motion. However, before this basis can be developed, it is essential to have a convenient language for *describing* wave phenomena.   The situation is analogous to that in particle mechanics, where a *kinematic* description of particle motion in terms of displacement, velocity, and acceleration must precede the more general *dynamical* questions of the relation of motion to the forces that produce it.   In the next section we shall consider such a descriptive language for a stretched string; several aspects will also be directly useful later in analyzing the relation of electromagnetic waves to the basic principles of electrodynamics, Maxwell's equations.

1-2   *Mathematical Description of Waves*

Let the x axis of a coordinate system be located along the equilibrium position of a string, as shown in Fig. 1-2.   We neglect any sag in the string due to gravity.   Denoting the equilibrium position of any point on the string by the coordinate x, and its instantaneous displacement from equilibrium by y, as shown, we may describe the configuration of the whole string at any instant by a function $y = f(x)$.   If at time t_1 the position is described by a function $f_1(x)$, then at a later time t_2 it will be described by a different function, $f_2(x)$, since the wave disturbance moves during this interval.   But if the wave travels with constant speed and maintains the same shape as it travels, these two functions are closely related; we shall now develop this relationship.

Fig. 1-2   *Coordinate system for a mathematical description of transverse waves on a string. The x axis is the equilibrium position of the string; the displacement of a point whose equilibrium position is x is denoted as y.   The equilibrium position of the string is shown as a shaded line.*

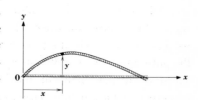

Let the speed of propagation of the wave, usually called the *wave speed*, be denoted by u.   If the initial configuration at time $t = 0$ is given by a function $y = f(x)$, what function describes the configuration at a later time t?   Since in time t the entire waveshape moves to the right a distance ut, the displacement y of point x at time t is just the same as the displacement of a point a distance ut to the left of x at time $t = 0$.   That is, the displacement of point x at time t is equal to the displacement of point $x - ut$ at time $t = 0$. This in turn is given simply by $f(x - ut)$, a function with the same form as $f(x)$ but with x replaced wherever it appears by the quantity $x - ut$. Thus if the waveshape at time $t = 0$ is $f(x)$ and if the wave propagates to the right with a constant speed u, the waveshape at any later time t is given by $f(x - ut)$.

Example: Suppose a transverse wave pulse on a rope is described at time $t = 0$ by the equation

$$y = \frac{1}{1 + x^2}$$

where x and y are both measured in meters. If the wave speed is 2 m/sec and the wave moves in the $+x$ direction, write expressions for the shape of the wave at $t = 1$ sec, $t = 2$ sec, and for any general value t.

Solution: In general, as just pointed out, the shape of the rope at any time t is given by

$$y = \frac{1}{1 + (x - ut)^2}$$

In the first case, $ut = (2 \text{ m/sec})(1 \text{ sec}) = 2$ m, and the expression at time $t = 1$ sec is

$$y = \frac{1}{1 + (x - 2)^2}$$

Similarly, at time $t = 2$ sec, it is

$$y = \frac{1}{1 + (x - 4)^2}$$

In these expressions, the waveshape has moved 2 and 4 m, respectively, from its position at time $t = 0$. The configurations of the rope at these three times are shown in Fig. 1-3.

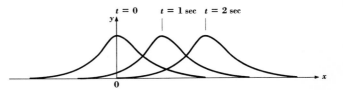

Fig. 1-3 *Motion of a transverse wave pulse. The pulse is shown at three successive times.*

The function $y = f(x,t)$ for any specific wave motion is a complete description of the motion, inasmuch as it gives the position of every point on the string at every instant of time. Such a function is called a *wave function;* it is clear that wave functions occupy a central position in the mathematical description of waves. The preceding discussion has shown that any wave function $y = f(x,t)$, which describes a wave propagating in the $+x$ direction with wave speed u, must contain the variables x and t only in the particular combination $x - ut$. The argument may be repeated for a wave traveling in the $-x$ direction to show that for such a wave the variables must appear only in the combination $x + ut$. An equivalent and sometimes more useful statement is that, for waves traveling in the $\pm x$ direction, the variables must appear in the combination $ax \mp bt$. This combination may be written as $a(x \mp bt/a)$, in which form it is clear that the wave speed u is given by $u = b/a$. This observation will be useful in a later discussion of the propagation of wave pulses.

The forms $y = f(x - ut)$ and $y = f(x + ut)$ for wave functions suggest another important observation. Since the wave function contains the two variables x and t, we can calculate its partial derivative with respect to either of these. These calculations are facilitated by introducing a single symbol to represent the combination $x \pm ut$. For a wave propagating in the $+x$ direction, let $z = x - ut$. Then application of the chain rule for derivatives leads to the following relations:

$$\frac{\partial y}{\partial x} = \frac{dy}{dz}\frac{\partial z}{\partial x} = \frac{dy}{dz} \quad (1)$$

$$\frac{\partial y}{\partial t} = \frac{dy}{dz}\frac{\partial z}{\partial t} = \frac{dy}{dz}(-u)$$

From these we conclude that the two derivatives must be related by the equation

$$\frac{\partial y}{\partial x} = -\frac{1}{u}\frac{\partial y}{\partial t} \qquad \text{for } y = f(x - ut)$$

A similar calculation for a wave propagating in the $-x$ direction yields the relation

$$\frac{\partial y}{\partial x} = +\frac{1}{u}\frac{\partial y}{\partial t} \qquad \text{for } y = f(x + ut)$$

Repeated application of the same procedure yields a relation between the *second* derivatives; this relation is the same for waves propagating in either direction:

$$\frac{\partial^2 y}{\partial x^2} = \frac{1}{u^2}\frac{\partial^2 y}{\partial t^2} \qquad\qquad (1\text{-}1)$$

This important differential equation, which must be satisfied by any wave function representing a wave traveling in *either* the $+x$ or $-x$ direction, is called the *wave equation* for this system.

To summarize: Any function $y = f(x,t)$ that describes a wave propagating in either direction on a string, with definite speed and unvarying waveshape, must satisfy Eq. (1-1).   Correspondingly, waves of this sort are physically possible if and only if this equation is consistent with the general laws of dynamics.   Thus the next logical step is to attempt to derive the wave equation, which we have already deduced from kinematic considerations, from the principles of dynamics.   In the course of this derivation it will become clear what properties the mechanical system must have in order to permit wave propagation.

The logical sequence just described will recur several times in our discussion of wave phenomena.   In introducing the concept of electromagnetic waves in Sec. 2-3 it will be shown that the functions describing the variation of electric and magnetic fields with position and time must satisfy a wave equation with exactly the same form as Eq. (1-1) if they are to be consistent with the appropriate general principles—in this case, Maxwell's equations.

1-3   Dynamics of Waves on a String

We shall now derive the wave equation for the string from Newton's laws of motion.   The string is not a point mass but rather a distribution of mass along a line, and so it is useful first to apply the laws of motion to a section of string sufficiently small so it may be considered a point.   Figure 1-4 shows a small element of string whose length in the equilibrium position would be Δx.   In the figure this element is displaced from the equilibrium position (represented by the x axis) and stretched, so that its actual length is somewhat greater than this.   Assuming that the string is uniform, we denote its mass per unit length in the equilibrium position by μ; this quantity is called the *linear mass density*.   Thus the mass of this section is $m = \mu \, \Delta x$.

Fig. 1-4   *Free-body diagram for an element of string whose length in its equilibrium position is Δx.   The force at each end of the string is tangent to the string at the point of application; each force is represented in terms of its x and y components.*

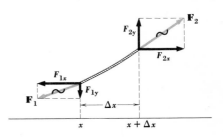

Neglecting gravity, the forces on this element of string are those shown in Fig. 1-4. The force applied to each end is in a direction tangent to the string at the corresponding point; these forces may be resolved into their x and y components. Under the assumption that the displacements are always transverse, there is no component of acceleration, hence of force, along the x axis. Thus it always must be true that $F_{1x} = F_{2x}$, where these symbols refer to the magnitudes of the corresponding components, regardless of sign. Since F_x does not change with the displacement of the string, each of these must be equal to the tension T in the string when it is not displaced from equilibrium. That is,

$$F_{1x} = F_{2x} = T \tag{1-2}$$

The transverse acceleration of the element of string is produced by the transverse component of force, $F_{2y} - F_{1y}$. To obtain the magnitudes of these forces, we note that the ratio F_{1y}/F_{1x} is equal to the *slope* of the string at the point x, and F_{2y}/F_{2x} to the slope at $x + \Delta x$. Thus we obtain the relations

$$\frac{F_{1y}}{F_{1x}} = \left(\frac{\partial y}{\partial x}\right)_x \qquad \frac{F_{2y}}{F_{2x}} = \left(\frac{\partial y}{\partial x}\right)_{x+\Delta x} \tag{1-3}$$

where the notation indicates that the derivatives are evaluated at the points x and $x + \Delta x$, respectively. Combining Eqs. (1-2) and (1-3),

$$F_{2y} - F_{1y} = T\left[\left(\frac{\partial y}{\partial x}\right)_{x+\Delta x} - \left(\frac{\partial y}{\partial x}\right)_x\right] \tag{1-4}$$

The net transverse force given by Eq. (1-4) is now to be equated to the product of the mass of the section and its acceleration:

$$F_{2y} - F_{1y} = \mu\,\Delta x\frac{\partial^2 y}{\partial t^2} \tag{1-5}$$

The question may arise as to whether the acceleration $\partial^2 y/\partial t^2$ should be evaluated at the point x or the point $x + \Delta x$. Since the next step is to let $\Delta x \to 0$, this is not really an important question.

Combining Eqs. (1-4) and (1-5) and dividing by $T\,\Delta x$,

$$\frac{(\partial y/\partial x)_{x+\Delta x} - (\partial y/\partial x)_x}{\Delta x} = \frac{\mu}{T}\frac{\partial^2 y}{\partial t^2} \tag{1-6}$$

We see that, in the limit as $\Delta x \to 0$, the left side of this equation becomes simply the derivative with respect to x of $\partial y/\partial x$, which is $\partial^2 y/\partial x^2$; in this limit we therefore have

$$\frac{\partial^2 y}{\partial x^2} = \frac{\mu}{T} \frac{\partial^2 y}{\partial t^2} \tag{1-7}$$

Any wave function $y = f(x,t)$ that describes a physically possible wave on the string must agree with Eq. (1-7).

This equation has precisely the same form as Eq. (1-1), which was derived from more general considerations. The fact that this equation can be obtained from Newton's laws of motion demonstrates that waves of the type under discussion are, in fact, compatible with the principles of mechanics. Furthermore, comparing Eqs. (1-7) and (1-1) gives an additional important result; the fact that these two equations must be identical shows that the wave speed u is directly related to the mechanical properties of the system. That is, it must be true that $1/u^2 = \mu/T$, or

$$u = \sqrt{\frac{T}{\mu}} \tag{1-8}$$

Increasing the tension in the string increases the wave speed, but increasing the linear mass density decreases the speed, as might be expected intuitively. Thus deriving the wave equation for the system not only shows that wave propagation is physically possible but also shows how the wave speed is related to the properties of the system. An analogous calculation will be made in Sec. 2-3 for electromagnetic waves.

1-4   *Sinusoidal Waves*

The discussion of wave motion on a string has been introduced with the idea of a wave pulse, localized at any given time in a certain region on the string, in which successive particles in the string undergo temporary displacements from equilibrium and then return. Some of the most important and interesting kinds of wave motion, however, are those in which each particle undergoes a repetitive, or *periodic*, motion. Suppose that the end of the string in Fig. 1-1 is given not just a single flip but a series of flips at regular time intervals. The number of repetitions per unit time is called the *frequency*, denoted by f, and the time for one repetition is called the *period*, denoted by T. Clearly, $T = 1/f$.

Since the motion of the end of the string is periodic, the wave pattern on the string at any instant is also repetitive. During one period T of the motion, the wave travels along the string a distance uT. Let us denote this distance by $\lambda = uT$. At the end of the time interval T, the end of the string begins to repeat the motion of the first interval. By the end of the second period, the wave has traveled a total distance 2λ, but since the motion of the end point during the second period is the same as that during the first period, the wave pattern on the string consists of two separate patterns, each of length λ, identical in shape. For example, the shape of the string between $x = 0$ and $x = \lambda$ is exactly the same as that between $x = \lambda$ and $x = 2\lambda$.

The distance λ is usually called the *wavelength;* it is equal to the distance between any pair of corresponding points on two successive repetitions of the waveform. The important relationship

$$\lambda = uT = \frac{u}{f} \tag{1-9}$$

is valid for any periodic wave motion.

An important example of periodic wave motion occurs when the end of the string is given a sinusoidal (i.e., simple harmonic[1]) motion, in some respects the simplest periodic motion of a point. Let the end of the string be at $x = 0$, and let this point be given a transverse displacement $A \cos 2\pi ft$, a simple harmonic motion with amplitude A and frequency f. Then, at the point $x = 0$, the wave function is

$$y(0,t) = A \cos 2\pi ft \tag{1-10}$$

The resulting wave motion is shown in Fig. 1-5.

To find the complete wave function, we recall from Sec. 1-2 that the function for a wave propagating in the $+x$ direction must contain x and t only in the particular combination $x - ut$, which is equivalent to stating that the coefficient of t in the wave function must be $-u$ times the coefficient of x. Here the coefficient of t is $2\pi f$, and so the coefficient of x must be $-2\pi f/u$; the general wave function is

$$y(x,t) = A \cos\left(2\pi ft - \frac{2\pi fx}{u}\right)$$

$$= A \cos 2\pi f\left(t - \frac{x}{u}\right) \tag{1-11}$$

As a check, we may substitute Eq. (1-11) into Eq. (1-1), which must be

---

[1] Any reader who is not familiar with simple harmonic motion would do well to review this important concept in an elementary mechanics text, such as H. D. Young, "Fundamentals of Mechanics and Heat," secs. 10-1 and 10-2, McGraw-Hill Book Company, New York, 1964.

Fig. 1-5 *A sinusoidal wave produced by giving the end of the string at x = 0 a sinusoidally varying displacement described by Eq. (1-10). The shape of the string at time t = 0, shown as a solid line, is described by the function y(x,0) = A cos 2πf (0 − x/u); the shape at a later time t, shown as a shaded line, is given by the general wave function of Eq. (1-11). In the time t the wave moves a distance ut to the right. The amplitude A and wavelength λ are also shown.*

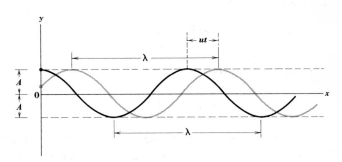

satisfied by any possible wave function. It is in fact satisfied; the calculation is left as a problem.

The significance of the wave described by Eq. (1-11) may be appreciated more fully by noting first that every particle in the string undergoes simple harmonic motion; for a fixed value of x, corresponding to a particular point on the string, the displacement is a sinusoidal function of time. The motions of various points differ in *phase;* they are out of step with respect to each other, but nevertheless each point moves with simple harmonic motion. Second, at any instant the *shape* of the string is described by a sinusoidal function of x. That is, for any fixed value t, y is a sinusoidal function of x.

An alternative form of Eq. (1-11), obtained with the help of Eq. (1-9), is

$$y(x,t) = A \cos 2\pi\left(\frac{t}{T} - \frac{x}{\lambda}\right) \tag{1-12}$$

In this form, the wave function shows directly that, when t changes by an amount equal to T, the argument of the sine function changes by 2π, corresponding to a complete cycle of motion of any point. Similarly, when x changes by an amount equal to λ, the argument of the function again changes by 2π, corresponding to a complete repetition of the waveform.

This discussion may be adapted to the case of a wave propagating in the $-x$ direction. Such a wave cannot be produced by shaking the end of the string at $x = 0$, since there is no string to the left of this point. But we may easily imagine a wave motion somewhere in the middle of the string, arising from sinusoidal motion of a point to the right of the region we are observing. Since any wave propagating in the $-x$ direction must contain x and t only in the combination $x + ut$, a possible wave function for a sinusoidal wave of amplitude A, frequency f, and speed u is

$$y(x,t) = A \cos 2\pi f\left(t + \frac{x}{u}\right) \tag{1-13}$$

which may also be written

$$y(x,t) = A \cos 2\pi\left(\frac{t}{T} + \frac{x}{\lambda}\right) \tag{1-14}$$

In order to save writing factors of 2π, it is often convenient to introduce two new parameters to describe the properties of waves. These are the *angular frequency* ω and the *wave number* k, defined as follows:

$$\omega = 2\pi f \qquad k = \frac{2\pi}{\lambda} \tag{1-15}$$

In terms of k and ω, Eq. (1-14) becomes

$$y(x,t) = A \cos (\omega t - kx) = A \cos (kx - \omega t) \tag{1-16}$$

The second form of Eq. (1-16), which is obtained by noting that, for any quantity a, $\cos (-a) = \cos a$, turns out to be more useful for our later work, and we usually adhere to this latter form, writing the x term before the t term in the wave function.

One further generalization of wave functions for sinusoidal waves is sometimes useful. A simple harmonic motion described by the equation

$$y = A \cos (\omega t + \phi)$$

has the same general character as one described by

$$y = A \cos \omega t$$

The two motions have the same frequency, period, and amplitude; they differ only in that they are out of step with respect to each other. When ϕ, called the *phase angle*, is equal to π (180°), the two motions are precise opposites of each other; otherwise they are out of step by some fraction of a cycle. From the foregoing discussion, it should be clear that if the free end of a string is given a motion $y(0,t) = A \cos(\omega t + \phi)$ the resulting wave is described by the wave function

$$y(x,t) = A \cos(kx - \omega t - \phi) \tag{1-17}$$

which is a wave differing from that described by Eq. (1-16) only in that at every point along the string, at any instant, the two waves are "out of step" by the same fraction of a period.

1-5   Superposition of Waves

In the wave phenomena discussed thus far, the wave motion originates in one region of the medium and propagates in one direction. But it may happen that two wave motions originate in different regions and propagate toward each other, such as the two wave pulses shown at the top of Fig. 1-6. While the two pulses are separated, no problem arises, but what happens when they reach the same region of the string and overlap?

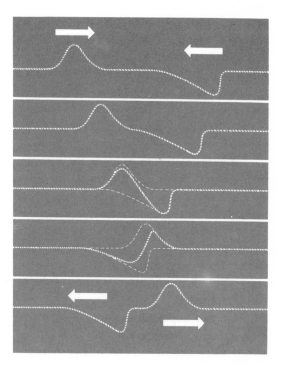

Fig. 1-6   *Two pulses with different shapes, moving toward each other, are produced in two separate sections of a string. The position of the string is shown at several successive times. The positions of the individual pulses, during the time of overlap, are shown as broken lines. The actual displacement, shown as a solid line, is the sum of displacements corresponding to the separate pulses. After the two pulses pass, they proceed with their original shapes.*

This expression can be simplified by expanding each of the cosine functions, using the identity $\cos (\alpha \pm \beta) = \cos \alpha \cos \beta \mp \sin \alpha \sin \beta$. The details of this calculation will be left for the reader; the result is

$$y(x,t) = -2A \sin kx \sin \omega t \tag{1-19}$$

Equation (1-19) deserves careful study. First, it should be observed that the variables x and t *do not* appear in the combination $x \pm ut$ characteristic of waves propagating in a single direction. Second, each point undergoes simple harmonic motion, as shown by the factor $\sin \omega t$, but all points move *in phase*. Third, the amplitude of the motion of a point depends on its position, because of the factor $\sin kx$. Points for which $\sin kx = 0$ (that is, $kx = 0$ or an integer multiple of π) do not move at all, and those for which $|\sin kx| = 1$ (that is, $kx = \pi/2$, $3\pi/2, \ldots$) have amplitude $2A$, which is twice the maximum displacement corresponding to each of the individual waves. In short, Eq. (1-19) does not represent a progressive wave but rather one with a stationary pattern which becomes larger and smaller with time. Such a wave is called a *standing wave*. The stationary points are called *nodes*, and the points of maximum amplitude are called *antinodes*. The standing wave represented by Eq. (1-19) is illustrated in Fig. 1-8.

Fig. 1-8 *Standing wave resulting from the reflection of a sinusoidal wave at a fixed point. The position of the string is shown at several times. The amplitude of the pattern becomes larger and smaller with time, but it does not move along the length of the string; hence the term standing wave. The nodes and antinodes are shown.*

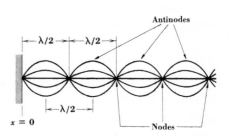

As previously, this example refers to a mechanical situation. However, there is a completely analogous phenomenon for electromagnetic waves, in which a standing wave is formed by reflection of a wave from the surface of a conductor. This will be discussed in detail in Sec. 2-5.

1-6   *Complex Exponential Functions*

Calculations with superposition of sinusoidal waves are often simplified considerably by making use of the close relationship that exists between sine and cosine functions and exponential functions with imaginary arguments. We recall that i represents the imaginary unit, having the property $i^2 = -1$. The equations relating the trigonometric and exponential functions, called the *Euler relations*, are as follows:

$$e^{ix} = \cos x + i \sin x$$
$$e^{-ix} = \cos x - i \sin x \tag{1-20}$$

These equations are derived in most texts on elementary calculus. From them one can obtain algebraically the inverse relations

$$\sin x = \frac{e^{ix} - e^{-ix}}{2i}$$

$$\cos x = \frac{e^{ix} + e^{-ix}}{2} \tag{1-21}$$

Any number containing imaginary as well as real parts is called a *complex number*. We now digress briefly to discuss some properties of complex numbers which are useful in their application to the description of sinusoidal motion. The number z is said to be a complex number if it can be expressed as $z = x + iy$, where x and y are real quantities. Conversely, every complex number can be written as the sum of a real and an imaginary quantity. The following notations are frequently used:

Real part of z = Re z = x

Imaginary part of z = Im z = y

Thus the real and imaginary parts of the complex quantity e^{ix} are, respectively,

Re e^{ix} = $\cos x$

Im e^{ix} = $\sin x$

Complex numbers may be represented graphically on a plane, using a rectangular coordinate system whose x axis corresponds to the real part of the complex number and y axis to the imaginary part. The x and y axes may also be called the real and imaginary axes, respectively. Any complex number is then represented as a point in this plane or as a vector joining the origin and the point, as shown in Fig. 1-9a. The length of this vector (the distance from the origin to the point) is given by $(x^2 + y^2)^{1/2}$. This quantity is called the *absolute value* of the complex

Fig. 1-9 *Complex plane.*
(a) Geometrical representation of
a complex number z and of
its real and imaginary parts.
The complex conjugate z* is also
shown. (b) Geometrical repre-
sentation of the complex number
Ae^{iωt}, showing its real and imagi-
nary parts, A cos ωt and
A sin ωt, respectively, and its
magnitude |Ae^{iωt}| = A. As the
vector representing this complex
number rotates counterclockwise
with constant speed, its projection
on the real axis varies
sinusoidally, with "simple har-
monic motion."

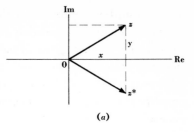

(a)

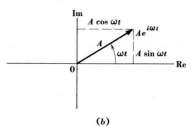

(b)

quantity z and is usually denoted by $|z|$. That is, if $z = x + iy$, then

$$|z| = (x^2 + y^2)^{1/2} \tag{1-22}$$

One additional notation is that of the *complex conjugate* of z, denoted by z^*, defined as a quantity with the same real part as z but an imaginary part with the opposite sign. That is, if $z = x + iy$, then by definition $z^* = x - iy$. More generally, the complex conjugate of any complex quantity can be obtained by replacing i everywhere by $-i$, provided all algebraic symbols represent real quantities.

To illustrate the usefulness of the above notation in describing sinusoidal motion, we consider the motion of a simple harmonic oscillator whose displacement from equilibrium is given as a function of time by $y = A \cos ωt$. This may be written as

$$y = A \cos ωt = A \operatorname{Re} e^{iωt} \tag{1-23}$$

The quantity $Ae^{iωt} = A(\cos ωt + i \sin ωt)$ can be represented graphically by a vector in the complex plane, as shown in Fig. 1-9b. The length of this vector is constant and is given by

$$|Ae^{iωt}| = (A^2 \cos^2 ωt + A^2 \sin^2 ωt)^{1/2} = A \tag{1-24}$$

Furthermore, consideration of Fig. 1-9b shows that the vector makes an angle $ωt$ with the real axis; this angle increases uniformly with time, corresponding to angular velocity ω.   That is, the vector in the complex plane representing the quantity $Ae^{i\omega t}$ has constant length A and *rotates counterclockwise* with constant angular velocity.   Thus the harmonic-oscillator motion described by Eq. (1-23) can be regarded as the *projection* on the real axis of the rotating vector just described.

As an example of the usefulness of the complex exponential representation of wave functions, we show how it can be used to obtain Eq. (1-19) from Eq. (1-18).   First, we note that

$$\cos (kx \pm \omega t) = \text{Re } e^{i(kx \pm \omega t)} = \text{Re } (e^{ikx} e^{\pm i\omega t}) \tag{1-25}$$

and so the wave function of Eq. (1-18), representing the superposition of two sinusoidal waves in opposite directions, can be expressed as

$$
\begin{aligned}
y(x,t) &= A \text{ Re } (e^{i(kx+\omega t)} - e^{i(kx-\omega t)}) \\
&= A \text{ Re } [e^{ikx}(e^{i\omega t} - e^{-i\omega t})]
\end{aligned} \tag{1-26}
$$

Reference to Eq. (1-21) shows that the quantity in parentheses is equal to $2i \sin \omega t$.   Thus

$$
\begin{aligned}
y(x,t) &= A \text{ Re } (e^{ikx} 2i \sin \omega t) \\
&= A \text{ Re } (2i \cos kx \sin \omega t - 2 \sin kx \sin \omega t) \\
&= -2A \sin kx \sin \omega t
\end{aligned} \tag{1-27}
$$

which agrees with Eq. (1-19).   This procedure may not seem to be much simpler than the direct use of trigonometric identities.   The real value becomes more evident when *several* sinusoidal waves are superposed; then the use of complex exponentials results in considerable simplifications.

The above discussion has been concerned only with the superposition of waves in one space dimension.   The most interesting and important kinds of wave phenomena occur as a result of the superposition of waves in two- or three-dimensional situations.   The familiar example is the interference pattern produced by the superposition of water waves from two point sources.   Each source produces sinusoidal waves with circular wavefronts spreading out from the source.   The total disturbance at any point on the surface of the water is equal to the sum of the two disturbances corresponding to the individual waves.   Such an interference pattern is shown in Fig. 1-10.   It is seen that the two disturbances reinforce each other along certain lines, but they cancel each other along other lines.   Interference patterns such as this are extremely important to an understanding of wave phenomena.   In fact,

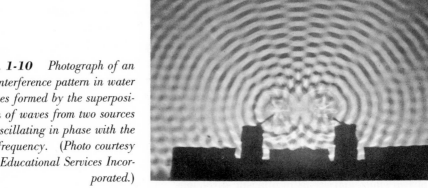

Fig. 1-10   *Photograph of an interference pattern in water waves formed by the superposition of waves from two sources oscillating in phase with the same frequency.   (Photo courtesy of Educational Services Incorporated.)*

just such an interference phenomenon provided the first direct experimental evidence of the wave nature of light.   In Chap. 3 we shall discuss in considerable detail the application of the principle of superposition to the understanding of various interference phenomena.

PROBLEMS

1-1   A wave pulse on a stretched string is described by the equation

$$y(x,t) = \frac{0.10}{4 + (2x - 10t)^2}$$

where x and y are measured in meters and t in seconds.
   a.   Sketch the pulse at time $t = 0$ and at time $t = 0.1$ sec.
   b.   What is the wave speed?   In what direction does the pulse move?
   c.   Write an equation describing a similar pulse moving in the opposite direction.

1-2   A wave pulse on a stretched string is described by the equation

$$y(x,t) = 0.1e^{-(0.5x - 50t)^2}$$

where x and y are measured in meters and t in seconds.
   a.   What is the maximum displacement of a point on the string as the pulse passes?
   b.   Sketch the shape of the pulse at time $t = 0$ and at $t = 0.01$ sec.
   c.   From the sketches, find the wave speed.
   d.   Find the wave speed directly from the functional form of the equation.

1-3   A certain wave motion on a string is represented by the function $y = A \sin k(x - ut)$, where A, k, and u are constants.

    a.   Derive an expression for the transverse velocity of a point on the string as a function of its equilibrium position x and time t.

    b.   Derive an expression for the slope of the string at point x and time t.

1-4   Verify that the wave function of Prob. 1-3 satisfies Eq. (1-1) by computing the required derivatives and substituting.

1-5   One end of a stretched string is moved transversely with a uniform speed of 1.0 m/sec until it is displaced 0.1 m; it is then returned to the original position with the same uniform speed. The resulting wave pulse is found to travel with a speed of 5.0 m/sec.

    a.   Sketch the shape of the string at $t = 0, 0.1, 0.2, 0.3$, and 0.4 sec.

    b.   What is the length of the wave pulse on the string?

    c.   Draw a graph showing transverse velocity as a function of position on the string for $t = 0.4$ sec.

1-6   Prove that, for any transverse wave on a string, the slope at any point x is equal to the ratio of the instantaneous transverse speed of the point to the wave speed.

1-7   A rope 40 m long has a total mass of 2.0 kg. If it is stretched horizontally to a tension of 500 nt, what is the speed of transverse waves on the rope?

1-8   A rope 10 m long is hung from the ceiling. The mass of the rope is 0.5 kg, and an object with a mass of 0.5 kg is tied to the bottom end.

    a.   How does wave speed vary with position on the rope?

    b.   If a wave pulse with a length of 0.1 m is produced at the bottom end, what is its length when it reaches the top end?

1-9   Write a wave function for a sinusoidal wave propagating in the $+x$ direction with an amplitude of 0.1 m, wavelength of 2.0 m, and frequency of 5 sec^{-1} if the point $x = 0$ has zero displacement at time $t = 0$. What is the wave speed?

1-10   Solve Prob. 1-9 if the point $x = 0$ has its maximum positive displacement at time $t = 0$.

1-11   The equation of a sinusoidal wave on a string is

$$y = 0.05 \sin 2\pi(0.1x + 2.0t)$$

where the distances are measured in meters and t in seconds. Draw a diagram showing the position of the string at $t = 0$ and at $t = \frac{1}{8}$ sec. From this diagram, find the wavelength, speed, and amplitude of the wave.

1-12   For the wave function of Prob. 1-11, find the wave speed, wavelength, period, frequency, wave number, and angular frequency directly from the wave function.

1-13   For the wave function of Prob. 1-11, find the maximum transverse speed of a point on the string and the maximum slope of the string.

1-14   One end of a stretched rope is given a periodic transverse motion with a frequency of 10 sec^{-1}.   The rope is 50 m long, has a total mass of 0.5 kg, and is stretched with a tension of 400 nt.
   a.   Find the wavelength of the resulting waves.
   b.   If the tension is doubled, how must the frequency be changed in order to maintain the same wavelength?

1-15   Suppose a sinusoidal wave on a string, having amplitude A and travel-ing in the $-x$ direction, is partially reflected at the point $x = 0$, so that the reflected wave is in phase with the incident wave at $x = 0$ but its amplitude is kA, where k is a number between 0 and 1, sometimes called the reflection coefficient.
   a.   Show that each point on the string undergoes simple harmonic motion with an amplitude that depends on x.
   b.   Find the ratio of maximum to minimum amplitude, known as the standing-wave ratio.

1-16   The frequency of a large organ pipe is determined by the condition that the length of the pipe is one-half wavelength.   If the frequency is to be 16 sec^{-1} and the speed of sound is $1,100$ ft/sec, what must be the length of the pipe?   (This is approximately the frequency of the note one octave below the lowest C on a piano and is the lowest note found on most large organs.)

1-17   For a stretched string whose equilibrium position is the x axis, con-sider the superposition of two transverse sinusoidal waves of equal amplitude and frequency but in perpendicular planes, one having dis-placements in the xy plane and the other in the xz plane.   Describe the motion of a point on the string if the two waves are in phase and if they are $90°$ out of phase.   For the latter case, prove that any point moves so that it has a constant distance from the equilibrium position.

1-18   For any two complex numbers A and B, prove that Re $(A + B) =$ Re $A +$ Re B.

1-19   For any complex number A, prove that Re $A = \frac{1}{2}(A + A^*)$ and Im $A = (A - A^*)/2i$.

1-20   Show that the complex number $-\frac{1}{2} + i\sqrt{3}/2$ is a cube root of unity.

1-21   Show that the sixth roots of unity are represented by points in the complex plane which lie on a circle of unit radius and are spaced $60°$

apart around the circle. Using this information, write each of the roots in the standard form $x + iy$.

1-22 Using Euler's relations, prove that $(\cos x + i \sin x)^n = \cos nx + i \sin nx$, which is called De Moivre's theorem.

1-23 Starting with Eqs. (1-21), prove the identity $\sin^2 x + \cos^2 x = 1$.

1-24 Evaluate $e^{i\pi/2}$, $e^{i\pi}$, $e^{3i\pi/2}$, and $e^{2\pi i}$.

VARIOUS CONCEPTIONS OF the nature of light and its present position as part of the spectrum of electromagnetic radiation are reviewed. It is shown that Maxwell's electromagnetic field equations predict the existence of electromagnetic waves, and certain simple types of waves are discussed in detail. These waves transport energy and momentum; they are reflected by conducting surfaces and refracted by an interface between two media. Finally, apparent frequency shifts associated with relative motion of source and observer are discussed.

2-1 Nature of Light

It is now known with a high degree of certainty that light is an electromagnetic disturbance, but this certainty was preceded by a long period of controversy as to the nature of light. The early scientists were familiar with two general mechanisms by which disturbances were propagated through space: motion of particles and wave motion. The first involves actual transport of material from one place to another; the other does not. It seemed natural to ask the question "Is light a particle or a wave?"

We now realize that, in a sense, this is an unfair question, inasmuch as there is no reason to think that light should fall completely into one or the other of these categories.   As we shall see, light partakes of *both* wave and particle properties.   More precisely, we should say that the *model* used to describe optical phenomena partakes of both wave and particle properties, since the ultimate function of any physical theory is to provide a model in terms of which phenomena may be described and understood.   To ask "What is light?" suggests that it ought to be just some other familiar phenomenon in disguise, such as a high-frequency sound wave or small particles of green cheese in transit; in fact, it has a fundamental identity of its own.

The speed of propagation of light has been measured quite precisely by a variety of means.   The earliest measurements made use of astronomical observations on the motion of the moons of Jupiter and apparent variations in the periods of their orbits resulting from the finite speed of propagation of light from Jupiter to earth.   Since then, terrestrial observations have been made with much greater accuracy, and at the present time the speed of light is one of the most precisely determined of all fundamental physical constants.   Its value in vacuum, usually denoted by c, is

$$c = 2.997924 \times 10^8 \text{ m/sec}$$

with a probable uncertainty of 0.000010×10^8 m/sec.   The approximate value $c = 3.00 \times 10^8$ m/sec is in error by less than 0.1 per cent.

During the seventeenth and eighteenth centuries a number of models were introduced to describe optical phenomena.   Geometrical optics had its origins in the early seventeenth century.   Propagation of light was described in terms of *rays*, which traveled in straight lines in a homogeneous medium but which could be bent by reflection at a shiny surface or refraction at an interface between two transparent media.   All optical phenomena involving lenses and mirrors can be described with considerable precision with the ray model and two simple postulates regarding reflection and refraction.   In this sense, geometrical optics is undoubtedly the simplest of all physical theories.

Even as early as 1800, however, it was clear that geometrical optics was not the last word.   A variety of interference phenomena were observed, the most famous of which was the two-slit experiment of Thomas Young, performed in 1802.   This experiment will be described in detail in Chap. 3.   By a brilliant interpretation of the results of his experiments in terms of a wave picture of light, Young was able to give very strong support to the theory that light is fundamentally a *wave* in nature.

Furthermore, he was able to determine with considerable precision the wavelengths of visible light, ranging from 7×10^{-7} m at the red end of the visible spectrum to 4×10^{-7} m at the violet end.

The wave theory of light was not immediately accepted, and controversy continued for many years. Now, however, evidence for the wave theory has become overwhelmingly convincing, and we now accept the fact that the wave model does provide a description of one important aspect of the behavior of light.

James Clerk Maxwell, the great pioneer in electromagnetic theory, predicted in 1862 the existence of *electromagnetic waves,* consisting of fluctuating electric and magnetic fields which propagate through space. His calculations included a prediction of the speed with which such waves should travel; to everyone's surprise, the predicted speed was identical with the measured value of the speed of light. This immediately suggested not only that light is a wave but that in particular it is an *electromagnetic* wave. In the words of Maxwell himself, the predicted speed of electromagnetic waves

. . . agrees so exactly with the velocity of light calculated from the optical experiments of M. Fizeau, that we can scarcely avoid the inference that *light consists in the transverse undulations of the same medium which is the cause of electric and magnetic phenomena.*

In 1887 Heinrich Hertz was able to produce in his laboratory electromagnetic waves with frequencies of the order of 10^6 to 10^8 cycles/sec, using circuitry which present-day electronics engineers would call an *oscillator.* The frequency was determined by computing the resonant frequency of an LC circuit, and the wavelength could be measured by various means, such as establishing standing waves with a reflector. In one experiment, in which the frequency of the oscillator was about 3×10^7 cycles/sec, Hertz measured the wavelength as 9.7 m. The corresponding speed of propagation of the waves, according to Eq. (1-9), is

$$u = \lambda f = (9.7 \text{ m}) (3 \times 10^7 \text{ sec}^{-1}) = 2.9 \times 10^8 \text{ m/sec}$$

which agrees well both with Maxwell's prediction and with the observed speed of light.

Hertz also showed that his electromagnetic waves could be *reflected* by plane polished metallic surfaces and *focused* by concave metallic reflectors, and that their directions could be altered by passage through dielectrics, such as wood, paraffin, and glass, in the manner of refraction of light. In short, electromagnetic waves were demonstrated to be so similar to light in behavior as to leave little doubt that light is, in fact, electromagnetic in nature. In the words of Hertz:

The described experiments appear, at least to me, in a high degree suited to remove doubt in the identity of light, heat radiation, and electrodynamic wave motion.

Following the pioneering experiments of Hertz, many other scientists and engineers investigated electromagnetic wave phenomena. In 1895, Marconi demonstrated the feasibility of wireless telegraphy, using "Hertzian waves," thus opening the door for the development of radio and television communication. It is now known that electromagnetic waves exist over an enormous range of frequencies and wavelengths; Fig. 2-1 shows this range and the common names associated with waves in various frequency ranges.

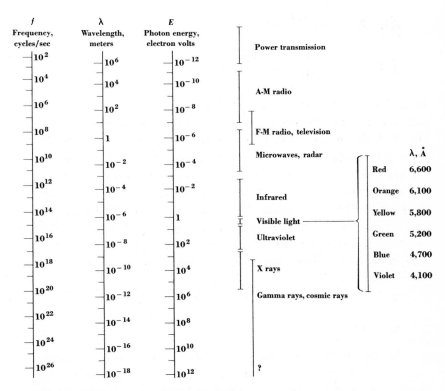

Fig. 2-1   *The electromagnetic spectrum. All scales are logarithmic. The scale ends in the vicinity of the highest-energy secondary cosmic rays that have been observed up to the present time.*

2-2   Maxwell's Equations

In this section it will be shown that the existence of electromagnetic waves can be predicted from Maxwell's electromagnetic field equations. It is assumed that the reader has already acquired some familiarity with these equations in integral form, but we begin by reviewing briefly the equations and their experimental basis.

When no material medium is present, the electric field **E** and the magnetic induction field **B** in vacuum are related to the electric charge density ρ and electric current density **j** by the following four equations, expressed in the mks system of units:

$$\int \mathbf{E} \cdot d\mathbf{S} = \frac{1}{\epsilon_0} \int \rho \, dV \tag{2-1a}$$

$$\int \mathbf{B} \cdot d\mathbf{S} = 0 \tag{2-1b}$$

$$\oint \mathbf{E} \cdot d\mathbf{l} = -\int \frac{\partial \mathbf{B}}{\partial t} \cdot d\mathbf{S} \tag{2-1c}$$

$$\oint \mathbf{B} \cdot d\mathbf{l} = \mu_0 \int \left(\mathbf{j} + \epsilon_0 \frac{\partial \mathbf{E}}{\partial t} \right) \cdot d\mathbf{S} \tag{2-1d}$$

In the first two equations, the integral on the left is taken over a closed surface and that on the right through the volume enclosed by that surface, with the convention that the direction of the surface element $d\mathbf{S}$ is out of the surface. In the last two equations, the integral on the left is taken over a closed curve and that on the right over any open surface bounded by that curve, with the convention that the directions of the line element $d\mathbf{l}$ and the surface element $d\mathbf{S}$ are chosen so that at a point near the edge the direction of $d\mathbf{l} \times d\mathbf{S}$ is away from the surface. The quantities ϵ_0 and μ_0 are called the *permittivity* and *permeability* of vacuum, respectively. Their numerical values in the mks system are

$$\epsilon_0 = \frac{1}{36\pi \times 10^9} \text{ coul}^2/\text{nt m}^2 = 8.85 \times 10^{-12} \text{ coul}^2/\text{nt m}^2$$

$$\mu_0 = 4\pi \times 10^{-7} \text{ weber/amp m}$$

We now review briefly the experimental basis of Maxwell's equations and their physical meaning. The first, a relation between the electric field **E** and its source (the charge density ρ), is Gauss' law of electrostatics, stating that the total flux of **E** out of a closed surface is proportional to the total electric charge enclosed by the surface. This in turn is derived from Coulomb's law expressing the force of interaction between electric charges.   The second, the corresponding relation for the magnetic field **B**, states that there is *no* "magnetic charge" analogous to the electric charge, so that the total flux of **B** through a closed surface is always zero.

The third equation is Faraday's law of induction, stating that the induced electromotive force in a loop, expressed as $\oint \mathbf{E} \cdot d\mathbf{l}$, is equal to the time rate of change of the total magnetic flux $\int \mathbf{B} \cdot d\mathbf{S}$ through the loop.   The fourth is a generalization of Ampère's law, giving the relation between the magnetic field **B** and its source, the current density **j**. Without the last term it is Ampère's law for magnetostatics, stating that the line integral of **B** around a closed path equals the total current linked by that path.   The last term, an essential generalization added by Maxwell, shows that a changing electric field acts as a source of magnetic field in exactly the same way as a real current.   In fact, the term $\epsilon_0\, \partial \mathbf{E}/\partial t$ in the fourth equation is usually called the *displacement current density* to emphasize its parallel with the ordinary current density **j** as a source of **B**.

For electric and magnetic fields not in vacuum but in a material, the equations have to be modified in two ways, corresponding to the phenomena of electric polarization and magnetization.   Both free charge and polarization charge act as sources of **E**, and magnetization provides an additional source of **B**; the first and fourth equations, which relate the fields to their sources, have to be modified accordingly.   The second and third equations retain their validity without modification.

In the following discussion, we shall consider only materials in which the electric polarization is directly proportional to the electric field, and the magnetization to the magnetic field.   For such materials the necessary modifications consist simply in replacing ϵ_0 and μ_0 by ϵ and μ, respectively, which are properties characteristic of the material, called its *permittivity* and *permeability*, respectively.   These are often expressed as

$$\epsilon = K_E\, \epsilon_0 \tag{2-2a}$$

$$\mu = K_M\, \mu_0 \tag{2-2b}$$

where K_E and K_M are called the *dielectric constant* and the *relative permeability*, respectively, of the material.   Finally, to include the possibility that the regions of integration may include more than one material, we include ϵ and μ inside the appropriate integrals.

When these modifications are made, and when no free charges or currents are present (the usual case in simple wave propagation), the Maxwell equations take the form

$$\int \epsilon \mathbf{E} \cdot d\mathbf{S} = 0 \tag{2-3a}$$

$$\int \mathbf{B} \cdot d\mathbf{S} = 0 \tag{2-3b}$$

$$\oint \mathbf{E} \cdot d\mathbf{l} = -\int \frac{\partial \mathbf{B}}{\partial t} \cdot d\mathbf{S} \tag{2-3c}$$

$$\oint \frac{1}{\mu} \mathbf{B} \cdot d\mathbf{l} = \int \epsilon \frac{\partial \mathbf{E}}{\partial t} \cdot d\mathbf{S} \tag{2-3d}$$

These equations can be expressed slightly more simply by introducing the auxiliary quantities **D** and **H**, defined by the equations

$$\mathbf{D} = \epsilon \mathbf{E} \tag{2-4a}$$

$$\mathbf{H} = \frac{\mathbf{B}}{\mu} \tag{2-4b}$$

When these quantities are used for calculations, it should be kept in mind that **E** and **B** are still the fields with the most direct physical significance.

2-3   Plane Electromagnetic Waves

We now proceed to show that the concept of an electromagnetic wave is permitted by Maxwell's equations. The procedure will be to make a simple assumption about a possible wave behavior of the electric and magnetic fields and then to show that the assumed field configurations are compatible with Maxwell's equations if the wave function for each field satisfies the wave equation. For simplicity, the discussion will be confined to the simplest possible wave.

The field configuration to be discussed has the following properties: The wave propagates in the x direction; the **E** field has a component only in the y direction, and the **B** field only in the z direction. These components are denoted in the usual way as E_y and B_z. Each of these depends on x and t, but *not* on y or z. That is, at any instant of time, each field is uniform over any plane perpendicular to the x axis. An example of a wave having these properties is shown schematically in Fig. 2-2.

We now show that such a wave is compatible with Maxwell's equations. First we note that the first two equations are satisfied automatically. At any instant the lines of force associated with the **E** field are parallel straight lines, parallel to the y axis. For any closed surface, there are precisely as many lines entering the enclosed volume on one side as leave it on the opposite side. Thus the total flux of **E** is always zero. The same argument also applies to **B**, and so Eqs. (2-3a) and (2-3b) are satisfied.

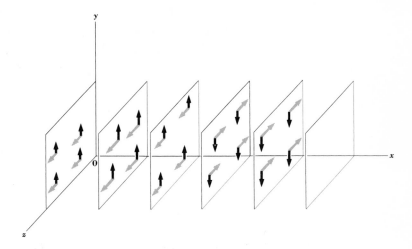

Fig. 2-2 *Schematic representation of a plane electromagnetic wave. The electric field* **E** *at various
points is shown by a solid vector; the magnetic field* **B**,
by a shaded vector. At each point, **E** *and* **B** *are
perpendicular to each other and to the direction of
propagation. At any instant, each field is uniform
over any plane perpendicular to the direction of
propagation.*

In applying the third of Maxwell's equations it is useful to consider
a surface lying parallel to the xy plane. By assumption, **B** is perpendicular to such a surface, and **E** is parallel to it. The choice of this
particular surface is made more reasonable by the observation that for
a surface parallel to either of the other two coordinate planes both sides
of the equation are identically zero, so that such a choice would not lead
to a useful result.

In particular, we consider the rectangular surface element shown
in Fig. 2-3a, with dimensions Δx and Δy. We shall write approximate
expressions for the integrals and then take the limit as Δx and Δy approach zero. Considering the integral $\oint \mathbf{E} \cdot d\mathbf{l}$, the top and bottom sections of the boundary make no contribution, since for these the line
element $d\mathbf{l}$ is perpendicular to **E**. Also, since E_y is independent of y,
the two contributions from the other two sides are $-(E_y)_x \, \Delta y$ and
$(E_y)_{x+\Delta x} \, \Delta y$, where the notation indicates the value of x at which E_y is
evaluated. Thus

$$\oint \mathbf{E} \cdot d\mathbf{l} = [(E_y)_{x+\Delta x} - (E_y)_x] \, \Delta y \tag{2-5}$$

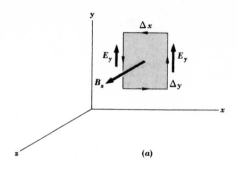

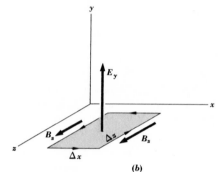

Fig. 2-3 (a) *Time variation of B_z is associated with space variation of E_y.* (b) *Space variation of B_z is associated with time variation of E_y. The directions of the line integrals are shown.*

Since the magnetic field is perpendicular to this surface element, the right-hand side of the third equation for this surface is simply

$$-\int \frac{\partial \mathbf{B}}{\partial t} \cdot d\mathbf{S} = -\frac{\partial B_z}{\partial t} \Delta x \, \Delta y \tag{2-6}$$

We now equate Eqs. (2-5) and (2-6), as indicated by Eq. (2-3c), and divide by $\Delta x \, \Delta y$. In the limit when $\Delta x \to 0$, the left-hand side becomes simply the partial derivative of E_y with respect to x, and we obtain finally

$$\frac{\partial E_y}{\partial x} = -\frac{\partial B_z}{\partial t} \tag{2-7}$$

This equation gives the electric field (expressed in terms of its derivative with respect to x) resulting from the time-varying magnetic field B_z.

A similar relationship results from applying Maxwell's fourth equation. Considering the directions of the fields involved, the appropriate surface to which to apply this equation is that shown in Fig. 2-3b. The calculation proceeds just as before. We have

$$\oint \frac{1}{\mu} \mathbf{B} \cdot d\mathbf{l} = -\frac{1}{\mu} [(B_z)_{x+\Delta x} - (B_z)_x] \, \Delta z$$

$$\int \epsilon \frac{\partial \mathbf{E}}{\partial t} \cdot d\mathbf{S} = \epsilon \frac{\partial E_y}{\partial t} \Delta x \, \Delta z$$

and finally, using Eq. (2-3d), dividing by $\Delta x \, \Delta z$, and taking the limit as $\Delta x \to 0$,

$$\frac{\partial B_z}{\partial x} = -\mu \epsilon \frac{\partial E_y}{\partial t} \tag{2-8}$$

Equations (2-7) and (2-8) are two simultaneous differential equations which relate the derivative of one field with respect to x to the time derivative of the other. The component B_z can be eliminated from these two equations by taking the derivative of Eq. (2-7) with respect to x and the derivative of Eq. (2-8) with respect to t and combining the results. We obtain

$$\frac{\partial^2 E_y}{\partial x^2} = \mu \epsilon \frac{\partial^2 E_y}{\partial t^2} \tag{2-9}$$

By a similar procedure, E_y can be eliminated; the resulting equation is

$$\frac{\partial^2 B_z}{\partial x^2} = \mu \epsilon \frac{\partial^2 B_z}{\partial t^2} \tag{2-10}$$

Both these equations have the general form of the wave equation introduced in Sec. 1-2:

$$\frac{\partial^2 f}{\partial x^2} = \frac{1}{u^2} \frac{\partial^2 f}{\partial t^2} \tag{2-11}$$

That is, the electric and magnetic fields we have postulated *are* solutions of Maxwell's equations, provided each varies with x and t in accordance with the wave equation. We see immediately that the speed u of the wave is given by

$$\mu \epsilon = \frac{1}{u^2} \qquad \text{or} \qquad u = \frac{1}{\sqrt{\mu \epsilon}} \tag{2-12}$$

We can now draw on our experience with solutions of the wave equation for the vibrating string to find possible wave functions for E_y and B_z. The simplest periodic solutions are sinusoidal. For example, a possible wave function for E_y is

$$E_y = E_0 \cos (kx - \omega t) \tag{2-13}$$

where E_0 is the amplitude of the wave, corresponding to the maximum value of E_y. The wave number k and angular frequency ω are related, as for any periodic wave, by $\omega = uk$, and u is given by Eq. (2-12).

The corresponding wave function for B_z can be found by using Eq. (2-7). We find

$$\frac{\partial E_y}{\partial x} = -\frac{\partial B_z}{\partial t} = -kE_0 \sin (kx - \omega t)$$

$$B_z = \frac{k}{\omega} E_0 \cos (kx - \omega t) = \frac{E_0}{u} \cos (kx - \omega t) \tag{2-14}$$

The above discussion has been somewhat formal, and it is well to pause here to consider its meaning. We have shown that Maxwell's electromagnetic field equations permit the existence of solutions representing electromagnetic *waves,* which in vacuum or a homogeneous medium propagate with a definite speed. In particular, we have found a solution corresponding to electric and magnetic fields which are perpendicular to the direction of propagation and to each other and which at any instant are uniform over a plane perpendicular to the direction of propagation. Because of this characteristic, such waves are called *plane* waves. Because both **E** and **B** are perpendicular to the direction of propagation, they are also *transverse* waves. In the case of sinusoidal waves, both **E** and **B** are, at any point in space, periodic functions of time, and at any point their time variations are in phase. At any instant,

$$B_z = \frac{E_y}{u} \tag{2-15}$$

and this relationship is independent of the frequency or wave number of the wave.

In vacuum, the wave speed given by Eq. (2-12) is $u = (\mu_0\epsilon_0)^{-1/2}$. Inserting the numerical values of the constants yields the result that the speed of electromagnetic waves in vacuum is

$$u = \frac{1}{\sqrt{(4\pi \times 10^{-7})(8.85 \times 10^{-12})}} \text{ m/sec} = 2.998 \times 10^8 \text{ m/sec} \tag{2-16}$$

which, as already pointed out, agrees with the observed value of the speed of light in vacuum. Since the days of Maxwell and Hertz, many other experimenters have measured the speeds of electromagnetic waves in vacuum over a wide range of frequency, and the results are all in agreement with Eq. (2-16).

From the fact that the differential equations we have developed are *linear* equations, we conclude that electromagnetic waves obey the *principle of superposition* discussed in Sec. 1-5. For example, we could superpose a wave described by Eqs. (2-13) and (2-14) with another having the same amplitude and frequency but propagating in the $-x$ direction. The resultant electric and magnetic field intensities, obtained by simply adding the corresponding fields for the separate waves, represent a standing wave, completely analogous to those discussed in connection with the vibrating string. In fact, standing waves were used by Hertz to determine the wavelength of his electromagnetic waves. In following sections many other important applications of the principle of superposition will appear.

2-4   Energy in Electromagnetic Waves

It has been mentioned that energy and momentum can be transported by electromagnetic waves. It is known from electromagnetic theory that associated with the presence of electric and magnetic fields in space or in a material is a density of energy w (energy per unit volume) given by

$$w = \frac{1}{2}\left(\epsilon E^2 + \frac{B^2}{\mu}\right) = \frac{1}{2}(\epsilon E^2 + \mu H^2) \tag{2-17}$$

where the vector field $\mathbf{H}$ defined by Eq. (2-4b) has been introduced to simplify later calculations. We now examine the implications of this expression in the case of the plane waves introduced in Sec. 2-3.

We consider a volume consisting of a small cube of dimensions Δx, Δy, and Δz, as shown in Fig. 2-4. The total electromagnetic field energy U in this volume is approximately

$$U = \tfrac{1}{2}(\epsilon E_y{}^2 + \mu H_z{}^2)\,\Delta x\,\Delta y\,\Delta z \tag{2-18}$$

This energy may change as a result of energy transported in or out of the volume by the electromagnetic field.

*Fig. 2-4   Energy flow in an elemental cube. The energy-flow vector **S** shows that energy enters the left face of the cube at a rate $(E_y H_z)_x$ and leaves the right face at a rate $(E_y H_z)_{x+\Delta x}$, per unit surface area. The difference of these quantities is the net rate of change of energy in the cube, dU/dt.*

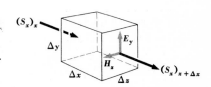

The time rate of change of U is

$$\frac{dU}{dt} = \left(\epsilon E_y \frac{\partial E_y}{\partial t} + \mu H_z \frac{\partial H_z}{\partial t} \right) \Delta x \, \Delta y \, \Delta z \tag{2-19}$$

With the help of Eqs. (2-7) and (2-8) and the relation $\mathbf{B} = \mu\mathbf{H}$, this can be written

$$\frac{dU}{dt} = \left[\epsilon E_y \left(-\frac{1}{\epsilon\mu} \frac{\partial B_z}{\partial x} \right) + \mu H_z \left(-\frac{1}{\mu} \frac{\partial E_y}{\partial x} \right) \right] \Delta x \, \Delta y \, \Delta z$$

$$= -\left[\frac{\partial}{\partial x} (E_y H_z) \, \Delta x \right] \Delta y \, \Delta z \tag{2-20}$$

Since Δx is small, the quantity in brackets in the last equation represents approximately the *change* in the quantity $E_y H_z$ from x to $x + \Delta x$. That is,

$$\frac{dU}{dt} = -[(E_y H_z)_{x+\Delta x} - (E_y H_z)_x] \, \Delta y \, \Delta z \tag{2-21}$$

This expression shows that the net rate of change of energy within the volume element depends on the *difference* of the values of the quantity $E_y H_z$ on the left and right faces and on the area $\Delta y \, \Delta z$ of these faces. This observation suggests that $E_y H_z$ represents a time rate of energy flow per unit surface area, so that $(E_y H_z)_x \, \Delta y \, \Delta z$ represents the energy flow *into* the cube at the left face and $(E_y H_z)_{x+\Delta x} \, \Delta y \, \Delta z$ the energy flow *out* at the right face. The direction of energy transport is clearly the same as the direction of propagation of the wave, and so it is natural to regard $E_y H_z$ as the x component of a vector quantity which represents both the magnitude and direction of the energy flow per unit time, per unit surface area. Denoting this vector quantity by $\mathbf{S}$, we have

$$S_x = E_y H_z \tag{2-22}$$

In this situation, the y and z components of $\mathbf{S}$ are zero.

The quantity $\mathbf{S}$ is called the *Poynting vector*. Its units are energy per unit time, per unit surface area; in the mks system the units of $\mathbf{S}$ are watts/m^2. Equation (2-22) is consistent with the more general definition

$$\mathbf{S} = \mathbf{E} \times \mathbf{H} \tag{2-23}$$

A more complete derivation, using Maxwell's equations and a theorem of vector calculus, yields the result

$$\frac{d}{dt} \int (\tfrac{1}{2}\epsilon E^2 + \tfrac{1}{2}\mu H^2) \, dV = -\int (\mathbf{E} \times \mathbf{H}) \cdot d\mathbf{S} \tag{2-24}$$

In this expression, the integral on the left side represents the total electromagnetic field energy in the volume V, and that on the right the total rate of energy flow out of the closed surface bounding this volume. Thus Eq. (2-24) states that the time rate of change of total energy in the volume is equal to the negative of the surface integral of **S**; this result justifies the interpretation of **S** as a rate of energy flow per unit area.

For the plane wave described by Eqs. (2-13) and (2-14) the Poynting vector is given by

$$S_x = \frac{E_0^2}{\mu\epsilon} \cos^2 (kx - \omega t)$$

$$= \sqrt{\frac{\epsilon}{\mu}} E_0^2 \cos^2 (kx - \omega t) \tag{2-25}$$

Thus S_x is proportional to $\cos^2 (kx - \omega t)$; the average value of this function can be shown to be ½, and so the *average* rate of energy flow is

$$S_{\text{av}} = \frac{1}{2} \sqrt{\frac{\epsilon}{\mu}} E_0^2 \tag{2-26}$$

The energy flow is always proportional to the *square* of the electric-field amplitude. The quantity S_{av} is referred to in optics as the *intensity* of the radiation.

Maxwell also demonstrated that electromagnetic waves transport *momentum*. When electromagnetic radiation carrying a total energy U is absorbed by a perfectly absorbing surface, the quantity of momentum p transferred to the surface is $p = U/c$. This result implies that associated with the energy flow given by the Poynting vector there is also a *momentum flow*, given by **E** $\times$ **H**$/c$. This result agrees with the predictions of the special theory of relativity, which shows that, for a particle with zero rest mass moving with a speed c, the energy and momentum are related by the equation $U = pc$. Remarkably, Maxwell's predictions preceded the development of the theory of relativity by over 30 years.

The momentum transfer caused by electromagnetic radiation has been measured directly by means of an apparatus shown schematically in Fig. 2-5. A mirror or a blackened disk is suspended by a fine fiber, forming a torsion balance similar in principle to that used by Cavendish to investigate gravitational forces. When light is permitted to strike the blackened disk, it is completely absorbed, and its momentum is transferred completely to the disk. If instead light strikes the mirror and is totally reflected, the momentum change is *twice* as great in magni-

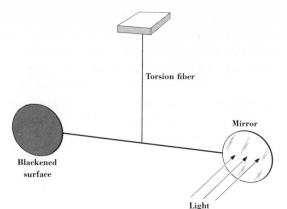

Fig. 2-5 *Torsion balance used to measure radiation pressure. The amount of twist in the horizontal beam is proportional to the force that the radiation exerts on the mirror or blackened surface.*

tude as the initial momentum, and the momentum transfer to the mirror is consequently also doubled. The radiation pressure is measured by observing the angle through which the horizontal beam twists.

The experiment is somewhat difficult to perform with precision; the pressure is very small (about 5×10^{-6} nt/m^2 for direct sunlight), and the experiment must be performed in a high vacuum to eliminate spurious effects resulting from convection currents in the surrounding air. Results of this experiment, performed first in 1903 by Nichols and Hull, confirm the above predictions.

2-5 Reflection and Refraction

Thus far, the discussion of electromagnetic waves has been confined to the propagation of waves in a homogeneous nonconducting medium. We now consider what happens when such a wave strikes a metallic conductor or an interface between two media having different electric and magnetic properties.

First, we suppose that a plane wave propagating in the $-x$ direction strikes a large perfectly conducting metallic plane coincident with the yz coordinate plane, as shown in Fig. 2-6a. What happens? We recall that in an ideal conductor there can never be an electric field because, if an attempt is made to establish an electric field, the mobile charges inside the conductor immediately readjust themselves so as to cancel it. Therefore, the electric field must always be zero at $x = 0$. But since the incident wave does not always have $\mathbf{E} = 0$ in this plane, the currents which flow in the conductor must generate another wave such that the superposition of it with the incident wave results in a *total* electric field intensity which is always zero in the plane $x = 0$.

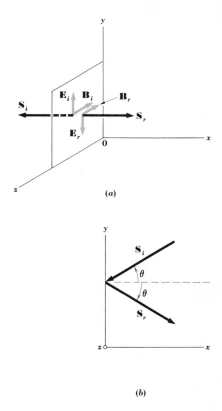

Fig. 2-6 (a) A plane wave strikes a metallic reflecting surface in the Oyz plane. The **E** and **B** fields and the Poynting vector for each wave are shown for a point near the surface. The total electric field **E** is zero near the surface, while **B** is not; the net rate of energy flow to the surface is zero if it is a perfect reflector (a metal with zero resistivity). (b) When the incoming wave direction is not perpendicular to the surface, the incident and reflected wave directions (shown by the directions of the **S** vectors) make equal angles with a perpendicular to the surface, and all three lines lie in a single plane.

(a)

(b)

This situation is completely analogous to that of reflection of waves at a fixed point on a vibrating string, discussed in Sec. 1-5. In that case the displacement at the fixed point was always zero, just as the conductor requires that the electric field be zero in a certain plane. The fixed point exerts forces on the string such as to generate a reflected wave, and the currents induced in the conductor generate a reflected electromagnetic wave. In order to provide complete cancellation at $x = 0$, the electric field of the reflected wave at $x = 0$ must have the same amplitude as that of the incident wave but must be $180°$ out of phase with it. Thus if the electric field E_i of the incident wave is given by

$$E_i = E_0 \cos (kx + \omega t)$$

then that of the reflected wave is given by

$$E_r = -E_0 \cos (kx - \omega t)$$

and the total electric field intensity is

$$E = E_i + E_r = -2E_0 \sin kx \sin \omega t \tag{2-27}$$

This result is obtained by the methods described in Sec. 1-5, used to develop Eq. (1-19). Just as for the similar case with the vibrating string, the result is a *standing wave*.

The corresponding expressions for the magnetic fields of the incident and reflected waves, and the total magnetic field, are

$$B_i = -\frac{E_0}{u} \cos (kx + \omega t)$$

$$B_r = -\frac{E_0}{u} \cos (kx - \omega t) \tag{2-28}$$

$$B = -\frac{2E_0}{u} \cos kx \cos \omega t$$

The negative sign in the first equation arises because, for a wave in the $-x$ direction, **B** must be in the $-z$ direction when **E** is in the $+y$ direction. We note that **B** does not vanish at the surface of the conductor, and there is no reason why it should.

An analysis which is precisely the same in principle but somewhat more complicated in detail shows that when the conducting plane is not perpendicular to the direction of propagation of the wave but is inclined at an angle, as shown in Fig. 2-6*b*, the reflected wave is not parallel to the incident wave but rather makes an angle with the plane equal to that of the incident wave, and in the opposite sense, as shown in the figure. Thus from the electromagnetic nature of light one can *derive* the familiar optical law that in reflection the angle of incidence equals the angle of reflection.

Next we consider the simplest possible example of *refraction* of an electromagnetic wave. Suppose that all space is divided by the *yz* plane into two regions, which are filled with different dielectric materials, with the material in the $x < 0$ half characterized by constants ϵ_1 and μ_1 and that in the $x > 0$ half by ϵ_2 and μ_2. When a plane electromagnetic wave propagating in the $+x$ direction strikes the boundary surface, some of the incident energy is reflected and the remainder is transmitted (refracted) in the second medium. This phenomenon is identical in principle to the familiar experience of looking into a store window and seeing both transmitted light from inside and reflected light from the street.

The wave frequency is the same in both media, but in general the wave number k is not, since the wave speed, given always by $u = (\mu\epsilon)^{-1/2}$, is different. We denote the values for $x < 0$ by u_1 and k_1, and for $x > 0$ by u_2 and k_2. Figure 2-7 shows electric and magnetic fields

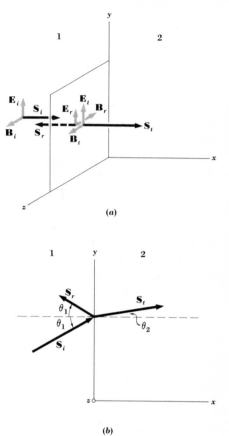

Fig. 2-7   (a) *Reflection and refraction of a plane wave at an interface between two media. The **E** and **B** fields and the Poynting vector **S** are shown for the incident, reflected, and transmitted waves near the interface at one instant.* (b) *When the incident wave is not perpendicular to the surface, the incident and reflected wave directions make equal angles to a perpendicular to the surface, and the angles of incident and refracted waves are related by Eq.* (2-38). *All three **S** vectors lie in a single plane perpendicular to the interface.*

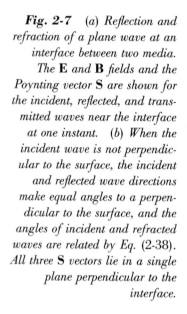

corresponding to the various waves; the Poynting vector for each is also shown to indicate the direction of propagation.

In the following development, the subscript i refers to the incident wave, r to the reflected wave, and t to the transmitted wave. Denoting by E_{0i}, E_{0r}, and E_{0t} the amplitudes of the incident, reflected, and transmitted waves, we may write for the total electric field E_1 in the region $x < 0$

$$E_1 = E_i + E_r = E_{0i} \cos (k_1 x - \omega t) + E_{0r} \cos (k_1 x + \omega t) \tag{2-29}$$

and for that (E_t) in the region $x > 0$

$$E_t = E_{0t} \cos (k_2 x - \omega t) \tag{2-30}$$

Equation (2-7) may be used as before to find the corresponding expressions for **B**, which are

$$B_1 = B_i + B_r = \frac{E_{0i}}{u_1} \cos (k_1 x - \omega t) - \frac{E_{0r}}{u_1} \cos (k_1 x + \omega t) \qquad (2\text{-}31)$$

$$B_t = \frac{E_{0t}}{u_2} \cos (k_2 x - \omega t) \qquad (2\text{-}32)$$

If the amplitude E_{0i} of the incident wave is known, the amplitudes E_{0t} and E_{0r} of the transmitted and reflected waves, respectively, can be calculated. The procedure is analogous to the case of reflection from a conductor. In that case it was shown that the total wave function for **E** must satisfy not only the wave equation but the boundary condition that its component parallel to the conducting plane is always zero everywhere in the plane $x = 0$. In the present case there are corresponding boundary conditions governing the behavior of the **E** and **B** fields at the interface between the two dielectrics. The boundary conditions, derived from Maxwell's equations, are most conveniently stated in terms of the components of each field parallel ($\parallel$) and perpendicular ($\perp$) to the interface on each side. They are

$$\epsilon_1 E_{\perp 1} = \epsilon_2 E_{\perp 2} \qquad (2\text{-}33a)$$

$$B_{\perp 1} = B_{\perp 2} \qquad (2\text{-}33b)$$

$$E_{\parallel 1} = E_{\parallel 2} \qquad (2\text{-}33c)$$

$$\frac{B_{\parallel 1}}{\mu_1} = \frac{B_{\parallel 2}}{\mu_2} \qquad (2\text{-}33d)$$

These equations are derived in most books on electricity and magnetism.[1] Very briefly, the first and second are derived by applying Maxwell's first and second equations, respectively, to a coin-shaped surface as shown in Fig. 2-8a, straddling the boundary surface and thin enough so that the contributions to the surface integrals from the edges are negligible. Correspondingly, the third and fourth equations are derived by applying Maxwell's third and fourth equations, respectively, to a long, narrow rectangular path straddling the interface as shown in Fig. 2-8b.

According to Eq. (2-33c), when the value $x = 0$ is substituted into Eqs. (2-29) and (2-30), they must agree for all values of t. Carrying out this calculation and dividing out the common factor $\cos \omega t$, we obtain the relation

$$E_{0i} + E_{0r} = E_{0t} \qquad (2\text{-}34)$$

---

[1] See, for example, A. F. Kip, "Fundamentals of Electricity and Magnetism," secs. 5-6 and 9-6, McGraw-Hill Book Company, New York, 1962.

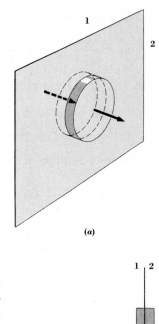

Fig. 2-8   *Regions of integration used to derive boundary conditions for* **E** *and* **B** *at an interface between two dielectrics.* (a) *A coin-shaped surface with faces parallel to the interface. The total flux of* **E** *or of* **B** *out of this surface is zero, according to Eq. (2-3a) or (2-3b). Hence Eqs. (2-33a) and (2-33b) are established.* (b) *A long thin rectangle whose area may be made arbitrarily small. Applying Eq. (2-3c) or (2-3d), the right side of each vanishes, and Eqs. (2-33c) and (2-33d) follow.*

A similar calculation using Eq. (2-33d) with Eqs. (2-31) and (2-32) leads to the relation

$$\frac{E_{0i}}{u_1 \mu_1} - \frac{E_{0r}}{u_1 \mu_1} = \frac{E_{0t}}{u_2 \mu_2} \tag{2-35}$$

These are two simultaneous equations for E_{0r} and E_{0t} in terms of E_{0i}, which is supposedly known. They may be solved simultaneously to obtain explicit expressions for E_{0r} and E_{0t}. Before completing this solution, however, it is useful to introduce a simplifying approximation. For many materials that are transparent to electromagnetic radiation, the magnetic permeability is very close to its value for vacuum. Thus in Eq. (2-35) we can make the approximation $\mu_1 = \mu_2 = \mu_0$. Furthermore, the *index of refraction n* of a material is defined as the ratio of the speed c of electromagnetic waves in vacuum to its value u_1 or u_2 in the material. That is,

$$n_1 = \frac{c}{u_1} \qquad n_2 = \frac{c}{u_2} \tag{2-36}$$

Thus Eqs. (2-34) and (2-35) can be rewritten

$$E_{0i} + E_{0r} = E_{0t}$$
$$n_1(E_{0i} - E_{0r}) = n_2 E_{0t}$$

Simultaneous solution of these equations yields the following:

$$E_{0r} = \frac{n_1 - n_2}{n_1 + n_2} E_{0i} \qquad E_{0t} = \frac{2n_1}{n_1 + n_2} E_{0i} \tag{2-37}$$

We note that, if $n_1 = n_2$, the reflected amplitude E_{0r} is zero and the transmitted amplitude E_{0t} is equal to that of the incident wave, as we should expect.

The first of Eqs. (2-37) shows another interesting result. When the index of refraction of the first medium is greater than that of the second, as with glass and air, the reflected wave near the boundary has the same phase as the incident wave. That is, the situation is just as shown in Fig. 2-7a. But in the reverse case, when $n_2 > n_1$, the amplitudes E_{0r} and E_{0i} have opposite signs, indicating that the reflected wave has its **E** field inverted with respect to the incident wave. This result will be useful in understanding some interference phenomena to be discussed in Chap. 3.

This analysis can be extended to the case where the direction of the incident wave is not perpendicular to the interface. The calculation is more complicated, because each field has at least two components. It turns out that in all cases the reflected wave makes an angle with the interface equal to that of the incident wave, just as in the case of reflection from a metallic surface. This is illustrated in Fig. 2-7b. The angle θ_2 of the refracted wave shown in Fig. 2-7b is always related to that of the incident wave θ_1 by

$$n_1 \sin \theta_1 = n_2 \sin \theta_2 \tag{2-38}$$

which is the familiar Snell's law of geometrical optics. Thus it is possible to *derive* from electromagnetic theory all the familiar laws of geometrical optics. These were originally discovered as empirical laws long before their theoretical basis was well understood.

In this case, the y and z components at any point are equal at each instant.   A little thought shows that the result is a plane-polarized wave with amplitude $\sqrt{2}\,E_0$ and plane of polarization at $45°$ to the xy and xz planes.

Another interesting case occurs when there is a phase difference of $\pi/2$.   Suppose the components are given by

$$E_y = E_0 \cos\,(kx - \omega t)$$

$$E_z = E_0 \cos\left(kx - \omega t - \frac{\pi}{2}\right) = E_0 \sin\,(kx - \omega t)$$

(2-40)

This pair of functions corresponds to Fig. 2-14 at time $t = 0$.   It is seen that, unlike the case of plane-polarized light, the total **E** field is never

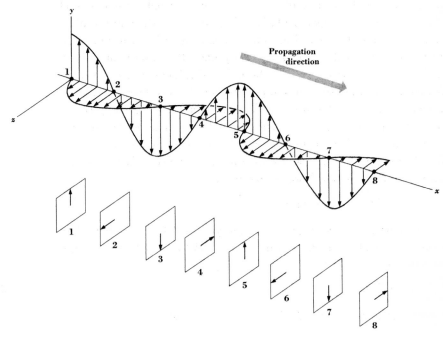

Fig. 2-14   *Superposition of two plane waves with equal amplitudes and wavelengths, plane-polarized in perpendicular planes and 90° out of phase.   The* **E** *fields are shown at one instant; the bottom diagrams show the resultant* **E** *field at several points.   At any point,* **E** *is never zero; it has constant magnitude but rotates with the angular velocity of the wave.   In the case shown, the resultant wave is right circularly polarized.*

zero. Instead, it has a constant magnitude, as shown by the fact that $(E_y{}^2 + E_z{}^2)^{1/2}$ is constant, and a direction that rotates uniformly about the direction of propagation with angular velocity equal to ω. This radiation is said to be *circularly polarized*. By convention, it is called right circularly polarized if, as in the above example, the **E** field at a fixed point in space rotates clockwise, as viewed looking backward toward the source, and left circularly if counterclockwise, as would be the case if the phase difference had the opposite sign.

If the phase difference is other than $\pi/2$, or if the two amplitudes are unequal, it can be shown that the electric-field vector at a given point traces out not a circle but an ellipse, and such light is said to be *elliptically polarized*.

Circularly polarized light may be made readily from plane-polarized light by means of a piece of birefringent crystal of such thickness that two perpendicularly polarized waves which are in phase when they enter the crystal are out of phase by $90°$ when they leave. Such a crystal is called a *quarter-wave plate*. Its action is most easily understood by observing that if the index of refraction of the material is different for the two planes of polarization the wavelength is also different. Let us call the two wavelengths λ_1 and λ_2, and suppose that $n_2 > n_1$, so that $\lambda_1 > \lambda_2$. Then the object is to choose the thickness d of the plate so that it contains a certain number N of the longer wavelength but $N + \frac{1}{4}$ of the shorter, in order to introduce a phase difference of $\pi/2$. Thus the condition to be met is

$$d = N\lambda_1 = (N + \tfrac{1}{4})\lambda_2 \tag{2-41}$$

Furthermore, the wavelengths are simply related to the indices of refraction n_1 and n_2 in the two directions and to the wavelength λ_0 in vacuum by

$$\lambda_0 = n_1\lambda_1 = n_2\lambda_2 \tag{2-42}$$

Combining Eqs. (2-41) and (2-42) yields the result

$$d = \frac{\lambda_0}{4(n_2 - n_1)} \tag{2-43}$$

for the thickness of the plate. Details of this derivation are left as an exercise. Finally, the requirement of equal components in the two perpendicular directions corresponding to n_1 and n_2 is achieved simply by using a plane-polarized beam at $45°$ to these directions. In a similar manner, a quarter-wave plate can be used to convert circularly polarized light into plane-polarized.

Radiation from individual atoms is sometimes circularly polarized. When the gas in a glow discharge tube emitting light is subjected to a strong magnetic field, shifts in the frequencies of the emitted light are observed, and various components of the emitted radiation are found to have various states of plane or circular polarization. The shift in frequency produced by the magnetic field is called the *Zeeman effect*. This effect was predicted in 1862 by Michael Faraday, but because of the smallness of the shifts it was not actually observed until 1896 (by Pieter Zeeman). It provides very direct experimental evidence that the sources of light are electric charges in motion in atoms. The Zeeman effect will be discussed in more detail in Chap. 8.

Polarization of light has many practical applications. The effectiveness of polaroid sunglasses is due in large measure to the fact that reflected glare from highways and water is partially polarized, and this glare can be reduced by polarizing filters. Some materials under stress become birefringent to a degree depending on the amount of stress. This phenomenon is the basis of the science of *photoelasticity*, which is an important tool in stress analysis. Many organic compounds in solutions, the most familiar examples being the sugars dextrose and levulose, have the effect of rotating the plane of polarization of a plane-polarized wave. This effect provides a useful analytical tool in distinguishing between two compounds which are so-called *mirror isomers*, that is, compounds whose molecular structures are mirror images of each other. The same effect can be used to measure concentrations of solutions of such compounds.

2-7   Doppler Effect

We conclude this chapter with a brief discussion of a phenomenon which, in this day of high-speed travel, is familiar to every child. When an automobile approaches, blowing its horn, the pitch seems to drop suddenly as the car passes the observer. Similarly, if the horn is stationary but the observer moves past, the pitch seems to drop as he passes. The frequency of a wave measured by an observer who is moving relative to the source is different from the frequency observed at the position of the source; when source and observer are approaching each other, the apparent frequency is increased, and when receding, decreased. This phenomenon, called the *Doppler effect* after its discoverer, occurs with all kinds of wave motion, although in the case of mechanical waves involving a material medium its nature is somewhat different from the case of electromagnetic waves, where no medium is involved.

We consider first the case of sound waves when the observer is at rest in the medium, such as air or water, but the source is traveling toward it with speed v. Let the frequency of the source be f, with corresponding period $T = 1/f$, and let the wave speed be u. In a time interval T, during which one cycle of the wave is emitted, the wave progresses a distance uT; but in this same interval the source moves in the same direction a distance vT, as shown in Fig. 2-15. Then the wavelength, which is the distance between successive maxima in the wave, is not uT, as it would be with a stationary source, but rather $(u - v)T$.

Fig. 2-15 *Doppler effect with a moving source. The wave pulses represent successive maxima of a periodic wave. During a time interval T between the emission of two successive pulses, each pulse moves a distance uT and the source a distance vT. The distance between successive pulses, which is the wavelength, is given by* $(u - v)T$.

The corresponding frequency, which we denote by f', is given by

$$f' = \frac{u}{(u - v)T} = \frac{u}{u - v}f = \frac{f}{1 - v/u} \tag{2-44}$$

which represents an apparent increase in frequency, as already noted. Correspondingly, when the source is receding from the observer, the frequency is smaller by an amount obtained by simply changing the sign of the term v/u in Eq. (2-44).

When the source is stationary relative to the medium but the observer is moving, the situation is somewhat different. This case is most easily analyzed as follows: Suppose the observer is moving away from the source with speed v; then the wave speed *relative to the observer* is not u but rather $u - v$. The frequency f' with which successive maxima of the wave pass this observer is therefore given not by u/λ but rather by

$$f' = \frac{u - v}{\lambda} \tag{2-45}$$

where λ is the wavelength measured in the stationary medium. This, in turn, is related to the frequency f of the stationary source by $\lambda = u/f$. Putting these equations together, we find for the apparent frequency

$$f' = \left(1 - \frac{v}{u}\right)f \qquad (2\text{-}46)$$

When the observer is moving away from the source, the apparent frequency is lower; if, instead, he is moving toward the source, it is necessary only to change the sign of the term containing v to find the apparent *rise* in frequency.

The two results contained in Eqs. (2-44) and (2-46) may be combined to obtain a formula for the case in which both source and observer are moving relative to the medium. This calculation is left as a problem.

In these calculations we have used nonrelativistic kinematic considerations. This is justified by the fact that ordinarily the speed of sound and the speeds of both source and observer relative to the medium are very much smaller than the speed of light, so that relativistic effects may be neglected. When we consider the Doppler effect for light, the situation is quite different, and relativistic kinematics must be used. Thus it should not be surprising that the results do not have quite the same form as those for sound. An additional distinction is that for light there is no material medium as there is for sound but rather, according to the theory of relativity, light propagates in vacuum with a speed that is independent of the motion of either source or observer.

The frequency shift corresponding to the Doppler effect for light can be derived by an argument quite similar to that used in the case of sound with a moving source. Suppose a light source moves toward an observer with speed v. Let T' be the period of the wave as measured by the stationary observer. During this time, the wave moves a distance cT' and the source moves a distance vT', and so the wavelength λ' measured by the stationary observer is

$$\lambda' = (c - v)T' \qquad (2\text{-}47)$$

Correspondingly, the frequency he observes is

$$f' = \frac{c}{\lambda'} = \frac{c}{(c - v)T'} \qquad (2\text{-}48)$$

The period T' is related to the period T measured in the frame of reference of the source, but it is *not* identical, since in relativistic kinematics the time interval between two events depends on the frame of reference of the observer. Now T is a *proper-time* interval in the reference frame of the source, since it is measured between two events at the same space point in that reference frame. Thus T' is of longer duration than T, according to the usual formula for dilation of time,

$$T' = \frac{T}{\sqrt{1 - v^2/c^2}} \tag{2-49}$$

Furthermore, $T = 1/f$, where f is the frequency measured in the frame of reference of the source. Combining these results with Eq. (2-48),

$$f' = \frac{c}{c - v} \sqrt{1 - \frac{v^2}{c^2}} f = \sqrt{\frac{c + v}{c - v}} f \tag{2-50}$$

The corresponding expression for the apparent frequency when the observer is *receding* from the source is

$$f' = \sqrt{\frac{c - v}{c + v}} f \tag{2-51}$$

The Doppler effect for light has important applications in the area of astronomy. Spectroscopic analysis of light from various distant galaxies reveals the presence of spectra which can be identified as belonging to certain elements, except that all the frequencies are shifted by a constant factor. The interpretation is that the galaxy is moving relative to the observer, and the shift in frequency is due to the Doppler effect. In practically all cases the Doppler shift is toward lower frequencies, indicating that the galaxy is *receding* from our solar system. Even more remarkable, the velocity predicted by this "red shift" is approximately proportional to the distance of the galaxy from the solar system. Observations of this kind have provided practically all the evidence for the "exploding-universe" cosmological theories, which picture the universe as having originated in a great explosion several billion years ago in a relatively small region of space, following which galaxies have ever since been receding from each other.

PROBLEMS

2-1   What is the wavelength of the radiation from (*a*) an a-m radio station with a frequency of 1,000 kc; (*b*) an f-m radio station with a frequency of 100 Mc?

2-2   What is the frequency of orange light with a wavelength of 6,000 Å?

2-3   A capacitor consisting of two parallel, coaxial disks is connected to a sinusoidal voltage source of frequency ω, and as a result the electric field between the disks varies with time according to $E = E_0 \cos \omega t$. Using Eq. (2-3d) for a circular path in a plane parallel to the disks and coaxial with them, find the induced magnetic field as a function of the distance from the axis.

2-4   Compare the magnitudes of conduction and displacement current for a vacuum tube operating at 100 Mc.   For example, the vacuum tube might have two electrodes each 1 cm^2 in area, separated by the order of 1 cm, with a maximum potential difference of the order of 100 volts and a maximum current of 10 ma.   Compute the electric field between the electrodes, and from this find the displacement-current density. At what frequency would the two become comparable?

2-5   Consider the flow of alternating current in a bar of copper (resistivity 1.7×10^{-8} ohm-m).   At what frequency are the conduction-current density and the displacement-current density equal in magnitude? What is their relative phase?

2-6   For the plane electromagnetic wave discussed in Sec. 2-3, prove that the magnetic field B_z must satisfy Eq. (2-10).

2-7   The maximum electric field in the vicinity of a certain radio transmitter is 10^{-3} volt/m.
   a.   What is the maximum magnetic field?
   b.   How does this compare in magnitude with the earth's magnetic field $(B = 0.5 \times 10^{-4}$ weber/m$^2)$?

2-8   An electromagnetic wave propagates in a ferrite material with the properties $K_E = 10$, $K_M = 1,000$.
   a.   What is the speed of propagation?
   b.   What is the wavelength of a wave having a frequency of 100 Mc?

2-9   For the standing wave represented by Eqs. (2-27) and (2-28), show that the **E** and **B** fields are 90° out of phase and that the positions of nodes for **E** correspond to antinodes for **B**, and conversely.

2-10   Find the Poynting vector 1 m away from a 100-watt light bulb, if it radiates uniformly in all directions.   From this, calculate the radiation pressure at this distance on (*a*) a perfectly absorbing black surface; (*b*) a perfectly reflecting polished surface.

2-11   For a 50,000-watt radio transmitting station, find the maximum electric and magnetic fields at a distance of 100 km from the antenna, if it radiates equally in all directions.

2-12   A radio station radiates 50,000 watts uniformly in all directions. If an electric-field strength of 100 volts/m is required to make a neon sign glow, how far away from the transmitter will it light neon signs?

2-13   For an electromagnetic wave, prove that the average energy associated with the **E** field is equal to that for the **B** field.

2-14   The intensity of sunlight on the surface of the earth is about 1,500 watts/m². Find the order of magnitude of the associated electric and magnetic fields.

2-15   A certain microwave antenna uses a parabolic reflector to beam its radiation essentially in a single direction. If the radiated power is 1,000 watts, find the reaction force on the structure which supports the reflector. Is this likely to be an important consideration in the design of the structure?

2-16   Is the Poynting vector **S** corresponding to the superposition of two waves equal to the sum $\mathbf{S}_1 + \mathbf{S}_2$ of the Poynting vectors of the individual waves? Explain.

2-17   The nineteenth-century inventor Nikolai Tesla proposed to transmit large quantities of electric power via electromagnetic waves. What field strengths would be required if an amount of power comparable to that in modern transmission lines (of the order of 200 kv and 1,000 amp) is to be transmitted in a beam with a cross-section area of 100 m²?

2-18   Calculate the Poynting vector for the standing wave in Fig. 2-6a resulting from total reflection at normal incidence on the surface of an ideal conductor, and show that its average value is zero.

2-19   How is the momentum density related to the Poynting vector for an electromagnetic wave traveling in a material medium (not vacuum)?

2-20   Derive an expression for the radiation pressure resulting from partial reflection of an electromagnetic wave at normal incidence on an interface between two materials, as in Fig. 2-7a.

2-21   Find the index of refraction for a glass whose dielectric constant is 2.5.

2-22   A beam of light strikes the surface of a puddle of water, at normal incidence.
  a. Find the amplitudes of reflected and transmitted waves, in terms of the amplitude of the incident wave.
  b. What fraction of the energy is transmitted? What fraction is reflected?

2-23   Unpolarized light is incident on a polarizing filter, and the emerging radiation strikes another polarizing filter with its polarizing axis at 45° to that of the first.

a. Describe the state of polarization of the light after the first filter, and after the second.

b. Find the electric-field amplitude and the intensity, after the first filter and after the second, in terms of the incident intensity.

2-24 Unpolarized light strikes a series of two polarizing filters whose polarizing axes make an angle θ with each other. Plot the emerging field amplitude and intensity as functions of θ. On the intensity graph, show the incident-light intensity.

2-25 A radio wave with a mixture of polarizations strikes a grid of parallel conducting wires. Describe the polarization of the radiation passing through the grid.

2-26 Three polarizing filters are stacked, with the axes of the second and third at 45 and 90°, respectively, with that of the first.

a. If unpolarized light of intensity I_0 is incident on the stack, find the intensity and state of polarization after each filter.

b. If the second filter is removed, how does the situation change?

2-27 Complete the derivation of Eq. (2-43) indicated in the text.

2-28 It is desired to make a "quarter-wave" plate from quartz, whose indices of refraction in two perpendicular directions are about 1.54 and 1.55. The plate is to be used with light with a wavelength of 6,000 Å.

a. What should be the thickness of the plate?

b. How should the plate be used to convert plane-polarized light into right circularly polarized? Left circularly polarized?

2-29 How can a right circularly polarized beam of light be converted into plane-polarized in a specified plane? Into left circularly polarized?

2-30 Can sound waves be polarized? Explain.

2-31 Write equations for the magnetic fields of the component waves in Fig. 2-14. From these, show directly that the resultant magnetic field at any point has constant magnitude but a direction that rotates uniformly about the direction of propagation.

2-32 Prove that Brewster's angle (cf. Sec. 2-6) is given by $\tan^{-1}(n_1/n_2)$.

2-33 A train approaches a station platform at 10 m/sec. Its whistle has a frequency of 100 sec^{-1}, as measured by the engineer. What frequency will be measured by an observer on the platform (*a*) when the train is approaching; (*b*) after the train has passed?

2-34   A passenger in a train moving at 10 m/sec measures the frequency of the whistle of a stationary train, which appears to its engineer to have a frequency of 100 sec^{-1}. What does the moving passenger measure (a) when his train is approaching the stationary train; (b) when the trains are separating?

2-35   Show that in the limit, when v/u is much smaller than unity, the expressions for the Doppler frequency shift for a moving source and for a moving observer [Eqs. (2-44), (2-46), and (2-50)] all become identical for both light and sound. [Hint: Expressions of the form $(1 + a)^n$ can be expanded using the binomial theorem, and if a is very small, $(1 + a)^n \simeq 1 + na$.]

2-36   A certain spectrum line in the light from a distant nebula is known to correspond to the hydrogen Balmer line at 4,340 Å but, because of the Doppler shift, appears to have a wavelength of 5,890 Å. Find the speed of the nebula with respect to the earth. Is it approaching or receding?

2-37   Radar systems utilizing the Doppler effect are used to measure velocities of moving objects, such as automobiles exceeding the speed limit. Derive an expression for the frequency shift for radiation reflected from a target moving at speed v relative to the source, and returned to the source position.

2-38   A space ship approaching the earth at a speed of $0.2c$ emits a green light with a wavelength of 5,000 Å. What wavelength is observed on earth? What color?

2-39   Derive an expression for the Doppler frequency shift for sound when both source and observer are moving relative to the medium. Show that, when both move with the same velocity, no Doppler shift is observed.

2-40   A sound wave produced by a stationary source with frequency f is reflected from a surface which is moving away from the source with constant speed v; the reflected wave then returns to the position of the source. What is the frequency of the reflected wave, measured by an observer at this position?

THIS CHAPTER DEALS with phenomena associated with the superposition of waves. We begin with a discussion of spherical waves and their relationship to the plane waves discussed in Chap. 2. Effects associated with superposition of spherical waves from several sources, called *interference* phenomena, are analyzed, and then we discuss phenomena associated with the emergence of a wave from an aperture or an edge, usually called *diffraction* effects. Finally, the variation of wave speed with frequency for light traveling through a material medium and its implications for the propagation of wave pulses are discussed.

3-1 Spherical Waves

The discussion of electromagnetic waves in Chap. 2 centered around plane waves. A plane wave propagates in one fixed direction, and the electric and magnetic fields at any instant are uniform over any plane perpendicular to this direction. At any point in space the fields are periodic functions of time, and in any plane perpendicular to the direction of propagation the electric field reaches its maximum intensity at all points simultaneously, is zero everywhere in the plane simultaneously, and so forth.   Thus the wavefronts, planes perpendicular to the direction of propagation, are *planes of constant phase.*

Although plane waves are the easiest waves to discuss theoretically, they are by no means the easiest waves to produce.   Indeed, everyday experience provides few, if any, examples of waves that are truly plane waves.   Much more common are the waves that originate in a small source and radiate outward in all directions from this source. A light bulb, a speaker in a hi-fi set, a radio-transmitter antenna, all radiate waves in all directions.   It is instructive to consider a simple example of an electromagnetic wave having this multidirectional feature.   The situation to be discussed is the simplest possible example of a *spherical* wave, in which the wavefronts or surfaces of constant phase are concentric spheres.

We take as the source of electromagnetic radiation an oscillating electric dipole.   Such a dipole can be constructed in a variety of ways, and the details need not concern us.   One possibility, shown in Fig. 3-1, uses two small metallic spheres separated by a distance l.   When these spheres are connected with an alternating source of potential difference, the charge on each sphere oscillates correspondingly.   If the maximum magnitude of charge is q, then the maximum dipole moment, which we denote by p_0, is simply $p_0 = ql$.   If the variation is sinusoidal, with

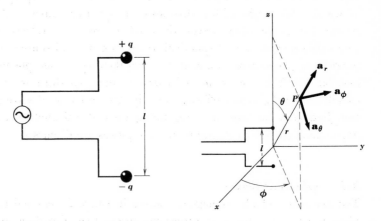

Fig. 3-1   *An oscillating electric dipole placed at the origin of a coordinate system with its axis along the z axis.   The spherical coordinates r, θ, and φ and the corresponding unit vectors are shown.*

angular frequency ω, the dipole moment p is given as a function of time by $p = p_0 \cos \omega t$. The electric field produced by this dipole also varies sinusoidally at each point in space; thus there is a displacement current and correspondingly a time-varying magnetic field, and an electromagnetic wave is produced.

Calculation of the electric and magnetic fields resulting from an oscillating dipole is a problem which is straightforward in principle but somewhat complicated in detail. This derivation will not be presented here; instead, we simply quote the results and then examine their meaning in detail. The fields are most easily described in terms of the spherical coordinates shown in Fig. 3-1, in which a point P is described by the distance r from the origin and the two angles θ and ϕ, as shown. Directions of vector quantities are specified by the use of the three unit vectors $\mathbf{a}_r$, $\mathbf{a}_\theta$, and $\mathbf{a}_\phi$, which point in the directions point P would move if r, θ, or ϕ, respectively, were given a small positive increment. As Fig. 3-1 shows, the unit vectors are mutually perpendicular and satisfy the relations

$$\mathbf{a}_r = \mathbf{a}_\theta \times \mathbf{a}_\phi \tag{3-1a}$$

$$\mathbf{a}_\theta = \mathbf{a}_\phi \times \mathbf{a}_r \tag{3-1b}$$

$$\mathbf{a}_\phi = \mathbf{a}_r \times \mathbf{a}_\theta \tag{3-1c}$$

For points far away from the dipole, compared with either its dimensions or the wavelength of the radiation, the electric and magnetic fields are given by

$$\mathbf{E} = -\frac{k^2 p_0 \sin \theta}{4\pi\epsilon} \frac{\cos (kr - \omega t)}{r} \mathbf{a}_\theta \tag{3-2a}$$

$$\mathbf{B} = -\frac{k^2 p_0 \sin \theta}{4\pi\epsilon u} \frac{\cos (kr - \omega t)}{r} \mathbf{a}_\phi \tag{3-2b}$$

These expressions contain a wealth of information and deserve careful study. Each contains the factor $\cos (kr - \omega t)$, characteristic of a wave propagating in the positive r direction, that is, radially outward in all directions from the source. The factor $1/r$ indicates that the electric and magnetic fields become less intense as the distance from the source increases; this is to be expected, since the wave spreads out in space. Furthermore, the field intensities also depend on the *direction* relative to the orientation of the dipole, according to the factor $\sin \theta$; both fields are strongest in directions perpendicular to the dipole axis and are zero along the axis. Neither field depends on ϕ; this is to be expected because of the axial symmetry of the source.

Considering the *directions* of the fields, we note that they are perpendicular to the radial direction and to each other. Since the wave propagates outward in all directions from the source, this shows that the wave is *transverse*, just as in the case of the plane waves. We also note immediately another similarity to the plane-wave situation; the maximum value of B is $1/u$ times the maximum value of E. That is, the ratio of E to B is the same as for the plane wave. Furthermore, the time variations of the two fields at any point in space are *in phase*, just as for plane waves. At any instant of time the loci of points in space at which the **E** or **B** field reaches its maximum magnitude, that is, the surfaces of constant phase, are spheres; hence the term *spherical waves*.

Figure 3-2 shows the electric and magnetic fields on cross sections of several concentric spheres. The spheres of constant phase move out uniformly with time; that is, their radii increase with speed u. In the particular case described, the **E** field at each point lies in a plane containing the z axis and the radial direction, while the **B** field is perpendicular to this plane and to the z axis.

This is by no means the only possible kind of spherical wave. Another one, different but equally simple, results from the use of a *magnetic* dipole, as, for example, a small circular loop or coil of wire carrying a current which varies sinusoidally with time. The result is a radiation field in which the directions of **E** and **B** are interchanged but in which the dependence of the field magnitudes on r and θ is the same as for the electric dipole. More complicated arrangements of oscillating charge or current, such as quadrupoles or higher multipoles, produce more complicated radiation fields. In all cases, however, when the charge or current producing the radiation field is confined to a small region surrounding the origin, the wave at distances sufficiently far from the origin is a spherical wave.

It is instructive to examine the *energy* transported by a spherical wave. This is most easily done by consideration of the Poynting vector, introduced in Sec. 2-4, defined by $\mathbf{S} = \mathbf{E} \times \mathbf{H}$. Using Eqs. (3-2) and (3-1a) together with the relations $\mathbf{H} = \mathbf{B}/\mu$ and $u = (\mu\epsilon)^{-1/2}$, we obtain for the Poynting vector

$$\mathbf{S} = \mathbf{E} \times \mathbf{H} = \frac{p_0{}^2 u k^4 \sin^2 \theta}{(4\pi)^2 \epsilon} \frac{\cos^2 (kr - \omega t)}{r^2} \mathbf{a}_r \qquad (3\text{-}3)$$

This equation reveals several additional important features of spherical waves. First, the direction of **S** is always radially outward, as expected; energy is always transported radially out from the source. Second, the radiated energy is proportional to k^4. The wave number k, we recall,

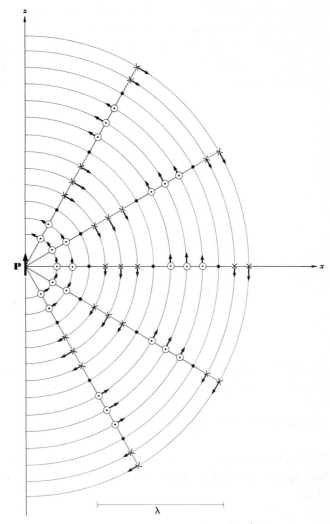

Fig. 3-2   *Cross section in the xz plane of dipole radiation, showing electric-field vectors at one instant of time. At the points with circles the* **B** *field comes out of the plane of the figure; at the points with crosses, it is into the plane.*

is related to the frequency and speed of the wave by $\omega = uk$, and so the rate of radiation of energy is proportional to ω^4. The *average* rate at which energy is radiated is obtained by taking the average of $\cos^2(kr - \omega t)$ over one cycle, which is ½. Thus the average rate of energy flow is

$$S_{av} = \frac{p_0^2 u k^4}{2(4\pi)^2 \epsilon} \frac{\sin^2 \theta}{r^2} \mathbf{a}_r \qquad (3\text{-}4)$$

The rate of energy flow is proportional to $1/r^2$, the familiar "inverse-square" law for intensity of illumination.

From Eq. (3-4) it is easy to find the *total* energy per unit time radiated from the dipole. **S** represents an energy flow per unit time, *per unit area*. To find the total rate of energy flow, we integrate over the surface of a sphere of arbitrary radius r. In Fig. 3-3, S_{av} has constant magnitude over the ring shown. The width of the ring is $r\,d\theta$, its

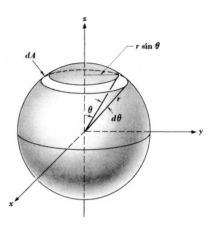

Fig. 3-3 *Spherical surface used to calculate total energy flow from an oscillating electric dipole. The area of the ring-shaped strip is $dA = 2\pi r^2 \sin \theta\, d\theta$. The average power radiated through this element of surface area is S dA, where S is the magnitude of the average Poynting vector on the ring.*

circumference approximately $2\pi r \sin \theta$, and its area $dA = 2\pi r^2 \sin \theta\, d\theta$. Thus the average power dP radiated through this strip is

$$dP = S_{av}\,dA = \frac{p_0^2 u k^4}{2(4\pi)^2 \epsilon} \frac{\sin^2 \theta}{r^2} 2\pi r^2 \sin \theta\, d\theta$$

The total average power P radiated through the sphere is the integral of this expression over θ, with limits 0 and π to include the entire surface. Since

$$\int_0^\pi \sin^3 \theta\, d\theta = \frac{4}{3}$$

we find

$$P = \frac{p_0^2 u k^4}{16\pi\epsilon} \int_0^\pi \sin^3 \theta\, d\theta = \frac{p_0^2 u k^4}{12\pi\epsilon} \tag{3-5}$$

This result is independent of r, which is essential; otherwise energy would be appearing or disappearing in the space separating the source and the sphere considered in the calculation.

As observed previously, plane waves are easier to deal with mathematically than spherical waves. Thus it is worthwhile to observe that, at points far away from the source, a small segment of a spherical wave may be considered as approximately a plane wave, as shown in Fig. 3-4. The surfaces of constant phase, small spherical segments, become approximately plane.   In the language of geometrical optics, the propagation of light is described not by means of waves and constant-phase surfaces but by means of *rays*.   For a spherical wave, the ray picture consists of many straight lines radiating out from the central source. For plane waves, the rays are simply straight parallel lines in the direction of propagation.   In each case, the lines used to represent the light in the ray picture are perpendicular to the constant-phase surfaces, or wavefronts, which represent the real physical basis of light.   This observation will be very useful in the following chapter, when we introduce the ray picture as a useful approximation for calculating certain kinds of optical phenomena.

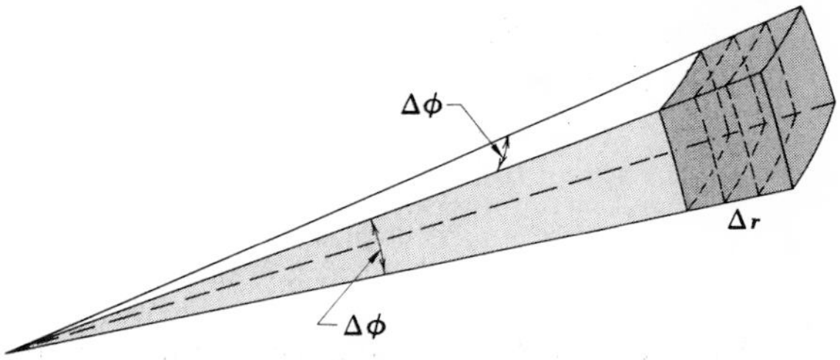

Fig. 3-4 *In a small region far removed from the source, a small segment of a spherical wave is very nearly a plane wave.*

3-2   Interference from Two Coherent Sources

To introduce the basic concepts of interference, as well as some techniques of calculation, we consider the following prototype problem. Two radio transmitting antennas, identical in all respects, are fed from the same oscillator; they emit sinusoidal waves which are identical in frequency, amplitude, phase, and state of polarization.   They are separated by a distance d which is of the same order of magnitude as the wavelength λ of the emitted radiation.   What are the characteristics of the resulting superposed radiation pattern?

For simplicity, we consider only the region far away (compared with a wavelength) from the antennas.   The situation is shown in Fig. 3-5.   First, we consider point O, equidistant from the two antennas. Because the two radiations are in phase, maxima of the two waves arrive simultaneously at O, resulting in values of **E** and **B** precisely twice those contributed by each separate wave, and an intensity four times as great.

Fig. 3-5 (a) Two identical radio antennas separated by a distance d. The antennas could be, for example, dipoles perpendicular to the plane of the figure, in which case the waves at points in the plane are plane-polarized perpendicular to it. (b) Detail showing the path difference for the two waves, in terms of the angle θ. The distance to P is so great that the lines from the two antennas may be considered parallel.

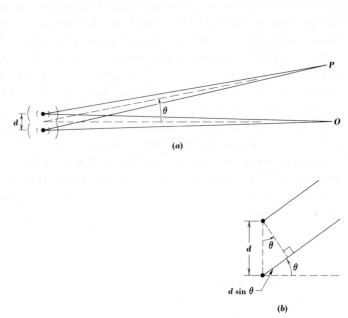

We now consider point *P* in the figure, exactly one-half wavelength closer to one antenna than the other. Because the two waves do not travel equal distances to *P*, they do not arrive at point *P* in phase but, rather, precisely one-half cycle out of phase. When one wave has its maximum electric field in one direction, the other has its maximum in the opposite direction; the result is that the vector sum of the two electric fields at this point is zero at every instant, and therefore the intensity of the total radiation field at this point is zero.

Thus the superposition of the two radiation fields produces a field which is more intense at some points and less intense at others than that corresponding to either wave separately. In terms of the angle θ in Fig. 3-5, the path difference between the two waves is $d \sin \theta$. If this optical path difference is zero or any integer number of wavelengths, waves from the two antennas arrive exactly in phase, while if it is any half-integer number of wavelengths, they arrive out of phase by 180°. These two conditions are called complete constructive interference and complete destructive interference or cancellation, respectively, and lead to maximum and zero intensity points, respectively. The condition for a point of maximum intensity is

$$d \sin \theta = n\lambda \qquad n = 0, 1, 2, \ldots \qquad (3\text{-}6)$$

and that for zero intensity is

$$d \sin \theta = (n + \tfrac{1}{2})\lambda \qquad n = 0, 1, 2, \ldots \qquad (3\text{-}7)$$

Wavelengths for radio transmission typically range from 1,000 m for the longest wave transmission to a few centimeters for radar and for television relay equipment.   Thus this is a macroscopic effect which can readily be observed with fairly modest equipment.   Precisely the same phenomenon can be observed with sound waves by replacing the transmitter antennas by two loudspeakers driven from the same amplifier.

The intensity distribution can be calculated in more detail by adding the contributions from the two sources to the total **E** field at point P.   Since this point is very distant compared with the separation of the sources, both contributions to **E** at point P have the same or opposite directions, and it is sufficient to add their magnitudes.   This is accomplished most conveniently by use of the representation discussed in Sec. 1-6.   The essential ideas are that a sinusoidal function can be represented as the projection on one coordinate axis of a rotating vector, which in turn can be represented in terms of an exponential function with imaginary argument.   We now illustrate these calculational techniques in detail.

Suppose that at point P in Fig. 3-5 the electric-field magnitude E_1 due to the bottom antenna is given by $E_1 = E_0 \cos \omega t$.   Then at P the field E_2 due to the top antenna has a similar time dependence $E_2 = E_0 \cos (\omega t + \phi)$ with a phase angle ϕ which depends on the difference in path length from the two sources.   We now introduce a two-dimensional rectangular coordinate system in a plane, and in it a vector with magnitude E_0 which makes an angle ωt with the positive horizontal axis, as shown in Fig. 3-6.   This vector rotates counterclockwise with time with constant angular velocity ω.   Furthermore, its projection on the horizontal axis, that is, its horizontal component, is given by $E_0 \cos \omega t$.   Thus this projection represents the field E_1.   Correspondingly, the field E_2 can be represented as the projection on the horizontal axis of another vector with magnitude E_0, making an angle $\omega t + \phi$ with the axis.   This vector also rotates with constant angular velocity, making a constant angle ϕ with the vector whose projection represents E_1.   Finally, the total E field at any instant is given by the sum of these two projections; this in turn is equal to the projection of the *vector sum* of the two vectors.

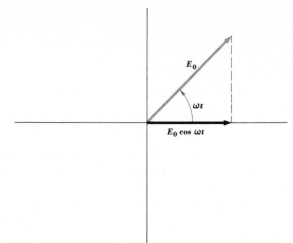

Fig. 3-6 *Rotating vector used to represent the quantity E_0 cos ωt. This vector rotates counterclockwise with constant angular velocity ω.*

This procedure may be clarified by reference to Fig. 3-7, which shows each vector as well as the vector sum at two different times. The entire triangle representing the vector sum rotates; the *maximum* value of the quantity $E_1 + E_2$, which is equal to the amplitude of the total field, is equal to the magnitude of the vector sum. Thus to calculate the amplitude of the field resulting from the superposition of several fields with phase differences, it is sufficient to draw the vector-addition diagram

Fig. 3-7 *Vector diagram showing vector addition of the two vectors whose projections on the horizontal axis are E_1 and E_2. The vectors are shown at two different times; the triangle representing the vector sum rotates, and the projection of the vector sum on the horizontal is the instantaneous total field at point P. The amplitude of this sinusoidally varying total field is the magnitude of the vector sum.*

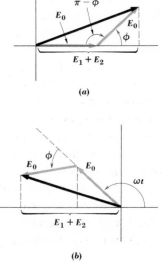

at one instant of time and from it to determine the magnitude of the vector sum. This magnitude depends on the relative orientation of the vectors, which in turn is determined by the phase difference of the component waves.

Application of the law of cosines to either triangle in Fig. 3-7 shows that the amplitude E of the resultant field is given by

$$E^2 = E_0{}^2 + E_0{}^2 - 2E_0{}^2 \cos(\pi - \phi)$$
$$= 2E_0{}^2 (1 + \cos \phi) \tag{3-8}$$

The intensity, according to Eq. (2-26), is given by

$$I = \tfrac{1}{2} \sqrt{\frac{\epsilon}{\mu}} E^2 = \sqrt{\frac{\epsilon}{\mu}} E_0{}^2 (1 + \cos \phi) \tag{3-9}$$

The intensity I_0 from a single antenna would be

$$I_0 = \tfrac{1}{2} \sqrt{\frac{\epsilon}{\mu}} E_0{}^2 \tag{3-10}$$

In terms of this quantity, we have

$$I = 2I_0(1 + \cos \phi) \tag{3-11}$$

Finally, we determine the phase difference ϕ in terms of the path difference $d \sin \theta$. It has already been shown that when the path difference is one-half wavelength the phase difference is π, and for a whole wavelength it is 2π. In general, ϕ is 2π times the *number of wavelengths* contained in the path difference; thus

$$\phi = 2\pi \frac{d \sin \theta}{\lambda} = kd \sin \theta \tag{3-12}$$

where k is the usual wave number, $k = 2\pi/\lambda$. In general, a path difference δ introduces a phase difference ϕ given by

$$\phi = k\delta \tag{3-13}$$

Finally, from Eqs. (3-11) and (3-12), the intensity distribution is given by

$$I = 2I_0[1 + \cos(kd \sin \theta)] \tag{3-14}$$

This same result can be obtained somewhat more analytically and less geometrically by representing each rotating vector in terms of a complex number whose real part represents the projection of the vector on the horizontal (real) axis. Thus the vector for E_1 is represented by the complex quantity $E_0 e^{i\omega t}$ whose real part is $E_0 \cos \omega t$, and the total field $E_1 + E_2$ can be represented as

$$E_1 + E_2 = \text{Re } [E_0 e^{i\omega t} + E_0 e^{i(\omega t + \phi)}]$$
$$= \text{Re } [E_0 e^{i\omega t}(1 + e^{i\phi})] \tag{3-15}$$

The *amplitude* E of the sinusoidally varying total field, represented by the magnitude of the vector sum, is the absolute value of the quantity in brackets in Eq. (3-15). To calculate the intensity, the *square* of this absolute value is needed; this is most easily obtained by using the fact that, for any complex number Z, $|Z|^2 = ZZ^*$. Thus E^2 is given by

$$E^2 = |E_0 e^{i\omega t} (1 + e^{i\phi})|^2$$
$$= E_0^2 [e^{i\omega t}(1 + e^{i\phi})][e^{-i\omega t}(1 + e^{-i\phi})]$$
$$= E_0^2 (2 + e^{i\phi} + e^{-i\phi})$$
$$= 2E_0^2 (1 + \cos \phi) \tag{3-16}$$

which agrees with the previous result [Eq. (3-8)].

Here is an example of the techniques just described. A certain radio station, operating at a frequency of $1{,}500 \text{ kc} = 1.5 \times 10^6 \text{ sec}^{-1}$, has two identical vertical dipole antennas spaced 400 m apart. What is the intensity distribution in the resulting radiation pattern?

First, the wavelength is $\lambda = c/f = 200$ m. The directions of the intensity maxima are those for which the path difference is zero or an integer number of wavelengths, as given by Eq. (3-6). Inserting the appropriate numerical values yields the following:

$$\sin \theta = \frac{n\lambda}{d} = \tfrac{1}{2}n$$

n	$\sin \theta$	θ
0	0	0
1	½	30°
2	1	90°

In this example, values of n greater than 2 give values of $\sin \theta$ greater than unity and thus have no meaning; there is *no* direction for which the path difference is three or more wavelengths. Similarly, the directions having zero intensity (complete destructive interference) are given by

$$\sin \theta = \frac{(n + \tfrac{1}{2})\lambda}{d} = \tfrac{1}{2}(n + \tfrac{1}{2})$$

n	$\sin \theta$	θ
0	¼	14.5°
1	¾	48.7°

In this case values of n greater than 1 have no meaning, for the reason just mentioned.

The complete intensity-distribution pattern is given by Eq. (3-14), which, with the appropriate values of k and d, becomes

$$I = 2I_0[1 + \cos (4\pi \sin \theta)]$$

This pattern is most conveniently represented graphically by a polar plot, as in Fig. 3-8.

It should be noted that, if the distance between antennas is less than one-half wavelength, there is *no* direction for which the intensity is zero. Even so, the variation of intensity with direction is given correctly by Eq. (3-14).

Clearly, the crucial consideration in interference phenomena is the relative *phase* of waves arriving at a given point from various sources. This in turn depends on the existence of a definite phase relationship between the sources and on the difference in path length from source to observation point. It should also be clear from the preceding discussion that in calculating the intensity pattern in an interference situation one must always add the amplitudes first, then calculate the intensity from the resultant amplitude; it would *not* be correct to calculate the intensity of each wave and then add intensities. That is, if the fields for two waves are E_1 and E_2, the intensity pattern is determined by $|E_1 + E_2|^2$, *not* by $(|E_1|^2 + |E_2|^2)$, which in general is a quite different quantity.

The phenomenon of interference with radio waves can occur with a single source, if the wave reaches the observer by two different paths. An example of practical importance is the case when radio waves reach a receiver by "straight-line" transmission and also by refraction in the

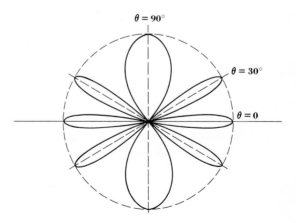

Fig. 3-8   *Polar plot of the intensity distribution in the interference pattern for two antennas in phase, for the particular case $d = 2\lambda$. For any angle θ, the distance of the curve from the origin represents the intensity in the corresponding direction. The line joining the antennas is vertical.*

ionosphere. The path lengths for the two waves are, in general, different. If the waves arrive with nearly equal amplitudes, there can be either almost complete constructive or destructive interference, depending on the relative phase. Since the ionosphere constantly changes in constitution, the path length of the refracted wave constantly changes. This accounts in part for the fading or rapid "buffeting" sound which sometimes occurs when one is trying to receive weak, distant a-m radio transmission.

Do similar interference effects occur with sources of visible light? Offhand, the answer might seem to be negative. One does not have to look far to find a light fixture with two bulbs in it, but interference effects are not observed. However, consider the situation of Fig. 3-9. We form two very narrow slits or apertures, perhaps by coating a sheet of glass with an opaque material and then scratching two very fine lines in it. We then illuminate one side of this plate with monochromatic (single-frequency) light, so as to avoid complications that would result from a mixture of wavelengths. As an example, light that is very nearly monochromatic can be obtained from a sodium vapor lamp or simply by heating a sodium compound in a flame.

We then look at the intensity of radiation at various points on a screen placed on the opposite side of the plate, as shown in Fig. 3-9. The pattern has precisely the same characteristics as that corresponding to interference of two radio waves, discussed above. The difference is one of *size*. The conditions for maximum and minimum intensity are still Eqs. (3-6) and (3-7), but the wavelengths are very much smaller than for radio waves and are of the order of 4 to 7×10^{-7} m.

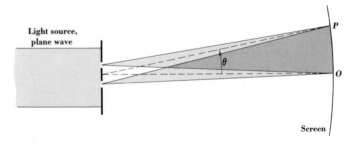

Fig. 3-9 *Interference pattern formed by two narrow slits illuminated from the left by a monochromatic plane wave. The interference pattern is formed on the screen at the right.*

The experiment just described was performed by Thomas Young in the year 1802, and he presented it as evidence of the wave nature of light. Furthermore, he was able to make determinations of wavelengths of light which, considering the crudeness of his apparatus, were remarkably precise. The ingenuity of his experiments and the insight which he applied to their analysis were among the brilliant scientific achievements of his time.

We now return to the question of why interference effects are not observed with two ordinary light bulbs. The two sources are not monochromatic, it is true; furthermore, the distance between them is ordinarily very much larger than a wavelength of light. But there is a much more fundamental reason than this, namely, the lack of a definite *phase relationship* between the two sources. In the basic mechanism of emission of light, atoms are given excess energy by thermal agitation, collisions of other atoms, or excitation in electric fields, and they subsequently radiate this energy away as electromagnetic radiation. Each atom radiates for a time (usually of the order of 10^{-6} sec) and then ceases when it has lost all the energy it can. Meanwhile, other atoms have begun to radiate. The phases of these emitted radiations are random; if there are two such sources, even if the intensities and spectral compositions are identical, there will be no definite phase relationship between the two radiations.

It is as though the two radio antennas discussed earlier were driven by different transmitters with the same frequency but each one was turned on and off at random so as to prevent a definite phase relationship between them. In this case no interference pattern would be observed, since the phase relationship at a given observation point would vary randomly with time, and so therefore would the intensity. By using a single transmitter we avoid this difficulty, and similarly when the two slits in Thomas Young's experiment are illuminated by the same source, radiation from them is in a definite phase relationship at each instant of time. Two sources having a definite phase relationship are said to be *coherent*, and two sources that do not have a definite phase relationship, such as two light bulbs, are *incoherent*. Clearly, coherent sources are an essential ingredient for the observation of interference phenomena. The most significant feature of light emitted by a laser is that the microscopic mechanism of emission in effect *synchronizes* the emission of many atoms, so that the emitted light maintains its definite phase relationship for time intervals much longer than that corresponding to the emission of a single atom.

3-3   *Interference from Several Sources*

The analysis of Sec. 3-2 can easily be extended to situations involving more than two sources. Figure 3-10*a* shows an array of four radio transmitting antennas, equally spaced along a straight line. Also shown in this figure are vector diagrams corresponding to the addition of amplitudes for various directions as shown. Just as in the case of two antennas, the phase difference ϕ between signals from adjacent antennas is given by Eq. (3-12).

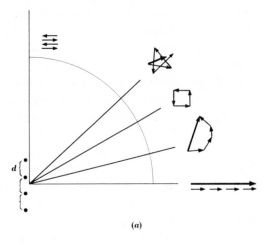

(*a*)

Fig. 3-10   (*a*) *Interference from four antennas in a row, for the case $d = \lambda/2$. Vector diagrams show the addition of amplitudes from individual waves at several points.* (*b*) *Graph showing intensity as a function of phase angle for the case of four sources.*

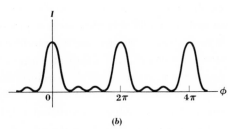

(*b*)

Figure 3-10*b* represents the general behavior of an interference pattern resulting from several coherent sources equally spaced along a straight line. It is possible to work out an expression for the intensity in the interference pattern, as a function of the angle θ, just as in the case of two sources. This is so easy that instead of doing it for four sources we shall do it for the general case of N sources of equal amplitude spaced equally along a straight line. Since there is a constant phase difference ϕ between waves arriving at P from adjacent sources, the vector diagram consists of a series of N vectors with equal magnitude E_0 and equal angle ϕ between directions of adjacent vectors. The vector diagram for the addition of amplitudes is shown in Fig. 3-11, which shows the constant phase difference ϕ between adjacent sources.

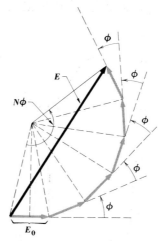

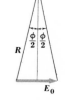

Fig. 3-11   *Graphical addition of amplitudes for N sources of equal strength with a phase difference ϕ between adjacent sources.   The case $N = 6$ is shown.*

As shown in the figure, the ends of the vectors lie on a circle whose radius R is given by

$$\frac{1}{2} E_0 = R \sin \frac{\phi}{2} \tag{3-17}$$

The resultant amplitude E is the length of the chord subtended at the center of the circle by the angle $N\phi$, as shown.   The length of a chord which subtends an angle $N\phi$ on a circle of radius R is given by $2R \sin (N\phi/2)$.   Combining this with Eq. (3-17), we find for the resultant amplitude

$$E = 2R \sin \frac{N\phi}{2} = E_0 \frac{\sin (N\phi/2)}{\sin (\phi/2)} \tag{3-18}$$

The intensity is

$$I = \frac{1}{2} \sqrt{\frac{\epsilon}{\mu}} E^2 = \frac{1}{2} \sqrt{\frac{\epsilon}{\mu}} E_0{}^2 \frac{\sin^2 (N\phi/2)}{\sin^2 (\phi/2)}$$

$$= I_0 \frac{\sin^2 (N\phi/2)}{\sin^2 (\phi/2)} \tag{3-19}$$

where again I_0 is the intensity from a single source, as in Eq. (3-10).

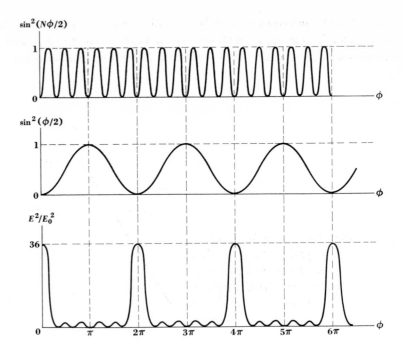

Fig. 3-12 *Interference pattern for six sources. The individual factors of Eq. (3-19) are plotted, with their quotient, which represents the intensity. The principal maxima are separated by several much smaller subsidiary maxima.*

The functional dependence of I on ϕ, which in turn depends on the angle θ in Fig. 3-10, consists of a rapid fluctuation given by the factor $\sin^2(N\phi/2)$ modulated by the more slowly varying function $1/\sin^2(\phi/2)$. Each factor, together with the product of the two functions, is plotted in Fig. 3-12. We note that the product is indeterminate at $\phi = 0, 2\pi, 4\pi, \ldots$, but it may be evaluated at these points by recalling that for very small angles $\sin x \simeq x$, so that we have approximately, for small ϕ,

$$\frac{\sin^2(N\phi/2)}{\sin^2(\phi/2)} \simeq \frac{(N\phi/2)^2}{(\phi/2)^2} = N^2$$

Thus at $\phi = 0, 2\pi, 4\pi, \ldots$,

$$I = \frac{1}{2}\sqrt{\frac{\epsilon}{\mu}}N^2 E_0^2 = N^2 I_0 \tag{3-20}$$

This corresponds physically to the case where signals from all N sources arrive at P in phase, so that the total amplitude is just NE_0.

To complete the intensity-distribution calculation, the phase difference ϕ must be expressed in terms of the angle θ giving the direction from the array of sources to the observer. When the sources are all in phase, this is determined entirely by the path difference and is given by Eq. (3-12), just as in the two-source case. If there are phase differences between the sources, they must be added to the phase angle resulting from the path difference. For example, if adjacent sources differ in phase by $45°$, then $\phi = kd \sin \theta + \pi/4$.

The interference pattern is seen to consist of sharp, large maxima, each separated by several much smaller subsidiary peaks. The larger the value of N, the sharper and more intense are the peaks, in contrast to the case of the two-slit diffraction pattern, where the maxima are rather broad. Practical use is made of this behavior in the design of directional radio antennas, when it is desirable to beam most of the power from a radio transmitter along a single line, as is the case in many communication situations.

Equation (3-19) can also be derived by using the complex exponential-function representation. The rotating vectors are represented by the quantities

$$E_0 e^{i\omega t}, \ E_0 e^{i(\omega t+\phi)}, \ E_0 e^{i(\omega t+2\phi)}, \ \ldots, \ E_0 e^{i[\omega t+(N-1)\phi]}$$

and their sum by

$$E_0 e^{i\omega t}(1 + e^{i\phi} + e^{2i\phi} + \cdots + e^{i(N-1)\phi}) \tag{3-21}$$

As explained previously, it is sufficient to calculate the vector sum at one instant of time, since its magnitude is constant. Clearly it is convenient to choose the time $t = 0$, which makes each factor $e^{i\omega t}$ equal to unity. Hence we drop this factor from here on. Expression (3-21) can be simplified by using the formula for the sum of terms in a geometric series:

$$1 + a + a^2 + \cdots + a^{N-1} = \frac{a^N - 1}{a - 1}$$

which can be verified by division. Dropping the factor $e^{i\omega t}$, we obtain

$$E = E_0 \frac{e^{iN\phi} - 1}{e^{i\phi} - 1}$$

which can be rearranged in the following form:

$$E = E_0 \frac{e^{iN\phi/2}}{e^{i\phi/2}} \frac{e^{iN\phi/2} - e^{-iN\phi/2}}{e^{i\phi/2} - e^{-i\phi/2}}$$

$$= E_0 e^{i(N-1)\phi/2} \frac{\sin (N\phi/2)}{\sin (\phi/2)} \tag{3-22}$$

The intensity I is given by

$$I = \frac{1}{2}\sqrt{\frac{\epsilon}{\mu}} |E|^2 = \frac{1}{2}\sqrt{\frac{\epsilon}{\mu}} EE^*$$

and so, finally,

$$I = \frac{1}{2}\sqrt{\frac{\epsilon}{\mu}} E_0{}^2 \frac{\sin^2 (N\phi/2)}{\sin^2 (\phi/2)} = I_0 \frac{\sin^2 (N\phi/2)}{\sin^2 (\phi/2)} \tag{3-23}$$

which agrees with Eq. (3-19).

One may again raise the question whether corresponding phenomena occur with visible light. They do indeed, and they are of considerable practical importance. One can construct an apparatus similar to that used in the two-slit experiment described above but having many slits. For interference effects to be readily observable, the spacing between sources should be of the same order of magnitude as the wavelength, which for visible light is less than 0.001 mm. The most widely used procedure is to scratch a series of very fine grooves with a diamond point either on a highly polished plane glass surface or on a polished metal mirror used as a reflector. It has been possible by very careful construction of machinery to obtain grids with up to about 30,000 lines/in. Such grids are called diffraction gratings. Those made from a transparent material and used in transmission are called *transmission gratings*, and those used as reflectors are called *reflection gratings*.

Diffraction gratings have found wide application in spectroscopy. When light of two different wavelengths is incident upon a grating with given line spacing, the maximum-intensity directions in the interference pattern will be different, since the phase relations depend on the wavelength. Thus it is possible to build an instrument to measure wavelengths. Furthermore, by proper choice of the line spacing in the grating, one can adjust the amount of spread or *dispersion* between maxima for different wavelengths. This is a considerable advantage over the prism spectrometer, in which one is at the mercy of the dispersive properties of the glass used; thus diffraction gratings are very widely used for precise spectroscopic measurements.

At this point a few notes on terminology are in order. The effects described above, resulting from the superposition of waves with phase differences, are called *interference* or *diffraction* effects. To an extent these terms are used interchangeably, but usually *interference* refers to superposition of only a few waves from different sources or from the same source with different optical paths, while *diffraction* usually involves superposition of a large number of waves, as in a diffraction grating. Physically, the basic principles involved are identical in the two classes of phenomena.

In the discussion of interference of light emerging from slits, it was assumed that all slits radiate in phase; this is true only when the primary source of light is far enough away so that the waves striking the slits may be considered plane waves, or when a lens system is used to convert spherical waves from a source at a finite distance into plane waves. Correspondingly, it was assumed that the position of the observer is essentially an infinite distance away. For historical reasons, interference phenomena in which both source and observer are infinitely far from the slit array are called *Fraunhofer diffraction*. Phenomena in which either source or observer or both are at a finite distance from the slits or other obstacle are called *Fresnel diffraction*. The distinction is illustrated in Fig. 3-13. Fraunhofer diffraction, because it involves plane waves, is easier to calculate in detail than Fresnel diffraction, but the physical principles are the same in both. Furthermore, by using lenses to convert spherical waves into plane waves, it is possible to observe Fraunhofer diffraction with finite distances. An example of a possible experimental arrangement is shown in Fig. 3-13.

We conclude this section with one additional example of an interference phenomenon involving the superposition of two waves. The situation is shown in Fig. 3-14. Two perfectly flat glass plates are in contact along one edge but are separated by a certain distance on the opposite edge, so as to form a wedge-shaped air space. Monochromatic light is incident from above. Reflections occur at all four surfaces; we consider in particular the interference between reflections from the two surfaces adjacent to the air wedge. In traveling from the source to the observer's eye, the wave reflected from the bottom surface has to travel somewhat farther than that from the top surface. The difference in path length varies with the distance from the line of contact between the glass plates, and so we expect an interference pattern. Near the line of contact, the path difference is very small; thus we expect a region of maximum constructive interference. Similarly, another region of constructive interference should occur when the path difference is one wavelength, corresponding to an air space of one-half wavelength. If the angle between the planes is α, as shown in the figure, the second

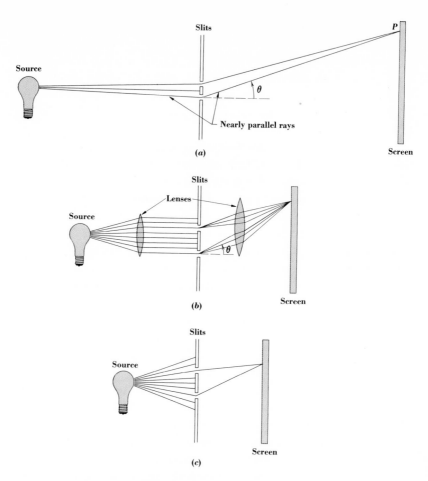

Fig. 3-13 (a) *Typical Fraunhofer diffraction situation, with both source and observer very far from the diffracting object.* (b) *Lens arrangement used to observe Fraunhofer diffraction with finite source and observer distances.* (c) *Typical Fresnel diffraction situation, with both source and observer at finite distances from the diffracting object.*

bright fringe should occur at a distance d from the line of contact, given approximately by

$$\alpha = \frac{\lambda/2}{d} \qquad \text{or} \qquad d = \frac{\lambda}{2\alpha} \tag{3-24}$$

More generally, there should be a succession of bright and dark fringes,

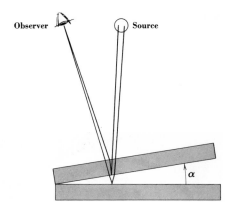

Fig. 3-14   *Reflection of light from the two surfaces shown. Depending on the difference in path length, constructive or destructive interference occurs.*

with adjacent bright fringes separated by the amount d given by Eq. (3-24).

This experiment is easy enough to perform, and the results are more or less what we have predicted, with one important exception. Near the line of contact, where we expect a bright fringe, a *dark* fringe is observed. The succession of alternate bright and dark fringes appears as predicted, but the positions are exactly reversed. It is as though somehow one of the reflected waves had suffered an additional phase shift of one-half cycle. This, in fact, is precisely what has happened. We recall the discussion of Sec. 2-5, where transmission and reflection coefficients were calculated for a plane wave striking an interface between two dielectric media. It was observed there that, if the second medium has a larger index of refraction than the first, the reflected wave is inverted with respect to the incident wave; that is, the reflection introduces a phase change of π. When the index of refraction in the first medium is greater than that in the second, no phase change occurs. Applying these results to the present situation, we see that the wave reflected internally from the top surface suffers no phase change but that reflected from the bottom surface is inverted. This additional phase change accounts for the positions of the fringes in the experiment just described and provides an interesting confirmation of the predictions of Sec. 2-5.

These *interference fringes*, as they are called, have many practical applications. One of the simplest is testing the flatness of a glass plate by putting it in contact with another plate known to be flat and observing the pattern of interference fringes resulting from the irregularities of the surface. These fringes are generally not along straight lines, as in the idealized situation described above, but are *contour lines* representing the irregularities of the surface. Two examples are shown in Fig. 3-15. By making use of these interference fringes it is possible to make surfaces that are flat within a fraction of a wavelength much more precisely than would be possible using ordinary mechanical measuring devices.

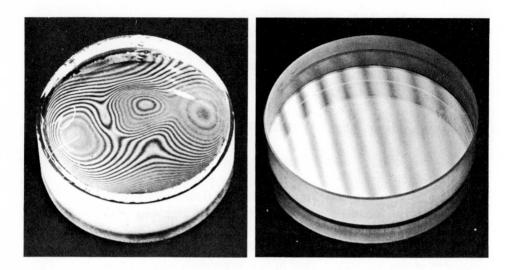

Fig. 3-15 *Interference fringes produced by interference between reflections at two air-glass interfaces. The ring-shaped fringes were first observed by Newton and are called Newton's rings.*

A similar phenomenon is responsible for the brightly colored rings observed when a thin film of oil floats on water. Here the radiation is not ordinarily monochromatic, and constructive interference occurs at different positions for different colors of light; hence the interference pattern appears as fringes of various colors rather than simply as light and dark fringes. Another important practical application of the interference between reflections from two adjacent surfaces is involved in anti-reflection coatings of lenses, in which a lens is coated with a thin film of material whose thickness is chosen to achieve maximum destructive interference of the reflected waves, with corresponding maximum transmitted intensity through the lens. Some of the details of design of such nonreflecting coatings are included in the problems for this chapter.

3-4   *Crystal Diffraction*

In the preceding section, the discussion of interference patterns from coherent sources of radiation separated in space was limited to sources in a straight line with equal spacing.   There is nothing to prevent an array of more complicated structure, with the sources of radiation distributed over a plane or throughout a region of space.   Detailed calculation of the resulting interference pattern may be more complicated, but the principles are the same as for the linear array of sources.

A simple example is shown in Fig. 3-16.   Each source in the square array emits radiation with the same amplitude and phase.   We observe the resultant interference pattern in the direction θ as shown.

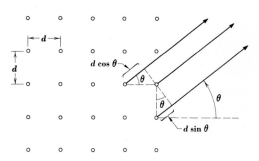

Fig. 3-16   *A two-dimensional array of antennas.   For radiation from all antennas to arrive at a distant point in phase, two conditions must be satisfied simultaneously; they are Eqs. (3-25) and (3-26).*

Constructive interference occurs between successive antennas in a horizontal row if the condition

$$d \cos \theta = m\lambda \qquad m = 1, 2, 3, \ldots \tag{3-25}$$

is satisfied, and constructive interference between successive elements in a vertical column occurs if

$$d \sin \theta = n\lambda \qquad n = 1, 2, 3, \ldots \tag{3-26}$$

For all the waves from the antennas to arrive at the point of the observer with identical phases, these two relations must be satisfied simultaneously.   Depending on the relative magnitude of d and λ, there may be several pairs of integers for which this relationship is satisfied, or perhaps none at all.   As a particular example, suppose that $d = \lambda\sqrt{2}$; then both conditions are satisfied when $\theta = 45°$, and we expect a strong maximum in the interference pattern in this direction.

Additional interesting features appear if, instead of being primary sources of radiation, the elements in the square array in Fig. 3-16 are *scatterers* of incident radiation.   Suppose, for example, they are small metal spheres and that a plane electromagnetic wave is directed at the array. The electric field at the position of each sphere induces a fluctuating electric dipole moment, so that each sphere acts as a source of a spherical wave. The total interference pattern is then the result of the superposition of the incident plane wave and the spherical waves, one for each of the metallic spheres. Since the spheres are at various distances from the primary source of the plane wave, the induced electric dipole moments are not all in phase. To compute the interference pattern we need to consider not just the differences in path lengths between the various radiators and the observation point but the *total* path difference from the primary source to each radiator, thence to the observation point.

Let us consider a plane wave incident upon a square array, as shown in Fig. 3-17. For the *row* of scatterers shown in the figure, the path length from source to observer is the same for all scatterers in the row if the lines to the source and observer are at equal angles, as shown in the figure. Now we examine the condition under which scattered radiation from adjacent rows is *also* in phase. As shown, the path difference for two scatterers in the same column but adjacent rows is $2d \sin \theta$. For constructive interference to occur, this must be an integer number of wavelengths. Thus the condition that must be satisfied in order for radiation from the *entire array* to arrive at the observer in

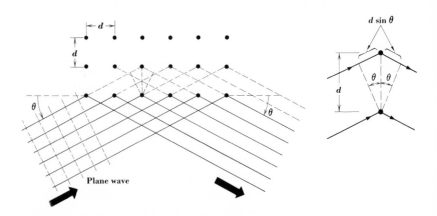

Fig. 3-17   *Scattering of radiation from a square array. Interference from successive scatterers in a row is constructive when the angles of incidence and reflection are equal. When Eq. (3-27) is satisfied, interference from adjacent rows is also constructive.*

phase is

$$2d \sin \theta = n\lambda \qquad n = 1, 2, 3, \ldots \tag{3-27}$$

When this condition is satisfied, a strong maximum in the interference pattern is observed. If the condition is not satisfied, no strong maximum is observed, since there is then *no* position of the observer for which all the radiation will arrive in phase from all scatterers. Equation (3-27) is called the *Bragg condition*, in honor of Sir William Bragg, one of the pioneers in x-ray diffraction analysis.

It is convenient to describe this interference effect in terms of *reflections* of the wave from the horizontal lines in Fig. 3-17. When strong interference maxima occur, they are always at angles such that the angles of incidence and reflection are equal, and there is the additional condition of Eq. (3-27), which must be satisfied for a strong reflection to occur. It would be possible in principle to enclose the array in a black box and determine the spacing of the radiators by observing the interference pattern, provided the wavelength of the radiation is known.

The entire discussion can be extended to a three-dimensional array of radiators. Again the concept of reflection planes is useful; if the array has regular structure, it is possible to construct a set of parallel planes passing through all the radiators. Again, all radiators in a given plane interfere constructively if the angles of incidence and reflection with respect to this plane are equal. Furthermore, the condition for constructive interference between adjacent planes spaced a distance d apart is again Eq. (3-27). The set of parallel planes is in general not unique; it is always possible to construct several different sets of parallel planes. Correspondingly, there are various sets of angles corresponding to directions of maximum intensity. Figure 3-18 illustrates two sets of planes for the simple case of a cubic array of radiators.

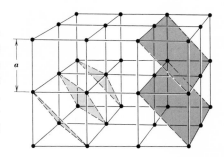

Fig. 3-18 *Simple cubic crystal lattice, showing two different families of crystal planes. The spacing of the planes on the left is $a/\sqrt{3}$; that of the planes on the right is $a/\sqrt{2}$. There are also three sets of planes parallel to the cube faces, with spacing a.*

The foregoing discussion may seem somewhat academic, but it has very important implications. What we have really been talking about is a three-dimensional diffraction grating, and its most important applications lie not in diffraction of radio waves but rather in x-ray diffraction. X-rays were discovered quite by accident in 1895 by Roentgen; the circumstances surrounding their origin immediately suggested their electromagnetic nature. All attempts at dealing with them by the usual optical methods were unsuccessful, however, and it became clear that their wavelength must be much shorter than that of visible light. In 1912 Laue suggested that, if the wavelengths of x-rays were of the same order of magnitude as the atomic spacing in crystals, a crystal could be used as a three-dimensional diffraction grating for the analysis of x-rays.

The experimental work that followed proved Laue's suggestion to be an extremely fruitful one. Directing a narrow beam of x-rays at a large single crystal whose orientation could be varied, and recording on photographic film the positions of the various maxima in the inter-

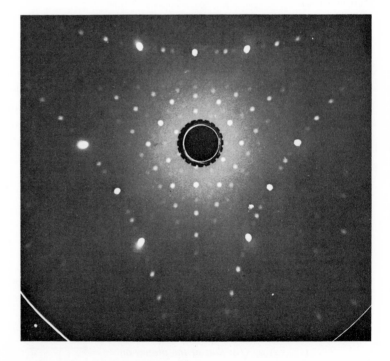

Fig. 3-19 *Photograph of an x-ray diffraction pattern; the spots represent directions of strong maxima in the interference pattern.*

ference pattern, make it possible to analyze the structure of crystals in considerable detail. An example of an x-ray diffraction pattern is shown in Fig. 3-19.

In the ensuing years, x-ray diffraction from crystals has been by far the most important experimental tool in the investigation of crystal structure of solids. It has been possible to measure atomic spacings in crystals quite precisely and to determine the details of crystal structure even in complex crystals. More recently, x-ray diffraction experiments have played a considerable role in investigations of the structure of liquids and even of organic molecules. Yet the basic principles involved in x-ray diffraction, those of superposition and interference, are the same ones responsible for a wide variety of other interference and diffraction phenomena.

3-5   *Diffraction from Apertures and Edges*

In this section we consider diffraction effects which occur when a plane wave strikes a barrier with an aperture or an edge. A typical situation is shown in Fig. 3-20; a plane electromagnetic wave is incident upon a sheet of material which is opaque to radiation except in one region where a hole has been cut. We place a screen at a considerable distance from the aperture and observe the radiation pattern on this screen. What do we see?

Fig. 3-20 *Plane monochromatic waves are incident on a barrier with an aperture, in the same plane as that of the waves. The intensity pattern on the screen is observed.*

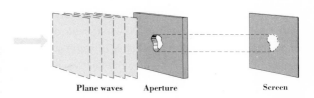

Plane waves   Aperture   Screen

The *ray* picture of light would provide a simple, clear-cut answer to this question. In that model, light travels in straight lines, and so the screen should be dark except for a uniformly illuminated spot the same size and shape as the aperture. Similarly, if instead of an opaque screen with an aperture we used a small opaque obstacle, the result should be a shadow on the screen with definite edges, the same size and shape as the obstacle. When actual observations are made, however, the edges are always somewhat fuzzy; if the experiment is done with monochromatic light, *fringes* appear at the edge of the shadow, reminiscent of interference fringes.   Such phenomena cannot be explained readily on the basis of a ray picture of light.

Even more strange, when a circular obstacle is used, a bright spot appears at the center of the shadow.   The existence of this bright spot was predicted in the year 1818 by the French mathematician Poisson, on the basis of a wave theory of light.   Ironically, Poisson himself was not a believer in the wave theory; he published this calculation, the result of which seemed absurd to him, as a final ridicule aimed at the supporters of the wave theory of light.   Poisson himself did not investigate the question experimentally, but when other physicists did so they found that his predictions were actually correct.   In fact, the existence of the bright spot had been observed 50 years earlier, but its significance was not understood at that time.

The various phenomena that involve departures from straight-line ray behavior of radiation are called *diffraction* phenomena.   Actual calculations of diffraction patterns are often quite complicated, but there are a few cases which can be handled relatively simply; we discuss the basic ideas here.   For light, diffraction patterns are usually calculated from the following principle: *In diffraction of a plane wave by an aperture in an opaque sheet, the radiation field for all points on the far side of the sheet is the same as would be produced by a uniform distribution of sources over the area of the aperture.*   We confine our attention to the case in which the opaque sheet is perpendicular to the direction of propagation of the incident plane wave, in which case we assert further that *all the sources in this distribution are in phase.*

This principle is called *Huygens' principle* in honor of Christian Huygens, a contemporary of Newton, who discovered it in the course of an investigation of the properties of water waves, long before the wave nature of light was understood.   In effect we have already used Huygens' principle in the analysis of a diffraction grating, which is an opaque screen containing a series of parallel slits equally spaced, illuminated by a plane wave.   We regarded each of the slits as a new source of radiation and calculated the resulting interference pattern.   The only new feature we are adding is that in general we must consider not just a discrete set of sources but a continuous distribution of sources over a surface.

The procedure prescribed by Huygens' principle may not seem to make any physical sense at all, since it is clear that there are not really any sources of radiation in the aperture; in fact, this is one place we can be certain there are *no* sources. Nevertheless, the assumption of a uniform distribution of sources across the aperture leads to the observed diffraction pattern. We now discuss an example of the use of this procedure and then present an argument to justify the use of the fictitious source distribution.

Let us apply the above prescription to calculate the diffraction pattern produced by an aperture in the form of a long, thin slit. In Fig. 3-21 the short dimension of the slit is vertical and its long dimension perpendicular to the page. According to the procedure just described, the resulting radiation pattern is the same as would be produced by a continuous distribution of sources over the area of the slit. Assuming that the length of the slit is much larger than its width, we may regard this as essentially a two-dimensional problem. We divide the

Fig. 3-21 *Calculation of the diffraction pattern for a slit of width a. The path difference between light from the bottom edge and that from a strip a distance s from the bottom edge is s sin θ. From this the phase difference of the two radiations can be found. The total intensity at any angle θ is found by adding the contributions of the source strips (integrating on s), taking account of the varying phase.*

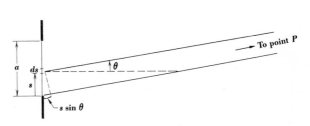

total width a into a series of elemental strips, a typical one of which is shown in the figure; the width of this elemental strip is denoted as ds. We can think of this strip as generating cylindrical wavefronts, that is, waves whose surface of constant phase are coaxial cylinders, with their axis along this strip.

We now calculate the total intensity in the direction θ toward the

distant point P.   Each elemental strip in the hypothetical source distribution across the slit contributes to the total field at P, but the various
contributions have various phases, resulting from the differences in path
length.   The path difference for the two strips shown is $s \sin \theta$, and so
the phase difference between them, according to Eq. (3-13), is

$$\phi = ks \sin \theta \tag{3-28}$$

which shows that the phase changes continuously with s across the slit.
Correspondingly, the total phase difference between the bottom and the
top of the slit, which we may call Φ, is given by

$$\Phi = ka \sin \theta \tag{3-29}$$

Fig. 3-22   (a) *Vector diagram
for addition of amplitudes for a
single slit.   The length of the
curve is the same for all angles;
the angle subtended is the total
phase difference between the top
and bottom edges of the slit.
The chord represents the resultant
amplitude.   (b) Vector diagrams
for several points in the diffraction pattern.*

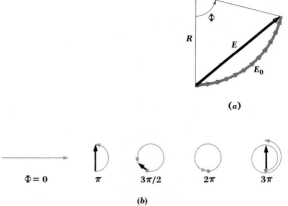

(a)

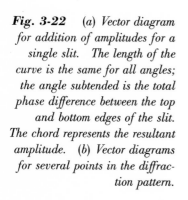

(b)

The intensity may be found by means of a vector diagram very
similar to that used for the interference pattern for N slits in Fig. 3-11.
Instead of the N slits, there is a continuous distribution of sources across
the slit; correspondingly, the construction to find the total amplitude is
not a vector sum of N vectors with equal magnitudes but rather an infinite sum of infinitesimal vectors, forming a smooth curve of constant
curvature R, as shown in Fig. 3-22a.   The *length* of this curve E_0, representing the sum of the magnitudes of the vectors, is constant, and the
chord length represents the amplitude of the resultant radiation.   The
total angle subtended at the center of the circle, labeled Φ in the figure,
is simply the total phase difference between the top and bottom of the
slit, which from Eq. (3-29) is $\Phi = ka \sin \theta$.   Just as in the case of Fig.
3-11, the chord length E is given by $\frac{1}{2}E = R \sin (\Phi/2)$; the constant

arc length E_0 is $E_0 = R\Phi$. Eliminating R and solving for E, we find

$$E = E_0 \frac{\sin{(\Phi/2)}}{\Phi/2} \tag{3-30}$$

where E_0 is the value of E when $\theta = 0$ and $\Phi = 0$. The intensity is

$$I = I_0 \frac{\sin^2{(\Phi/2)}}{(\Phi/2)^2} = I_0 \frac{\sin^2{(\frac{1}{2}ka \sin\theta)}}{(\frac{1}{2}ka \sin\theta)^2} \tag{3-31}$$

where I_0 is the intensity at $\theta = 0$. Vector diagrams corresponding to several points in the diffraction pattern are shown in Fig. 3-22b.

This result may also be obtained by use of the complex-number representation. The electric field dE resulting from a strip of width ds at the bottom of the slit $(s = 0)$ is

$$dE = E_0 \text{ Re } (e^{i\omega t}) \frac{ds}{a} \tag{3-32}$$

where the factor $1/a$ is included for dimensional consistency and so that in the final result E_0 will represent the amplitude in the direction $\theta = 0$. Similarly, the contribution dE from a strip of width ds a distance s from the bottom is

$$dE = E_0 \text{ Re } [e^{i(\omega t + \phi)}] \frac{ds}{a} \tag{3-33}$$

where the phase angle ϕ is given as before by Eq. (3-28).

To find the total field at P, we integrate Eq. (3-33) over the width of the slit, using for ϕ the expression given by Eq. (3-28). Since the factor $e^{i\omega t}$ drops out in taking the absolute value, we omit it from here on. The amplitude at P is then given by

$$E = E_0 \left| \frac{1}{a} \int_0^a e^{iks \sin\theta} \, ds \right| = E_0 \left| \frac{e^{ika \sin\theta} - 1}{ika \sin\theta} \right|$$

$$= E_0 \left| e^{(1/2)ika \sin\theta} \frac{\sin{(\frac{1}{2}ka \sin\theta)}}{\frac{1}{2}ka \sin\theta} \right| \tag{3-34}$$

Finally, the intensity distribution is

$$I = I_0 \frac{\sin^2{(\frac{1}{2}ka \sin\theta)}}{(\frac{1}{2}ka \sin\theta)^2} \tag{3-35}$$

in agreement with Eq. (3-31).

Figure 3-23 shows a graph of this function and under it a photograph of a diffraction pattern, which agrees well with the theoretical

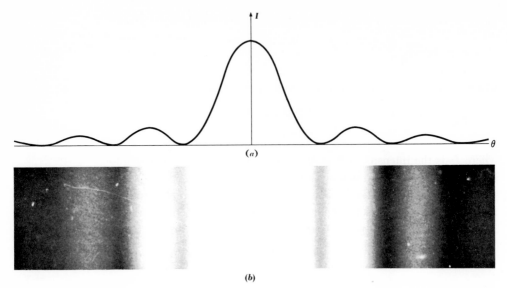

(a)

(b)

Fig. 3-23 (a) *Intensity distribution for the diffraction pattern formed from a single slit on a very
distant screen.* (b) *Photograph made by placing
photographic film in the plane of the screen.*

prediction. Thus, at least in this particular case, the recipe for calculating diffraction patterns leads to a result which agrees with experimental observations.

We now outline briefly an argument to show *why* the seemingly
fictitious source distribution across apertures leads to correct results in
diffraction-pattern calculations. If the opaque sheet has *no* aperture, it
blocks the radiation completely. But how does it accomplish this?
When a plane wave is incident on the left side of the sheet, it induces
oscillating dipoles in the sheet; these produce an additional radiation
field which, when superposed on the incident field, results in a total field
with zero intensity at all points to the right of the sheet. If the incident
wave is a plane wave, the sources of this secondary wave, which precisely
cancel the incident wave at points to the right of the sheet, must be a
uniform distribution of sources over the sheet.

Now, what happens when we remove a certain area of the sheet?
In doing so, we remove the secondary sources in that area. Let a typical
secondary source be S_i, and let its radiation field be $\mathbf{E}_i$. We note that
we could produce the same effect as removing these sources if, instead,
we allowed them to remain and added to each one a corresponding source
S_i', which produces a radiation field precisely the negative of that of S_i,

that is, $-\mathbf{E}_i$. But the latter arrangement also corresponds to the super-position of the waves associated with an opaque sheet with no aperture (i.e., no radiation field to the right of the screen) and the radiation field associated with the distribution of sources S_i. Thus on the right side the total radiation field is just that of the uniform distribution of sources S_i' over the area of the aperture; this fact justifies calculating the radiation pattern on this basis.

Some important points are left out of this argument. One of the most important omissions is that we have not considered any peculiarities associated with induced sources at the *edges* of the aperture. To the extent that we have neglected these, our results are independent of the material of which the opaque sheet is made. But in cases where edge effects cannot be neglected, the properties of the material *are* relevant, and the calculations become considerably more complicated. In general, it is usually legitimate to neglect edge effects whenever the dimensions of the aperture are much larger than the wavelength of the radiation. This is usually the case with visible light, but it is practically never the case with radio waves of microwave frequencies, in which case more detailed calculations must be made.

Diffraction patterns can be calculated for other kinds of apertures, circular, rectangular, and so on, and for single edges. Except in the

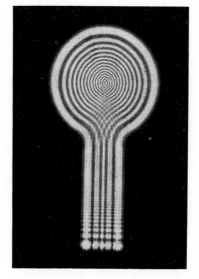

Fig. 3-24 *Diffraction pattern formed by an irregularly shaped aperture.*

simplest cases, the calculations become very complicated and often are made numerically, using a high-speed computer. An interesting example of diffraction from an aperture is shown in Fig. 3-24. Photographs such as this are almost always made not by placing the photographic film an infinite distance from the aperture but by using a converging lens as shown in Fig. 3-13b.

3-6 *Dispersion*

In the development of the fundamental properties of electromagnetic waves in Sec. 2-3, it was shown that these waves travel in matter with a speed given by

$$u = \frac{1}{\sqrt{\mu\epsilon}} \tag{3-36}$$

which in vacuum reduces to $c = (\mu_0\epsilon_0)^{-1/2}$. The index of refraction n of the material is defined as the ratio of the speed of light in vacuum to its value in the medium, $n = c/u$. Thus

$$n = \sqrt{\frac{\mu\epsilon}{\mu_0\epsilon_0}} \tag{3-37}$$

When the electric and magnetic properties of the material are given in terms of the dielectric constant K_E and the relative permeability K_M, introduced in Eqs. (2-2), the index of refraction becomes simply

$$n = \sqrt{K_E K_M} \tag{3-38}$$

Furthermore, as mentioned in Sec. 2-5, K_M for most materials (with the notable exception of the ferromagnetic materials) differs from unity by at most a few parts in 10^4, and often by less than 1 part in 10^6. Thus the approximation $K_M = 1$ almost never introduces any appreciable error, and we find the even simpler result

$$n = \sqrt{K_E} \tag{3-39}$$

It is necessary, however, to use a certain amount of discretion in applying Eq. (3-39). An example will illustrate some of the possible problems. Water is composed of highly polar molecules and in a static electric field has an unusually large relative dielectric constant, approximately $K_E = 80$. Equation (3-39) gives a predicted value of the index of refraction of about 9. The *measured* index of refraction for water, for visible light, is about $n = 1.33$. What went wrong?

The difficulty is that we have used the value of K_E obtained from *static* measurements, that is, measurements where the field and the polarization do not change with time. But the transmission of electromagnetic radiation is a highly *dynamic* phenomenon, since the fields oscillate at very high frequencies. In water, the large static polarization is associated with rotation of molecules possessing electric dipole moments. At sufficiently high frequencies inertial effects prevent the molecules from rotating appreciably, and thus the effective dielectric constant at high frequencies is much *less* than its static value. To account for the observed value of the index of refraction, the effective dielectric constant has to be not 80 but about 1.8. In Eqs. (3-36) and (3-39) we must use not the properties of a material measured under static conditions but rather values measured under *dynamic* conditions of the same frequency as that of the radiation.

In general, both K_E and K_M can be expected to vary with frequency, and therefore we expect the index of refraction of a material also to be a function of frequency. The variation of index of refraction with wavelength (and therefore with frequency) is a well-known phenomenon. In 1666, Sir Isaac Newton discovered that the refraction of a beam of light by a glass prism is different for different colors, although the relation between color and wavelength was not firmly established until 140 years later. This variation in refractive power, which has come to be known as *dispersion*, is the mechanism by which white light is broken up into a rainbow, and the same effect is used in prism spectrometers. Thus the variation of refractive index with wavelength is not particularly astounding. For most glasses, at optical frequencies the index of refraction *increases* with increasing frequency; in refraction the shorter wavelengths (the violet end of the spectrum) are bent more sharply than the longer ones (the red end of the spectrum). Variation of index of refraction with wavelength for two glasses is shown in Fig. 3-25.

The dependence of index of refraction on frequency can be understood on the basis of the microscopic structure of matter. We consider here a model which is very simple and not entirely realistic but which affords some insight into the dependence of dielectric properties on frequency. We shall use the following very simple model of a dielectric. Electrons are distributed through the material, with an average density of N electrons per unit volume. Each particle has charge e and mass m, and each is bound to a certain equilibrium position by a force which is proportional to the displacement from that equilibrium position. Thus, in the absence of any external field, the particles can vibrate with simple harmonic motion about their equilibrium positions. Such a model is

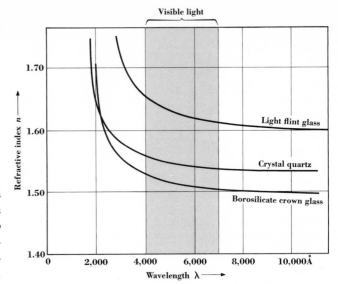

Fig. 3-25 *Variation of index of refraction with wavelength for two glasses of different composition and for crystalline quartz.*

reminiscent of the old Thomson model of the atom, in which the positive charge was regarded as a blob occupying the whole volume of the atom, with electrons embedded in the same manner as raisins in a pudding. The "pudding" was given elastic properties so that the electrons could vibrate harmonically about their equilibrium positions. We now know that the positive charge is actually concentrated in a small nucleus in the interior of the atom and that the electrons are not at rest. Nevertheless, it is not completely unreasonable to represent the *changes* in their motion which result from a periodic external field in terms of this simple model.

Proceeding with the analysis, we note that in the presence of a periodic external field the electrons undergo periodic motions with the frequency of the field. As a result, each one has a time-varying dipole moment resulting from its displacement with respect to the positive charge of the atom. Our program is to calculate this displacement as a function of time, from which we can calculate the *polarization* of the material, which is the dipole-moment density, as a function of time. By definition the electric displacement D is given by $D = \epsilon_0 E + P$ and, for a medium in which D is proportional to E, $D = \epsilon E$. As the calculation will show, P is proportional to E, so that from the results of the calculation we can determine ϵ.

In the presence of a sinusoidally varying electric field $E = E_0 \cos \omega t$, an electron experiences a force $F = eE_0 \cos \omega t$ in addition to the elastic force $(-kx)$ tending to restore it to its equilibrium position. Applying Newton's second law to the motion of the electron, we find

$$-kx + eE_0 \cos \omega t = m\frac{d^2x}{dt^2} \tag{3-40}$$

As pointed out above, the resulting motion of the electron is expected to be a sinusoidal function of t, with the same frequency as that of the radiation. That is,

$$x = A \cos \omega t \tag{3-41}$$

where the amplitude A of the motion is an as yet unknown constant. Substituting Eq. (3-41) and its second derivative into Eq. (3-40), we find that this is a solution of the differential equation only if A obeys the condition $-kA + eE_0 = -m\omega^2 A$, or

$$A = \frac{eE_0}{k - m\omega^2} \tag{3-42}$$

This equation is somewhat more illuminating when expressed in terms of the natural frequency ω_0 of the oscillator, defined by $\omega_0 = (k/m)^{1/2}$. This is the frequency with which the electron would vibrate, as a result of the elastic force, if there were no external periodic field. In terms of ω_0,

$$A = \frac{eE_0/m}{\omega_0{}^2 - \omega^2}$$

and

$$x = \frac{e/m}{\omega_0{}^2 - \omega^2} E_0 \cos \omega t = \frac{e/m}{\omega_0{}^2 - \omega^2} E \tag{3-43}$$

This shows that the displacement x from equilibrium of each electron is proportional to the applied sinusoidal field E. When the frequency ω of the field is less than the natural vibrational frequency ω_0 of the electron, the displacement is *in phase* with the field; if larger, x and E have opposite signs, indicating that their variations with time are 180° out of phase.

Each electron contributes a dipole moment xe, and so the polarization, or density of dipole moments, is $P = xeN$; thus

$$P = \frac{e^2NE/m}{\omega_0{}^2 - \omega^2} \tag{3-44}$$

The electric displacement is

$$\mathbf{D} = \epsilon_0 \mathbf{E} + \mathbf{P} = \left(\epsilon_0 + \frac{e^2 N/m}{\omega_0{}^2 - \omega^2} \right) \mathbf{E} \tag{3-45}$$

which shows that the permittivity ϵ is given by

$$\epsilon = \epsilon_0 + \frac{e^2 N/m}{\omega_0{}^2 - \omega^2} \tag{3-46}$$

Thus we see that a frequency-dependent dielectric constant results from even such a simple model as this.   Equation (3-46) also shows that, when the frequency of the incident radiation is close to the natural frequency of the oscillators, the dielectric constant becomes very large, corresponding to a very small velocity of propagation.   Physically, what happens then is that energy is strongly *absorbed* from the incident radiation.   Our model contains no mechanism for energy absorption, but one can easily be included by adding to the equation of motion [Eq. (3-40)] a velocity-dependent damping force analogous to a viscous friction force in a harmonic oscillator.   The analysis will not be given in detail; if the damping force is represented as $-2m\gamma \, dx/dt$, where γ is a constant characterizing the magnitude of the damping effect, the dielectric constant is given by

$$\epsilon = \epsilon_0 + \frac{e^2 N}{m} \frac{\omega_0{}^2 - \omega^2}{(\omega_0{}^2 - \omega^2)^2 + 4\gamma^2\omega^2} \tag{3-47}$$

and energy is absorbed from the radiation at an average rate per unit volume of

$$\frac{dE}{dt} = \frac{e^2 N E_0{}^2}{m} \frac{\gamma\omega^2}{(\omega_0{}^2 - \omega^2)^2 + 4\gamma^2\omega^2} \tag{3-48}$$

In the case of $\gamma = 0$, corresponding to the absence of damping force and therefore the absence of a mechanism for absorption of energy, Eq. (3-47) reduces to the simpler case of Eq. (3-46), and the rate of energy absorption becomes zero.   Figure 3-26 shows the variation of permittivity and energy absorption with frequency, for this simple microscopic model.

The phenomena illustrated by Fig. 3-26 are observed in many common materials.   Ordinary glass has a dielectric constant which is very nearly independent of frequency at low frequencies; in the region of visible light the index of refraction and the dielectric constant increase with frequency, and the material becomes opaque in the ultraviolet

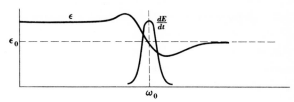

Fig. 3-26 *Permittivity and rate of energy absorption as functions of frequency.*

region. Clearly, the quantitative details of the preceding discussion should not be taken too seriously, because of the obvious shortcomings of the model. But it does give some qualitative insight into the microscopic mechanisms of dispersion and absorption.

The microscopic mechanism by which electrons dissipate energy absorbed from an electromagnetic wave is closely related to the microscopic basis of electrical resistance. In any material, not all electrons are completely bound to individual atoms; some are more or less free to move through the material. As a result, no material is a perfect electrical insulator. When an electron moves through a material, it can undergo inelastic collisions with atoms. In the case of crystalline solids, this energy then appears in the form of crystal lattice vibrations and is interpreted macroscopically as a rise in temperature of the material.

Thus the absorption of radiation by a material is related to its electrical conductivity. It can be shown that the differential equation for the electric field in a conducting medium is, for plane waves in the x direction,

$$\frac{\partial^2 E}{\partial x^2} = \mu\epsilon\frac{\partial^2 E}{\partial t^2} + \mu\sigma\frac{\partial E}{\partial t} \tag{3-49}$$

which differs from the wave equation for an insulator in having the additional term which depends on the conductivity σ and which arises from the presence of electric currents in the material. Solutions of Eq. (3-49) can be obtained by methods similar to those we have already used. When an electromagnetic wave enters a conducting medium, its intensity I decreases with the distance x it penetrates into the material, according to

$$I = I_0 e^{-\alpha x} \tag{3-50}$$

where the quantity α, called the *absorption coefficient*, is given by

$$\alpha = \mu\sigma u = \sigma\sqrt{\frac{\mu}{\epsilon}} \tag{3-51}$$

The derivations of Eqs. (3-50) and (3-51) are left as problems.

3-7   *Interference with Different Frequencies*

We conclude this chapter with a general discussion of some interference phenomena involving the superposition of waves having different frequencies and wavelengths. For example, let us suppose two waves, both plane-polarized in the same plane, have equal amplitudes E_0 at a certain point in space but slightly different frequencies ω_1 and ω_2. Their electric fields can be added to find the total electric field at the point:

$$E = E_0 \cos \omega_1 t + E_0 \cos \omega_2 t = E_0 \, \text{Re} \, (e^{i\omega_1 t} + e^{i\omega_2 t}) \tag{3-52}$$

This expression is more illuminating when written in terms of the average frequency $\omega_0 = (\omega_1 + \omega_2)/2$ and the amount $\Delta\omega$ by which each differs from the average. That is, we write

$$\begin{aligned} \omega_1 &= \omega_0 - \Delta\omega \\ \omega_2 &= \omega_0 + \Delta\omega \end{aligned} \tag{3-53}$$

In terms of these, Eq. (3-52) becomes

$$\begin{aligned} E &= E_0 \, \text{Re} \, (e^{i(\omega_0 - \Delta\omega)t} + e^{i(\omega_0 + \Delta\omega)t}) \\ &= 2E_0 \, \text{Re} \, e^{i\omega_0 t} \cos \Delta\omega t \\ &= (2E_0 \cos \Delta\omega t) \cos \omega_0 t \end{aligned} \tag{3-54}$$

This function represents a field oscillating with a frequency ω_0 with an amplitude (in parentheses) which is modulated by the time-dependent amplitude factor $\cos \Delta\omega t$ with a smaller frequency $\Delta\omega$.

For sound waves, this phenomenon is the familiar one of *beats*. When two tuning forks, one having a frequency of 440 cycles/sec and the other 442 cycles/sec, are sounded together, the ear perceives the superposition of these waves as a sound with a frequency of 441 cycles/sec, with an intensity which varies from zero to maximum and back with a frequency of 2 cycles/sec. We note that this is just twice the frequency ($\Delta\omega = 1$ cycle/sec) with which the amplitude factor varies, since the ear perceives only the magnitude of the amplitude, not its sign.

Next, we consider the space variation of the waves. If both waves are plane waves propagating in the $+x$ direction, the superposed-wave function is

$$E = E_0 \, \text{Re} \, [e^{i(k_1 x - \omega_1 t)} + e^{i(k_2 x - \omega_2 t)}] \tag{3-55}$$

where each wave number k is related to the corresponding frequency ω by $\omega = uk$, as usual. At the particular time $t = 0$, this is

$$E = E_0 \text{ Re } (e^{ik_1 x} + e^{ik_2 x}) \tag{3-56}$$

Just as with the frequencies, it is convenient to introduce the quantities k_0 and Δk:

$$\begin{aligned} k_1 &= k_0 - \Delta k \\ k_2 &= k_0 + \Delta k \end{aligned} \tag{3-57}$$

In terms of k_0 and Δk, Eq. (3-56) becomes

$$\begin{aligned} E &= E_0 \text{ Re } [e^{i(k_0 + \Delta k)x} + e^{i(k_0 - \Delta k)x}] \\ &= [2E_0 \cos (\Delta k)x] \cos k_0 x \end{aligned} \tag{3-58}$$

This equation is plotted in Fig. 3-27, which also shows the individual wave functions at the time $t = 0$.

Fig. 3-27 *Superposition of sinusoidal waves with different wave numbers ($k_1 < k_2$) results in a wave that appears locally sinusoidal but whose amplitude varies from zero to twice the amplitude of each individual wave. The locally sinusoidal nature is described by a wave number $k_0 = \frac{1}{2}(k_1 + k_2)$, while the envelope curve has a slower variation with x given by the smaller wave number $\Delta k = \frac{1}{2}(k_2 - k_1)$.*

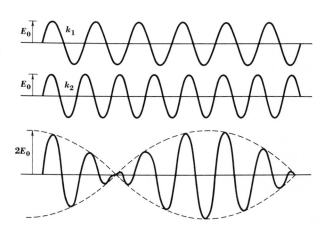

This picture can be obtained directly by a graphical superposition of the two waves. They are in phase at $x = 0$, and the maximum amplitude there is $2E_0$. Moving along the x axis, the two waves grow farther and farther out of phase because of their slightly different wavelengths, until a point is reached where a maximum in one direction for one wave corresponds to a maximum in the opposite direction for the other, and then complete destructive interference occurs. Thus, just as in the consideration of the time dependence, the resulting wave has the appearance of a sinusoidal wave whose amplitude changes slowly as a function of x, over a distance long compared with the individual wavelength. The factor in Eq. (3-58) that represents the varying amplitude is

$$2E_0 \cos \Delta kx \tag{3-59}$$

This factor is usually called the *envelope* of the wave, since it is the boundary line along which the maxima of the wave function lie.

Although Fig. 3-27 shows the resultant wave only at one particular time, it is clear that, if both waves have the same speed u, the entire pattern, including the envelope curve, moves with the same speed as the individual waves. But the speed of electromagnetic waves in a material medium is, in general, a function of frequency. When we superpose two waves having not only different frequencies but also different speeds, some important new features develop. In particular, the speed of propagation of the *envelope* of the interference pattern will not necessarily be equal to the speed of *either* of the individual waves.

For example, let us suppose that two sinusoidal waves have frequencies ω_1 and ω_2 and wave numbers k_1 and k_2, respectively, and that ω_1 and k_1 are slightly larger than ω_2 and k_2, respectively. The wave speeds u_1 and u_2 are given by $\omega_1 = u_1 k_1$ and $\omega_2 = u_2 k_2$. Suppose also that the wave speed is an increasing function of frequency, so that $u_1 > u_2$. Qualitative insight into the behavior of the interference pattern can be gained by imagining that we run alongside the waves with the same speed u_2 as the *slower* of the two waves. Figure 3-28 shows the individual waves and their superposition at two different times. In the first case, the envelope of the interference pattern has a maximum at the position of the observer. In the second case, the observer and the second wave have traveled the same distance, and so the second wave still looks the same, but the first has gained a little, as shown in the figure. The region where the two waves interfere constructively has moved considerably *farther* than the first wave; thus the speed of the envelope is considerably *greater* than that of either of the waves. Correspondingly, if the first wave travels somewhat more slowly than the second wave, we find that the envelope of the interference pattern travels more slowly than either of the two waves.

A precise relationship between the individual wave speeds and the speed of the envelope can be derived. In terms of the quantities ω_0, $\Delta\omega$, k_0, and Δk defined by Eqs. (3-53) and (3-57), the superposed

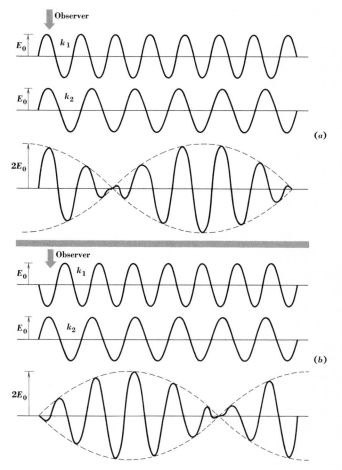

Fig. 3-28 (a) Interference pattern seen by an observer moving with the second wave. At this instant he is at a maximum in the envelope. (b) Slightly later, the second wave has not moved relative to the observer, but the first has moved ahead slightly. The envelope of the interference pattern has now moved so that the observer is at a minimum rather than a maximum. The velocity of the envelope is greater than that of either of the waves.

wave is

$$E = E_0 \, \mathrm{Re} \left[e^{i(k_1 x - \omega_1 t)} + e^{i(k_2 x - \omega_2 t)} \right]$$

$$= E_0 \, \mathrm{Re} \left[e^{i[(k_0 + \Delta k)x - (\omega_0 + \Delta\omega)t]} + e^{i[(k_0 - \Delta k)x - (\omega_0 - \Delta\omega)t]} \right]$$

$$= E_0 \, \mathrm{Re} \left[e^{i(k_0 x - \omega_0 t)} \left(e^{i(\Delta k x - \Delta\omega t)} + e^{-i(\Delta k x - \Delta\omega t)} \right) \right]$$

$$= [2E_0 \cos (\Delta k x - \Delta\omega t)] \cos (k_0 x - \omega_0 t) \qquad (3\text{-}60)$$

In the last form of this equation, the quantity in brackets represents the envelope of the superposed wave, and the second term represents a sinusoidal wave with the average frequency ω_0 and wave number k_0. We recall from Sec. 1-2 that a wave function for a wave traveling in the $+x$ direction always contains x and t in the combination $ax - bt$, where a and b are constants, and that the speed of propagation of the wave is given by the quotient of the coefficient of t and the coefficient of x, that is, b/a. Examining the last form of Eq. (3-60), we see that the wave characterized by k_0 and ω_0 propagates with a speed $u_0 = \omega_0/k_0$ characteristic of these average values, but the speed of the *envelope* of the wave is something quite different. Denoting that speed by v, we find

$$v = \frac{\Delta\omega}{\Delta k} \tag{3-61}$$

If the speed u were the same for all frequencies, the ratio ω/k would be constant, and $\Delta\omega/\Delta k$ would be equal to ω/k. But in general this is not the case, and the velocity of the envelope is different from the velocity of either individual wave. The speed of propagation of the envelope of an interference pattern is usually called the *group velocity*. We shall see later that the validity of the result given by Eq. (3-61) is not restricted to this particular situation but that it is more general in scope.

Superposing two waves with different wave numbers has the interesting effect of *bunching* the wave, that is, of concentrating the wave in certain regions of space. Although the superposed wave, like each of the individual waves, extends throughout space and is not localized, the superposed wave has a considerably more "lumpy" nature than the individual waves. This suggests the possibility that by adding more waves of still different frequencies and wave numbers we might be able to produce a *wave pulse* with a finite extension in space such as, for example, the wave shown in Fig. 3-29, which resembles a half cycle of the superposition of two sinusoidal waves. A more general superposition of several sinusoidal waves can be represented, at one instant of time, as

$$E = \sum_n A_n e^{ik_n x} \tag{3-62}$$

or even

$$E = \int A(k) e^{ikx}\, dk \tag{3-63}$$

in which a continuous distribution of values of k is used, and the function $A(k)$ represents the amplitude of the component wave having wave number k. Representation of functions as superpositions of sinusoidal functions is called *Fourier analysis*. The expression in Eq. (3-62) is called a Fourier series, and Eq. (3-63) a Fourier integral. Fourier analysis is of considerable importance in many different areas of physics.

By an appropriate choice of the function $A(k)$ it is possible to construct a localized *wave pulse,* also called a *wave packet.* If the speed

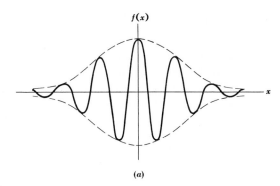

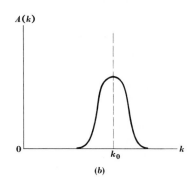

Fig. 3-29   (a) *Wave pulse formed by the superposition of a continuous spectrum of sinusoidal waves with wave numbers centered around k_0. (b) The corresponding function $A(k)$. It can be shown that successive zeros of the wave pulse (corresponding to half-wavelengths of a sinusoidal wave) are spaced a distance π/k_0 apart.*

of the individual sinusoidal waves is independent of frequency (and therefore of k) the pulse also moves with this speed, and its shape is constant.   But if the wave speed is a function of frequency, then the pulse speed is the *group velocity* introduced above, which is, in general, different from the wave speed.   It can be shown that, if the pulse is constructed from waves whose wave numbers are all in the vicinity of a central wave number k_0, the group velocity is given by

$$v = \frac{d\omega}{dk} \tag{3-64}$$

where the derivative is evaluated at $k = k_0$.   This agrees with Eq. (3-61), which was derived for the special case of the superposition of only two sinusoidal waves.   Equation (3-64) is derived in Appendix D.

Wave packets are of great importance in the area of quantum mechanics.   In some experiments, elementary particles behave as though they were waves instead of particles.   The concept of a wave packet provides the means of reconciling the apparently incompatible wave and particle aspects of the behavior of matter.   We shall return to this important subject in Chap. 6.

PROBLEMS

3-1 Two identical oscillating dipoles of the type shown in Fig. 3-1 are located at the origin of a coordinate system, at right angles to each other, one along the y axis, one along the z axis. The two oscillators are in phase. Find the total radiation field for points along each of the three coordinate axes. Describe the state of polarization of the radiation in each case.

3-2 Repeat Prob. 3-1 for the case where the two oscillators are $90°$ out of phase. Also show that the total radiation field is the same as that produced by a permanent dipole p_0 which *rotates* in the yz plane with angular velocity ω.

3-3 A dipole such as that shown in Fig. 3-1 is made from two metallic spheres separated by a distance of 1 m. A sinusoidal potential difference is applied to produce an oscillating dipole, and the maximum charge on each sphere is 10^{-8} coul. If the frequency is 10^6 sec^{-1}, find the total power radiated from the dipole.

3-4 An electric-dipole antenna for a radio station operating at 1,000 kc produces a maximum electric field of 10^{-3} volt/m at a distance of 10 km. If the dipole is vertical, find the maximum dipole moment of the antenna.

3-5 Two identical radio antennas separated by one-half wavelength operate $180°$ out of phase.
   a. Draw vector diagrams to determine the resultant intensity, for intervals of $30°$ around the antennas.
   b. Derive an expression for the intensity as a function of angle, in terms of the intensity that would be produced by a single antenna.

3-6 Two identical radio antennas separated by one-half wavelength are operated with a phase difference of ϕ. Derive an expression for the intensity of the resultant radiation pattern, as a function of angle, in terms of the intensity of a single antenna.

3-7 Two radio antennas are driven from the same source, in phase, but are oriented so that for points on a horizontal plane the radiation of one is polarized in this plane but that of the other is polarized in a vertical plane. Find the intensity of the resultant radiation as a function of angle, for points in the horizontal plane.

3-8 In a two-slit interference experiment with light of a wavelength of 5,000 Å, what must be the spacing of the slits if the distance from the central maximum to the first adjacent maximum, on a screen 10 m away, is 1 cm?

3-9 If the apparatus of Prob. 3-8 is immersed in water, what should the slit spacing be?

3-10 Two identical radio antennas spaced one-quarter wavelength apart are fed from the same source but are 90° out of phase because of phase-shifting networks. Find the resultant intensity as a function of angle.

3-11 Four identical radio antennas in a line, spaced one-half wavelength apart, are all driven in phase. Calculate the resulting intensity pattern, and draw vector diagrams showing addition of amplitudes at several points.

3-12 A diffraction grating is to be constructed to give the first maximum at 30° for the sodium line at 5,890 Å.
   a. What should be the line spacing of the grating?
   b. What is the angular separation of the lines in the sodium doublet (5,890 and 5,896 Å)?

3-13 A certain diffraction grating has 5,000 lines/cm. For a certain spectrum line a maximum is observed at 30° to the normal. What are the possible wavelengths of the line?

3-14 Suppose the range of the visible spectrum is defined as 4,000 to 7,000 Å. Design a diffraction grating which spreads (disperses) the first diffraction maxima over 30° for this range.

3-15 An antenna array consists of N identical antennas in a straight line one-quarter wavelength apart. The phase difference between successive antennas in the row is 90°. Calculate the resulting intensity distribution, and show that for large N this scheme directs nearly all the energy in a single direction.

3-16 Lenses are often coated with magnesium fluoride ($n = 1.38$) to reduce reflections. How thick should the layer be if reflections from the coating surface interfere destructively with those from the coating-glass interface for a wavelength in the center of the visible spectrum (say yellow light at 5,500 Å)? Assume that, for the glass, $n = 1.50$.

3-17 Suppose the coating material in Prob. 3-16 has an index of refraction of 1.70. What should be the thickness of the film?

3-18 Lenses coated with magnesium fluoride as described in Prob. 3-16 appear bluish. Why?

3-19 Suppose that the plates of Fig. 3-14 are 10 cm wide and are separated at one edge by 0.1 mm. The plates are made of glass with $n = 1.50$, and the space between them is filled with an oil having $n = 1.33$. Compute the spacing between interference fringes, and determine whether the fringe at the line of contact is dark or bright.

3-20   Repeat Prob. 3-19 for the case when the space between the plates is filled with carbon disulfide, for which $n = 1.62$.

3-21   A plano-convex lens rests with its convex surface on a plane glass surface. The radius of curvature is 30 cm, and the setup is illuminated from above with light of a wavelength of 6,000 Å.
  a.   Is the point of contact a bright or dark area in the interference pattern?
  b.   Derive expressions for the radius of the nth bright ring in the pattern, and for the nth dark ring.

3-22   A simple cubic crystal lattice has a lattice spacing of 2.0 Å. At what angles will constructive interference from planes parallel to a cube face occur, if x-rays with a wavelength of 1.0 Å are used?

3-23   In Prob. 3-22, at what angles will constructive interference be observed for each of the sets of planes shown in Fig. 3-18?

3-24   A certain hexagonal crystal lattice consists of sets of parallel planes spaced a distance b apart, with atoms arranged in each plane in an array of equilateral triangles of side a. Atoms in adjacent planes are all in straight lines perpendicular to the planes. If the spacing between adjacent atoms in a plane is a, for what wavelength will constructive interference occur at 30° for sets of vertical planes, perpendicular to the planes of the triangular arrays?

3-25   In a single-slit diffraction experiment, the slit is 0.1 mm wide and is illuminated by monochromatic light with a wavelength of 5,000 Å. The diffraction pattern is observed on a screen 10 m away. What is the spacing between successive minima in the pattern?

3-26   Derive a formula for the angular spacing of dark fringes in the diffraction pattern for a single slit, by observing that when the width of the slit is divided into halves, there are certain angles for which corresponding regions in the two halves are exactly 180° out of phase so that complete destructive interference occurs.

3-27   Consider the limit of the intensity distribution for diffraction from a single slit [Eq. (3-31)] when the width of the slit is much larger than a wavelength. Describe the resulting pattern.

3-28   The relative dielectric constant K_E of water is strongly temperature-dependent, decreasing from 88 at 0°C to 55 at 100°C. How can this behavior be understood?

3-29   Is the phenomenon described in Prob. 3-28 consistent with the fact that the index of refraction of water for visible light (5,890 Å) varies only from about 1.33 to 1.32 over the same temperature range? Explain.

3-30   Make a calculation of the dielectric constant of a material, similar to that leading to Eq. (3-46), but starting with the assumption that the electrons are completely free instead of elastically bound. This resembles the state of affairs in the ionosphere. Show that the displacements are exactly out of phase with the electric field, and so the relative dielectric constant is less than unity.

3-31   Show that the function

$$E_y = E_0 e^{i(kx - \omega t)} e^{-\lambda x}$$

is a solution of Eq. (3-49). From this, derive Eqs. (3-50) and (3-51).

3-32   Why is the sky blue?

3-33   By combining Eq. (3-44) for the induced dipole moment of an elastically bound electron with the formulation of Sec. 3-1 concerning energy radiated by an oscillating dipole, find the total energy scattered by an elastically bound electron in the presence of an electromagnetic wave of amplitude E_0 and frequency ω. What is the limit of this expression as the binding force becomes very small (a nearly free electron)?

3-34   Why does the sky appear red in a sunset?

3-35   What order of magnitude of conductivity of water would be needed to account for the fact that total darkness occurs at a depth of a few hundred meters? (The eye can respond to intensities of the order of 10^{-6} to 10^{-8} that of daylight.)

3-36   Calculate the energy density and the Poynting vector for a superposition of two sinusoidal electromagnetic waves, as discussed in Sec. 3-6, for the case where the wave speeds are slightly different. Show that the speed of energy transport is given by the group velocity, not the wave velocity of either wave.

GEOMETRICAL OPTICS IS an approximate method of calculating optical phenomena; it is based on a description of light as *rays* which travel in straight lines in a homogeneous medium. We discuss first the relationship of the ray and wave pictures. Reflection and refraction of spherical waves at plane surfaces are discussed, first using the wave description and then in terms of rays, and it is shown that the laws of reflection and refraction for rays can be derived from wave considerations. In this connection, the concept of *images* is introduced. Next, reflection and refraction of a spherical wave at a spherical surface are considered, and an approximate analysis of a thin lens is given. Finally, we discuss briefly some applications of lenses and mirrors in optical instruments.

4-1 Waves and Rays

In Chaps. 2 and 3 it was mentioned that some aspects of the propagation of plane and spherical waves can be described in terms of lines called *rays* in the direction of propagation, perpendicular to the wavefronts. For a plane wave, the rays are parallel lines in the direction of propagation; for spherical waves they radiate outward in all directions from the source of the radiation.   Figure 4-1 shows the relationship between rays and wavefronts for these two kinds of waves.   In situations where diffraction effects can be neglected, the methods of geometrical optics provide a very simple and convenient set of principles for calculating the behavior of optical systems such as lenses and mirrors.

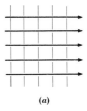

(a)

Fig. 4-1   *Relation of wave and ray descriptions.   Solid lines are rays; broken lines are wavefronts (surfaces of constant phase).   The two sets of lines are perpendicular at their intersections.   (a) Plane wave; (b) spherical wave.*

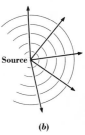

(b)

To illustrate the relationship between the wave and ray pictures, we consider first the reflection of a spherical wave from a plane surface, such as a polished metal surface.   The mechanism of reflection is exactly the same as for reflection of a plane wave, discussed in Sec. 2-5.   When the incident wave strikes electrons in the metal, these electrons undergo oscillatory motions of the same frequency as that of the incident wave and thus serve as secondary sources of radiation, producing a reflected wave.   With the assumption that the metal is a perfect conductor, the secondary sources must produce a radiation field such that in the plane of the reflector the component of **E** parallel to the plane is always zero at the surface.   Now suppose we remove the reflector and place at the point Q shown in Fig. 4-2 another source which is the mirror image of the source at P except that all charges at Q have the opposite sign to those at P.   Then in the plane equidistant between P and Q (the former location of the reflector) the two radiation fields add to form a total field whose parallel component of **E** is zero, as shown in the figure.

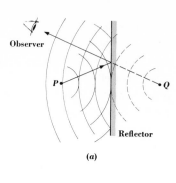

Fig. 4-2 (a) Incident and reflected spherical waves. The reflected wave is the same as though it had originated at a source at Q. (b) Electric fields $\mathbf{E}_i$ and $\mathbf{E}_r$ of incident and reflected waves, respectively, at a point on the reflector. The vector sum shows that the resultant field $\mathbf{E}_{tot}$ has no component parallel to the surface. To an observer to the left of the mirror, the reflected rays seem to come from Q, which is called an image of P.

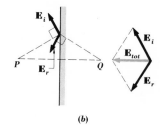

The reflected radiation field is determined, as just pointed out, by the condition that $E_{\parallel} = 0$ at the boundary surface and by the associated induced sources. But this boundary condition is satisfied equally well by the situation where the reflector is removed and the source Q added. Thus for all points to the left of the reflector the reflected radiation is exactly the same as though it had been emitted by the source Q. In the real physical situation, of course, Q does not exist, but it nevertheless provides a very convenient way of describing the resultant radiation field. It is called a *virtual source* or an *image* of the real source P.

A somewhat different but equivalent analysis is the following: Consider a small sector of the spherical wavefront, striking a small area of the reflecting surface. A sufficiently small sector of a spherical surface can be considered as approximately plane; the reflection from this small area is therefore expected to behave in the same way as the reflection of a plane wave, which results in another plane wave reflected with equal angles to the surface. Thus the part of the wave reflected from this element of surface is part of a spherical wave having the property that perpendiculars to the new spherical wavefronts (represented by the rays in Fig. 4-2) have just the angles that are predicted by the "image source" shown.

In terms of the ray picture, a ray originates at the point P, is reflected, and reaches the observer's eye so that the angle of incidence is equal to the angle of reflection. The observer in Fig. 4-2 judges the position of the source by the directions of the rays (or wavefronts) reaching his eyes; to this observer it appears that the source is at point Q. Thus the mirror is said to produce an *image* of the source P at the point Q. In general, a plane mirror always produces an image, behind the mirror a distance equal to the source distance, such that the line joining P and Q is perpendicular to the plane of the mirror.

A similar analysis can be carried out in the case of the *refraction* of spherical waves by a plane surface between two media having different indices of refraction. Just as above, the general features can be predicted by considering a small area of the interface and regarding the spherical wave striking that small area as practically a plane wave. The relationships governing the reflection and refraction of a plane wave at a plane surface have been discussed in Chap. 2; the reflected wave obeys the law of reflection just stated, and the direction of the refracted wave is determined by Snell's law, which is

$$n_1 \sin \theta_1 = n_2 \sin \theta_2 \tag{4-1}$$

where n_1 and n_2 are the refractive indices in the two media, and θ_1 and θ_2 are the angles the rays make with a line perpendicular to the interface. Thus, the small segments of spherical wave can be expected to proceed as shown in Fig. 4-3, in which the ray representation of the segments is shown. The result is a reflected spherical wave in the first medium, and a transmitted wave in the second medium. Just as in the previous case of reflection, the reflected wave proceeds backward in the first medium as though it had originated at a point Q in the second medium, as shown in Fig. 4-3a.

The transmitted wave is somewhat more complicated. For a transmitted ray (segment of a spherical wave) near the axis of Fig. 4-3b, the backward projection of the corresponding ray crosses the axis at a distance s' given by

$$s \tan \theta_1 = s' \tan \theta_2 \tag{4-2}$$

If the rays are nearly parallel to the axis, the angles θ_1 and θ_2 are small, so that, approximately,

$$\tan \theta_1 \simeq \sin \theta_1 \quad \text{and} \quad \tan \theta_2 \simeq \sin \theta_2 \tag{4-3}$$

Making this approximation in Eq. (4-2) and combining the result with Eq. (4-1), we find

$$\frac{s'}{s} = \frac{n_2}{n_1} \tag{4-4}$$

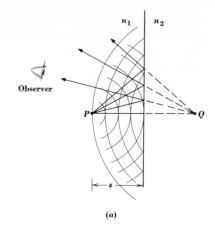

(a)

Fig. 4-3 (a) Spherical wave partially reflected by the interface between two media. The reflected wave is as though it had originated at point Q, independent of the relative magnitudes of n_1 and n_2. (b) Spherical wave partially transmitted through the interface. The refracted wave near the horizontal axis is approximately a spherical wave with its center at the point Q, whose position is given by Eq. (4-2). For the case shown, $n_2 > n_1$; note that the wavelength is smaller in the second medium.

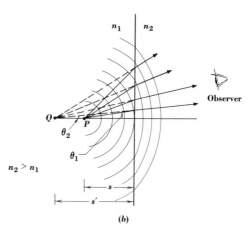

(b)

The central part of the transmitted spherical wave, that is, the part proceeding almost perpendicular to the refracting surface, has the same shape as though it had been emitted by a source at Q as shown; it is said that there is an *image* of the real source at this point. It is important to note that this result is correct only for that part of the wave whose propagation is approximately perpendicular to the interface. Taken as a whole, the refracted wave is not precisely a spherical wave but has a more complicated form. Thus Eq. (4-4) is an approximation, valid for the condition known as "normal incidence," that is, when the rays are all nearly normal (perpendicular) to the interface.

The image associated with the refracted wave in the above discussion is responsible for the fact that, when one looks down at a body of water from the air above, objects under water always seem to be closer than they really are.   In this case, n_2 is the index of refraction of air, approximately unity, while n_1 is the index of refraction of water, about 1.33.   Thus the image position s' is closer to the surface than the actual position s.

We now have all the necessary ingredients of a complete ray treatment of light.   The three principles of geometrical optics are:

1.   In a homogeneous medium, rays of light travel in straight lines.
2.   At a reflecting surface, a ray is reflected so that the incident and reflected rays make equal angles with the surface.
3.   At an interface between two media having indices of refraction n_1 and n_2, the ray of light is bent in accordance with *Snell's* law [Eq. (4-1)].

In principles 2 and 3, the reflected and refracted rays lie in the plane determined by the incident ray and the line normal to the surface at the point of incidence.

As far as the ray picture is concerned, these principles are *complete;* they describe all phenomena in geometrical optics and are sufficient to solve any problem.   In this sense, geometrical optics is the *simplest* of all physical theories.   Detailed calculations of optical phenomena can easily become extremely complicated, however.   Even in the simple case of the refraction of a spherical wave by a plane surface between two media, we found that it was necessary to make an approximation in order to obtain a simple result.   Similar approximations have to be made in the next section, where we deal with the reflection and refraction of spherical waves by spherical surfaces in lenses.   In the remainder of this chapter we shall concentrate on the simplest possible calculations, making approximations where necessary to avoid the complications inherent in more precise treatments.

4-2   Reflection at a Spherical Surface

We consider next the reflection of a spherical wave by a spherical surface.   We can distinguish two general cases.   In one, the source is much closer to the mirror than its center of curvature C, as in Fig. 4-4a.   In this case, the reflected wave should have characteristics similar to the case of a spherical wave reflected from a plane surface and thus should proceed away from the mirror as though it had originated at an image point Q, as shown in the figure.   On the other hand, if the distance from source to mirror is large compared with the radius of curvature of the

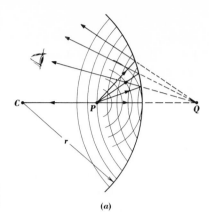

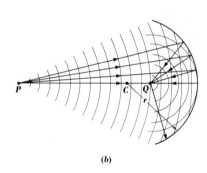

Fig. 4-4 *Reflection of a spherical wave from a spherical mirror of radius r. (a) When the source P is much closer than the center of curvature C, the reflected wave proceeds as though it had originated at Q, which is the image of P. (b) When the source P is much farther away than the center of curvature, the reflected wave converges toward a real image point Q.*

(a)

(b)

mirror, a spherical wavefront strikes the edges of the mirror before striking its center; consideration of the resulting phase relationship shows that the curvature of the reflected wave should have the opposite sense; that is, it should *converge* toward an image point Q, as shown in Fig. 4-4b. This also happens when the source P is located *at* the center of curvature, for then spherical waves reach all parts of the spherical mirror simultaneously and are reflected back exactly in phase, so that the reflected spherical wave has precisely the same center of curvature as the original spherical wave. In this case, the image point and the source coincide.

Now we shall analyze this reflection in more detail, using the ray picture together with appropriate approximations. The basis for the calculations is Fig. 4-5. The line through the center O of the mirror, perpendicular to a tangent plane at that point, is called the *optic axis* of the mirror. A ray originates at point P, a distance p from O, making a small angle α with the optic axis. It is reflected through the point Q, a distance q from O. The radius of curvature of the mirror is r; C is its center of curvature, and, following the law of reflection, the

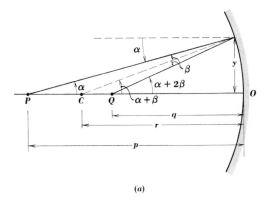

(a)

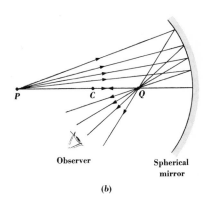

Fig. 4-5 (a) *Ray diagram used to derive the object and image distance relation for a spherical mirror. For rays nearly parallel to the axis, all rays originating at P are reflected through Q, resulting in a real image at Q. (b) Several rays originating at P, reflected through Q.*

Observer

Spherical mirror

(b)

incident and reflected rays make equal angles with the radius line from the center to the mirror surface. In terms of the angles in Fig. 4-5, the distance y shown in the figure may be variously expressed as

$$y = p \tan \alpha = r \sin (\alpha + \beta) = q \tan (\alpha + 2\beta) \tag{4-5}$$

If the angles α and β are sufficiently small, the angle, its sine, and its tangent are all very nearly equal. Thus Eqs. (4-5) become approximately

$$p\alpha = r(\alpha + \beta) = q(\alpha + 2\beta) \tag{4-6}$$

We may divide these equations by β and eliminate the ratio α/β to obtain

$$\frac{1}{p} + \frac{1}{q} = \frac{2}{r} \tag{4-7}$$

The most important feature of this equation is what it does *not* contain, namely, the angles α and β. This shows that a ray originating from point P is reflected through point Q, no matter at what angle it leaves P, provided that the angle is *small*.

Figure 4-5*b* shows several rays originating at *P* and reflected through *Q*. The rays then diverge again from *Q*, so that to an observer to the left of this point it seems that *Q* is the source of the rays. Thus *Q* is an *image* of the source at *P*. In contrast to some of the images previously considered, the rays actually *do* diverge from this point. For this reason, *Q* is said to be a *real* image. Conversely, images consisting of rays that only *appear* to diverge from a certain point are usually called *virtual* images.

When the source distance becomes very great, $p \to \infty$, the incoming waves are very nearly plane waves. In this case, Eq. (4-7) gives for the image distance $q = r/2$. Thus, an incoming plane wave is reflected through a point at a distance $r/2$ away from the mirror. Conversely, a source at this point is reflected as a parallel beam, that is, a plane wave. This point, labeled *F* in diagrams, is called the *focus* of the mirror; its distance from the mirror is the *focal length*, usually denoted by *f*. Thus, for a spherical mirror, $f = r/2$ and

$$\frac{1}{p} + \frac{1}{q} = \frac{1}{f} \tag{4-8}$$

We emphasize again that, because of the approximations made in deriving this equation, only those rays striking the mirror near its center can be expected to be reflected precisely through the focus. The deviations occurring for rays far from the optic axis or making large angles with it are called *spherical aberrations*. It is possible to design a mirror that precisely focuses a parallel beam (plane wave); such a mirror is *paraboloidal* in shape. Reflecting astronomical telescopes are always used to view very distant objects, where the light rays are very nearly parallel, and mirrors for such telescopes are usually paraboloidal rather than spherical.

When the source distance *p* is less than the focal length *f*, Eq. (4-8) gives a negative value for the image distance *q*. This corresponds to a reflected wave which is a diverging spherical wave, appearing to originate from a virtual source to the right of the mirror, as in Fig. 4-4*a*. Thus a negative value of *q* means a virtual image to the right of the mirror, rather than a real image to the left. A similar consideration can be applied to the case where the incoming wave is produced by another mirror or lens and is a *converging* spherical wave, as shown in Fig. 4-6, rather than a wave that appears to originate from a point. In this case it is useful to introduce the concept of a *virtual object*, defined as the point at which the incoming rays would converge if they were not

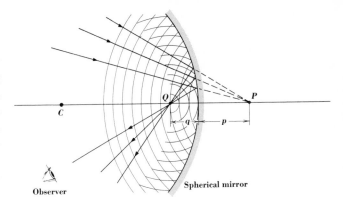

Fig. 4-6 *A converging incident spherical wave can be represented as a virtual source at P, toward which the wave would converge if the mirror were not present. The corresponding object distance p is negative.*

first reflected by the mirror.   Further developments involving these concepts are left as exercises.

The discussion of formation of images by a spherical mirror can easily be extended to the more general case when the source, or *object*, is not a single point but is extended in space.   For each point P of the object there is a corresponding image point Q, lying on the line through P and the center of curvature C.   The distance q of each image point from the center O of the mirror is again related to the distance p of the corresponding object point, according to Eq. (4-8).   An immediate corollary is that, for an object whose points all lie in a plane perpendicular to the optic axis, the distance p is (in the small-angle approximation) the same for all points, and so all the image points are also equidistant from O.   That is, in this approximation, *the image of a plane object is also plane.*

Understanding of the formation of images of extended objects is facilitated by a construction called a *principal-ray diagram*.   We select a point on the object, such as point P in Fig. 4-7.   There are four rays which can always be located easily:

1. A ray that leaves P parallel to the optic axis is reflected through the focus F.
2. Conversely, a ray from P that passes through the focus F is reflected back parallel to the optic axis.
3. A ray that passes through the center of curvature C strikes the mirror perpendicularly and is reflected back along itself.
4. A ray striking the center O of the mirror is reflected so as to make equal angles with the optic axis.

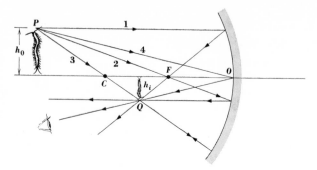

Fig. 4-7   *Principal-ray diagram, showing the formation of a real image by a spherical mirror. Numbers on the four principal rays correspond to those in the text.*

These four rays are shown in Fig. 4-7. They converge at a point Q, which is therefore a real image of point P. This figure could be used for an alternative derivation of Eq. (4-8); it also provides a useful relation between the *sizes* of object and image. By considering the similar triangles formed by P, Q, O, and the optic axis, we see that the sizes of object and image, which we may call h_o and h_i, respectively, are directly proportional to the distances from the mirror:

$$\frac{h_i}{h_o} = \frac{q}{p} \tag{4-9}$$

This equation is useful when it is necessary to know the relative lateral sizes of object and image, as in computing magnifying powers of optical instruments.

4-3   Refraction at a Spherical Surface

Next, as a step toward analysis of the behavior of lenses, we consider the *refraction* of a spherical wave by a spherical surface between two optical media. As in the case of refraction by a plane surface, the wave is partly reflected and partly refracted (transmitted). The reflected wave is governed by the considerations given in Sec. 4-2, and so in this section we shall concentrate entirely on the *refracted* wave. In Fig. 4-8, a spherical wave originating at point P is refracted at a spherical interface with radius of curvature r between two media with indices of refraction n_1 and n_2. The resulting wave is, at least for small angles near the optic axis, a converging spherical wave corresponding to rays which converge at the point Q in the second medium. Thus this point is a *real image* of the source, or object, at P.

Just as with the spherical mirror, we can derive a relationship between object and image distances. The appropriate ray diagram is

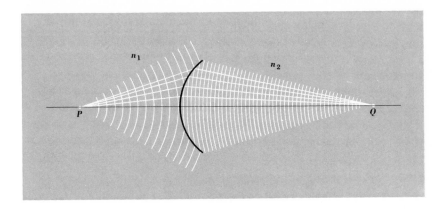

Fig. 4-8   *A spherical wave from P in the first
medium is refracted at the spherical interface, resulting
in an approximately spherical wave converging
toward the real image point Q in the second medium.
Corresponding rays are shown.*

shown in Fig. 4-9. The various angles are related by the requirement
that the sum of interior angles in a triangle must be 180°. Applying
this to each of the triangles that share the side passing through C, we
obtain the relations

$$\alpha + \gamma + (180° - \theta_1) = 180° \qquad \text{or} \qquad \theta_1 = \alpha + \gamma$$
$$\theta_2 + \beta + (180° - \gamma) = 180° \qquad \text{or} \qquad \gamma = \theta + \beta$$

(4-10)

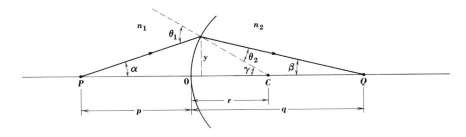

Fig. 4-9   *Ray diagram for the derivation of the
equation relating object and image distances for refraction by a spherical surface. All angles are actually
very small but are exaggerated here for clarity. For
the case shown, $n_2 > n_1$.*

Next, the distance y can be expressed in a variety of ways, as follows:

$$y = p \tan \alpha = q \tan \beta = r \sin \gamma \qquad (4\text{-}11)$$

which, for small angles, gives

$$\alpha p = \beta q = \gamma r \qquad (4\text{-}12)$$

Finally, Snell's law in the small-angle approximation is

$$n_1 \theta_1 = n_2 \theta_2 \qquad (4\text{-}13)$$

Now it is possible to combine the five simultaneous equations for the angles [Eqs. (4-10), (4-12), and (4-13)] to eliminate all the angles, just as was done with the spherical mirror. The reader can supply the details of this calculation; the result is

$$\frac{n_1}{p} + \frac{n_2}{q} = \frac{n_2 - n_1}{r} \qquad (4\text{-}14)$$

the general form of which is pleasingly similar to Eq. (4-7) for the spherical mirror.

Just as with the spherical mirror, it is possible for the image distance q to turn out negative. In such a case, the refracted wave does not converge to the right of the interface but *diverges* in such a way as to appear to have originated at a point to the left of the surface a distance $-q$. Correspondingly, when the incident wave is a converging spherical wave that would converge at a certain distance to the *right* of the interface if the interface were not there, the object distance p is negative. Lastly, the curvature of the surface may be opposite to that shown. When the center of curvature is to the left, r is a negative quantity. These sign conventions are summarized as follows:

1. p is positive when the object point is to the left, negative otherwise.
2. q is positive when the image point is to the right, negative otherwise.
3. r is positive if the center of curvature is to the right, negative otherwise.

We might now proceed to discuss the action of a spherical surface on plane waves and define a focus and a focal length, just as in the case of the spherical mirror. In practical situations, however, spherical surfaces are usually used in pairs, in the form of *lenses*, and so we proceed immediately to a discussion of the situation where there are two spherical surfaces adjacent to each other.

4-4   *Thin Lenses*

We now consider an optical system consisting of a thin piece of material of index of refraction n_2, with spherical surfaces of radii r_1 and r_2, respectively, embedded in a medium of index of refraction n_1. Such a system is called a *lens*. When the lens is in vacuum, $n_1 = 1$; for air at ordinary temperature and pressure, $n = 1.00028$, and the approximation $n_1 = 1$ is often used. It is, however, useful to include in the analysis the possibility that the lens may be immersed in some other fluid, for which n_1 is different from unity.

The analysis proceeds as follows: If the second surface were not present, the first would form an image of any object placed to the left of it. The second surface may interfere with the actual formation of this image, but it does not alter the fact that rays emerge from the first surface in directions characteristic of a particular image position. If they are converging, the image position is to the right of the first surface; if diverging, to the left. Thus it is perfectly legitimate to regard this image as an *object* for the second surface, even though it may not actually be formed when the second surface is present. The image still exists in the sense that the directions of the rays emerging from the first surface are characteristic of a certain image position. Let p_1 and q_1 represent the object and image positions for the first surface, and p_2 and q_2 those for the second surface, with the usual sign conventions. Applying Eq. (4-14) to the two surfaces, we find

$$\frac{n_1}{p_1} + \frac{n_2}{q_1} = \frac{n_2 - n_1}{r_1} \tag{4-15a}$$

$$\frac{n_2}{p_2} + \frac{n_1}{q_2} = \frac{n_1 - n_2}{r_2} \tag{4-15b}$$

In the second equation the roles of n_1 and n_2 are reversed, since for the second surface the medium characterized by n_1 is on the right rather than on the left.

Next, we note that the *image* formed by the first surface is the *object* for the second. Furthermore, if the first image distance q_1 is positive, the corresponding object distance for the second surface is negative, and conversely; thus if the thickness of the lens is negligible, we have $q_1 = -p_2$. Using this relationship together with Eqs. (4-15), we can eliminate q_1 and p_2 to obtain a single equation relating the original object distance p_1 and the final image distance q_2. The result is

$$\frac{1}{p_1} + \frac{1}{q_2} = \left(\frac{n_2}{n_1} - 1\right)\left(\frac{1}{r_1} - \frac{1}{r_2}\right) \tag{4-16}$$

Having derived this equation, we now describe the lens as a single unit; we drop the subscripts on p and q and simply state that the first object position p and the final image position q are related by

$$\frac{1}{p} + \frac{1}{q} = \left(\frac{n_2}{n_1} - 1\right)\left(\frac{1}{r_1} - \frac{1}{r_2}\right) \tag{4-17}$$

The same sign conventions apply to this equation as for the single-surface equation (4-14).

When the source or object is very far away, the incident waves are practically plane waves. The value of q at which such plane waves are focused is called the *focal length* of the lens and is denoted by f, just as in the case of the spherical mirror. That is, an incident plane wave, corresponding to rays parallel to the axis, is brought to focus at a distance f from the lens, where

$$\frac{1}{f} = \left(\frac{n_2}{n_1} - 1\right)\left(\frac{1}{r_1} - \frac{1}{r_2}\right) \tag{4-18}$$

Equation (4-18) shows that, within the approximations we have made, the lens is *symmetric;* if it is reversed, side to side, the focal length and all the other characteristics remain unchanged. This can be verified by noting that turning it over corresponds to interchanging r_1 and r_2 and changing the signs on both. Once the focal length f is known, the lens equation can be written somewhat more simply:

$$\frac{1}{p} + \frac{1}{q} = \frac{1}{f} \tag{4-19}$$

Consideration of Eq. (4-18) reveals that in the usual case, when $n_2 > n_1$, f is a positive quantity whenever the lens is thicker in the middle than at the edge, while f is negative if the lens is thicker at the edge. In the latter case, a beam of parallel rays is not brought to a real focus but rather *diverges* from the lens as though it originated from a virtual focus a distance f to the left of the lens. Similarly, it is possible for q to be negative, indicating the existence of a virtual image, or for p to be negative, corresponding to a virtual object describing rays which converge as they approach the first surface of the lens.

Understanding of the formation of an image by a lens is facilitated by constructing a principal-ray diagram of the same sort used for the spherical mirror, Fig. 4-7. The principal rays which are most easily drawn are:

1.   A ray parallel to the optic axis, which is refracted through the focus.

2. A ray passing through the focus, refracted parallel to the optic axis.
3. A ray which passes straight through the center of the lens and which is not deviated at all.

Figure 4-10 shows principal-ray diagrams for two cases. In Fig. 4-10a the object is farther from the lens than the focal length, and a real image results. In Fig. 4-10b, the object is closer than the focal length, resulting in a virtual image. In such cases it is sometimes necessary to project the rays backward to find the intersection point corresponding to the position of the virtual image. Similar diagrams can be drawn for the case of lenses having negative focal lengths. In all cases, as the principal-ray diagrams show, the ratio of object to image

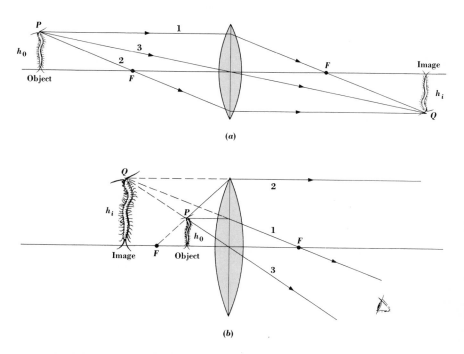

Fig. 4-10 *Principal-ray diagrams showing image formation by a convex lens. (a) When the object distance is greater than the focal length, a real, inverted image is formed. (b) When the object distance is less than the focal length, a virtual, erect image is formed; its position is obtained by projecting the principal rays backward. The rays appear to come from point Q.*

size is equal to the ratio of distances from the lens, just as for the spherical mirror, and Eq. (4-9) holds for lenses as well as mirrors.

We emphasize again that this entire discussion of lenses is an approximate one. We have assumed throughout that all rays are very nearly parallel to the optic axis. For rays sufficiently far from the optic axis, various deviations, called *aberrations,* begin to appear. In the design of precise optical equipment, such as camera lenses, it is always necessary to use several lenses in combination, to cancel partially the effects of these aberrations.

Another factor which is important in many optical devices is dispersion; in general the index of refraction of the material varies with wavelength, so that the focal length of the lens is a function of wavelength. This results in *chromatic aberration,* which in precise optical equipment is corrected in part by using combinations of lenses having different indices of refraction and dispersion.

The design of such optical systems is an extremely complex operation, frequently involving a considerable amount of trial-and-error calculation. The development of high-speed digital computers in recent years has made possible the design of lens systems which otherwise would be hopelessly complicated to calculate. These include "zoom" lenses with variable focal length, extremely wide-angle lenses, and many other special-purpose lenses. Even in the most complicated cases, however, the same basic principles are involved as in the simple examples discussed here.

4-5   *Optical Instruments*

We conclude this chapter on geometrical optics with a brief discussion of several simple applications of lenses and mirrors in optical instruments. One of the simplest is the use of a lens in a camera, as shown in Fig. 4-11a. The function of the lens is simply to create at the position of the film a real image of the object being photographed, as shown. The simplified discussion of this chapter would indicate that this can be accomplished with a single lens; actually camera lenses usually contain several elements, in order to reduce various aberrations.

A similar problem is that of a slide or motion-picture projector. Here the function is just opposite that of a camera lens: The lens creates an enlarged real image on a screen of a transparent film or slide, as shown in Fig. 4-11b. These two applications of lenses have several features in common. In both cases the ratio of object to image size is the same as the ratio of object and image distance from the lens; the

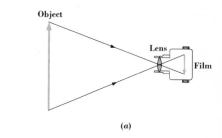

(a)

Fig. 4-11   (a) *A camera lens forms a real inverted image, reduced in size, at the position of the film.* (b) *Projector forms a real, inverted, enlarged image of a slide or other transparent object, on a projection screen. The lenses between bulb and slide serve to concentrate light from the bulb on the slide; they are called condenser lenses.*

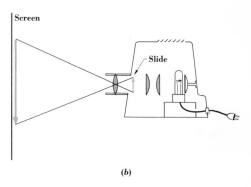

(b)

image is real and is inverted with respect to the object. These features and the same general principles are characteristic of the operation of the human eye, in which the lens produces a real inverted image on the retina.

A slightly more subtle application of a single lens is that of a simple magnifying glass. The closer an object is to the eye, the more detail can be seen, but most persons cannot focus their eyes comfortably on an object closer than about 10 in. (about 0.25 m). The function of a magnifying glass is to form an enlarged image at a distance sufficiently far away from the eyes to be comfortable for viewing. Unlike the case of the camera or slide projector, the image need not be real. Figure 4-12, which is drawn approximately to scale, shows how a magnifying glass with $f = 3$ in. forms an enlarged, erect virtual image of an object located closer to the lens than the focus. It is customary to define the *magnification* of an optical system as the ratio of the *angular size* (ratio of size to distance from the eye) of the image using the instrument to that without the instrument, under the most favorable conditions. For the magnifying glass, "most favorable conditions" means as close as possible with comfort, namely, 0.25 m away from the eye. Thus in the example of Fig. 4-12 the magnification is about 3, often written as 3×.

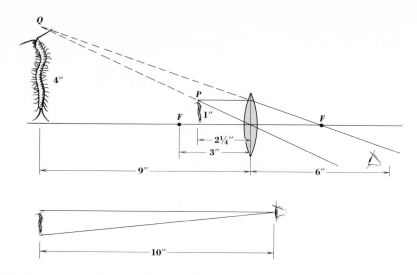

Fig. 4-12 *A magnifying glass forms an enlarged, erect virtual image. The angular size of this image in the situation shown is approximately 4 in./15 in. or 4/15. The angular size of the object at the closest distance for comfortable viewing is 1 in./10 in. or 1/10. The magnification in this situation is (4/15)/(1/10), or 2⅔.*

For greater magnification it is often desirable to use two or more lenses in combination. We consider here only the two simplest examples of such schemes, the compound microscope and the astronomical telescope. Figure 4-13 shows the general construction of a compound microscope. The lens closest to the object, called the *objective lens*, forms a real, enlarged, inverted image of the object in the barrel of the microscope. The second lens, called the *eyepiece lens*, uses this image as its object and forms a final virtual, enlarged, erect image, which can be located at a distance from the eye convenient for comfortable viewing. Compound microscopes constructed according to this general scheme but using more complex lens groupings can be made with a magnification of several hundred.

The operation of the refracting astronomical telescope, shown in Fig. 4-14, is very similar to that of the compound microscope, except for differences in magnitudes of the various focal lengths. Like the compound microscope, it makes use of an objective lens, forming a real image in the barrel of the telescope, and an eyepiece lens which forms

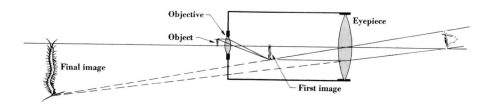

Fig. 4-13 *A compound microscope. The objective lens, whose focal length is usually only a few millimeters, forms a real image in the microscope barrel. This image forms the object from which the eyepiece forms the final virtual image. Sizes of object and images, as well as the diameter of the barrel, have been exaggerated for clarity.*

an enlarged virtual image of the first image. The final image, as in the case of the compound microscope, is inverted with respect to the object. This is the principle of operation of most ordinary binoculars, which also use a pair of prisms for each eye, in which internal reflections invert the image (up and down and right to left) back to the same orientation as the object. Binoculars typically have a magnification of 5 to 20,

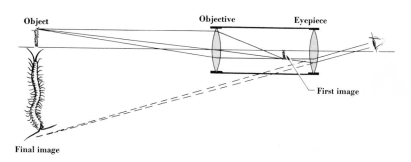

Fig. 4-14 *A refracting astronomical telescope. The objective lens forms a real image in the telescope barrel, and the eyepiece forms a final virtual image. Object and image sizes are exaggerated. In telescopic sights and transits, the cross hairs may be located at the position of the first image; they then appear to be superimposed on the actual object. The final image is usually located far away, for most comfortable viewing.*

although telescopes with much greater magnifying powers can be made using this principle.

Finally, we consider briefly the principle of the reflecting telescope. Its operation is similar to that of the telescope just described, except that the objective lens is replaced by a concave mirror. When the telescope is to be used only with very distant objects, this scheme has several advantages. One is that a mirror is intrinsically free from chromatic aberration. Another is that by making the mirror paraboloidal instead of spherical, the spherical aberrations mentioned in Sec. 4-2 can be completely eliminated in the first image. A third is that it is usually easier and cheaper to make large mirrors than lenses of comparable size. The general shape of a reflecting telescope is shown in Fig. 4-15.

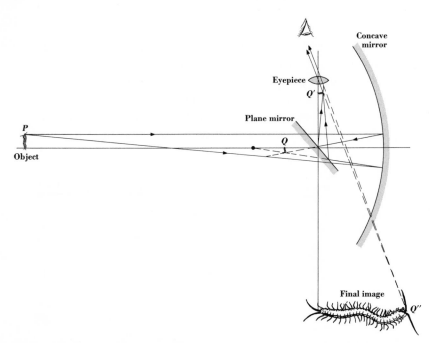

Fig. 4-15   *A reflecting telescope. The image formed by the mirror is brought away from the optic axis by a small plane mirror placed at 45° to the optic axis. Q shows the image the concave mirror would form if the plane mirror were not present; Q' is the (real) image formed of this image by the plane mirror. The eyepiece forms a final virtual image as shown. Not all the rays in this diagram are principal rays.*

Throughout this chapter we have neglected effects associated with diffraction. Since the apertures involved in optical instruments for visible light are usually very large compared with the wavelengths of light, it might seem that diffraction effects are completely negligible. Nevertheless, in very precise work, such as photographic work requiring very high resolution, diffraction effects usually determine the ultimate limit of the sharpness of image produced by a lens. Clearly, diffraction effects are more important with small lens apertures than with large apertures. This is one of the reasons for constructing reflecting telescopes with extremely large reflectors, such as the 200-in.-diameter reflector at Mount Palomar. The other reason is that the intensity of the final image depends on the light-gathering capacity of the objective lens or mirror, which in turn is proportional to its area.

The limitations on resolving power of lenses and mirrors imposed by diffraction phenomena have been studied extensively, but it is not appropriate to consider them further here. Diffraction effects, together with limitations of mechanical precision of lens manufacture, set the ultimate limits on the quality of images formed by lenses and mirrors.

PROBLEMS

4-1 A fish in a pool appears to a fisherman to be 5 ft below the surface. What is its real depth below the surface?

4-2 An observer 1 m away from a glass slab 1 m thick, having $n = 1.5$, looks at an object 1 m away from the opposite side of the slab, 3 m away from him.

    a. How far away does the object appear to be?

    b. At what distance would a camera have to be focused to photograph the object in this situation?

4-3 Consider a "corner" constructed from three mutually perpendicular plane mirrors, such as an inside corner of a cube. Show that a ray of light directed into this corner always emerges after reflection in a direction parallel to its original direction. This principle is used in the design of reflectors for highway safety and other uses.

4-4 It is often said that the image formed by a plane mirror reverses right and left but not top and bottom. Is this true? Explain.

4-5 What minimum height must a wall mirror have, and how should it be located on a vertical wall, so that a person 6 ft tall whose eyes are

6 in. below the top of his head can see himself from shoes to top of head?

4-6 Show that a mirror with parabolic cross section exactly focuses a parallel beam to a point.

4-7 Show that reflections from the inside of a prolate ellipsoid of revolution have the property that light from a source at one focus of the ellipsoid is focused at the other focus. A similar effect with sound accounts in part for the unusual acoustic properties of some buildings with rounded ceilings, such as the Mormon Tabernacle in Salt Lake City.

4-8 For a concave spherical mirror of radius r, plot a graph showing the image distance q as a function of object distance p. Indicate the radius and focal length on the p scale.

4-9 A concave spherical mirror has a radius $r = 10$ cm. Find the location, size, and orientation of the image of an object 1 cm high, and draw a principal-ray diagram showing formation of the image, for the cases:
a. $p = 10$ cm
b. $p = 4$ cm

4-10 Consider a convex spherical mirror with $r = -10$ cm.
a. Under what conditions does the mirror form a real image of a real object?
b. Describe the position, size, and orientation of the image formed of an object 1 cm high 10 cm from the mirror. Draw a principal-ray diagram.

4-11 For a spherical interface of radius r between two optical media, with the same orientation as Fig. 4-8, draw graphs showing image position q as a function of object position p when:
a. $n_2 > n_1$
b. $n_2 < n_1$

4-12 A spherical interface of radius $r = 5$ cm separates two media whose indices of refraction are $n_1 = 1$ and $n_2 = 1.5$. The surface is concave to the right. Find the image size, position, and orientation for an object 1 cm high placed:
a. 20 cm to the left of the surface
b. 5 cm to the left

4-13 Repeat Prob. 4-12 for the case where the surface is concave to the left.

4-14 A parallel beam (plane wave) strikes a transparent sphere of radius R and index of refraction n. At what point is the beam focused?

4-15   A small object is located in the center of a transparent glass marble of radius 1.0 cm and index of refraction 1.5. Where does the object appear to be, and how does its apparent size compare with its actual size?

4-16   Show from Eq. (4-18) that any thin lens which is thicker at the center than at the edges has a positive focal length, and conversely.

4-17   Discuss quantitatively the effect of a cylindrical interface between two media on a parallel beam incident on the interface.

4-18   For a thin lens with spherical surfaces, plot the image position q and the image size as functions of the object distance p, for an object of a given size, for the case $f > 0$.

4-19   Repeat Prob. 4-18 for the case $f < 0$.

4-20   The size of film used for a single picture in a 35-mm camera is about 24×36 mm, or roughly $1 \times 1\frac{1}{2}$ in. What focal-length lens should be used to take a picture of:
a.   A mountaineer 10 ft away?
b.   A deer 50 ft away?

4-21   A slide projector designed for 35-mm slides (about $1 \times 1\frac{1}{2}$ in.) projects a picture on a screen 40×50 in., 10 ft away.
a.   What is the focal length of the lens?
b.   What is the distance from slide to lens?

4-22   The equation relating object and image distances for a thin lens [Eq. (4-19)] can be expressed in terms of the distances of object and image from the focal points, rather than from the lens. Denoting these distances by s and s', respectively, prove that

$$ss' = f^2$$

This form of the thin-lens equation was developed by Newton.

4-23   Two thin lenses whose focal lengths are f_1 and f_2 are placed in contact. Prove that the effect of this combination is the same as that of a single thin lens of focal length f given by

$$\frac{1}{f} = \frac{1}{f_1} + \frac{1}{f_2}$$

4-24   A double-convex lens whose surfaces both have radii of curvature of 10 cm is silvered on one side. The index of refraction is $n = 1.5$. Show that this lens acts as a mirror of focal length f, and find f:
a.   When the light approaches from the silvered side
b.   When the light approaches from the unsilvered side

4-25   For a converging lens, show that, in the case of real images, $p + q \geq 4f$.

4-26   A compound microscope has objective and eyepiece lenses of focal lengths 0.5 and 5.0 cm, respectively. The first image is formed 10 cm from the objective lens. Find the magnification:
    a.   If the final image is 25 cm from the eyepiece
    b.   If the final image is at infinity

4-27   A telescope is to be made from two lenses, having focal lengths of 5 and 1 cm.
    a.   What should be the distance between lenses if the initial object and the final virtual image are both very far away?
    b.   What is the magnification under these circumstances?

4-28   The first image of a reflecting telescope is formed 5 m from the mirror, and this image is observed with a compound microscope having $200 \times$ magnification.
    a.   What is the radius of curvature of the mirror?
    b.   What is the overall magnification?

IN THE FIRST four chapters we have been concerned primarily with *classical optics*, that is, with optical phenomena that can be understood on the basis of a *ray* or *wave* model. We began by examining some general properties of waves, in the familiar context of mechanical waves. The general language developed in the opening chapter is applicable to a wide variety of wave phenomena, including not only the prototype example of waves on a stretched string but also sound waves, waves on the surface of a liquid, elastic waves in solids, and many others.

Next we introduced the idea of waves whose nature is *electromagnetic* rather than *mechanical*. The existence of electromagnetic waves was predicted by Maxwell's electromagnetic field equations, which form the foundation of classical electrodynamics. A variety of experimental evidence demonstrates conclusively that light is an electromagnetic wave and that it is a small part of a very broad spectrum of electromagnetic waves with frequencies ranging from less than 1 cycle/sec to the order of 10^{25} cycles/sec and probably even higher.

The wave model of light and other electromagnetic radiation proves to be satisfactory for the understanding of a variety of phenomena associated with *propagation* of light, including interference and diffraction, polarization, and related physical phenomena. Furthermore, in certain special cases the wave picture of light can be simplified even more by representing the propagation of wavefronts by rays. The ray representation forms the basis of *geometrical optics*, the model usually used in the analysis of optical instruments such as lenses, mirrors, and combinations of these. The range of applicability of geometrical optics is much more limited than that of the more general wave theory, but within its range it is much simpler; indeed, in some respects geometrical optics is the simplest of all physical theories.

In summary, the wave and ray models of classical optics provide a description of a wide variety of optical phenomena associated with the propagation of light and other electromagnetic radiation, and within this context the theory may be regarded as fairly complete. Yet there are many other phenomena, especially those associated with *emission* and *absorption* of radiation, in which the wave picture is far from complete. The latter class of phenomena forms the subject matter for the next three chapters.

First, although we have regarded the propagation of an electromagnetic wave as a continuous process, a variety of evidence shows that the energy associated with this radiation is emitted and absorbed only in discrete units, sometimes called *quanta*. The wave model gives no hint as to why these quanta should exist or how they are emitted or absorbed.

Second, the existence of characteristic spectra of elements, in which each element emits radiation only of a number of discrete frequencies, different for each element, shows that the emission of radiation by atoms of an element must be related to the internal structure of the atoms. But again, wave optics, based as it is on classical electrodynamics, provides no clue to the understanding of this relationship.

As we shall see in the next three chapters, the understanding of phenomena associated with the emission and absorption of radiation and of its interaction with matter requires sweeping changes in our concepts of the nature both of radiation and of matter itself. First, there is the apparent inconsistency of the *discreteness* of the energy of radiation with the continuous nature of wave propagation. Then there is the problem of describing and understanding the internal structure of atoms. As we shall see, an atom is basically a mechanical system; yet when classical new-tonian mechanics is applied to the system, even in the simplest cases, the results cannot account for the existence of characteristic spectra and so cannot be a completely correct description of the internal structure of atoms.

The key to the understanding of these problems is *quantum mechanics,* which involves fundamental changes in our conception of how a mechanical system is to be described. In particular, it is necessary to abandon the idea of describing a particle as a local-ized point in space, moving at each instant with a definite velocity. Instead, particles must be regarded as spread-out entities which are not completely localized in space. As these entities move with time, the spread-out nature partakes of some of the characteristics of a *wave.* Thus under some circumstances particles exhibit wave properties, and in fact these wave properties can be demonstrated very directly in some experiments.

Thus, while the first four chapters have concentrated on the successes of classical optics, the next three chapters will concen-trate on its failures. But from these failures emerges a more sophisticated physical theory which *does* provide at least a partial basis for the understanding of emission and absorption of radiation and of its relation to the internal structure of atoms. In recognition of the discrete, or *quantum*, nature of the energy associated with radiation and with changes of internal states of atoms, this new theory is called *quantum mechanics*.

5 *Particle Nature of Radiation*

MANY OPTICAL PHENOMENA can be understood on the basis of the wave nature of light and other electromagnetic radiation. Many other phenomena, however, exhibit a different aspect of the nature of light and suggest that it should be regarded not as a wave but as a stream of particles. Several phenomena which exhibit the particle nature of light are discussed and interpreted in terms of the fundamental assumptions of the quantum theory. Finally, it is shown that the wave and particle aspects of radiation are not necessarily mutually inconsistent but that they can be regarded as two aspects of a single fundamental phenomenon.

5-1 *Emission and Absorption*

In order to comprehend the enormous significance of the discoveries outlined in this chapter, we first consider briefly the state of knowledge of optics and the structure of matter around 1890. As we have seen in the first four chapters, the wave theory of light accounted completely for the phenomena then known concerning the *propagation* of light, such as geometrical optics, interference, diffraction, and polarization.

Insofar as these phenomena were concerned, the wave theory of light was *complete*.

Furthermore, the development of electromagnetic theory, crowned by the brilliant achievements of James Clerk Maxwell, predicted the existence of electromagnetic waves whose speed in vacuum should be the same as the observed value of the speed of light. These developments, together with the experimental work of Heinrich Hertz, who in 1887 convincingly demonstrated the existence of electromagnetic radiation, provided conclusive evidence that light is indeed an electromagnetic wave; it is now recognized as a small part of a very broad spectrum of electromagnetic radiation.

With respect to the structure of matter, the existence of atoms was firmly established by an abundance of chemical phenomena, the kinetic theory of gases, and other evidence. The work of Faraday and others on electrolysis showed that there exist elementary units of charge; by 1890 it was fairly clear that atoms consist of positive and negative charges and that part of the negative charge can be removed under some conditions. Finally, in 1897, the experimental work of J. J. Thomson with what were then called "cathode rays" showed definitively the existence of electrons and also provided a measurement of the charge-to-mass ratio of the electron. Thus it became clear that atoms are not indivisible, as had once been thought, but have some internal structure. The details of this internal structure, however, were completely unknown and had to wait to be investigated and understood until the pioneering experiments of Rutherford and his colleagues in 1911.

Phenomena associated with the *emission* and *absorption* of light by matter were not nearly so well understood as its *propagation*. There was, to be sure, a certain degree of qualitative understanding; it was clear that electromagnetic radiation is produced by oscillating charges or currents, just as Hertz had produced electromagnetic radiation by means of oscillations in a resonant circuit. To account for the observed wavelength of light, as determined from interference and diffraction phenomena, the frequency must be of the order of 10^{15} cycles/sec, compared with frequencies of the order of 10^8 in the experiments of Hertz. It was suspected that vibrations of optical frequency must be associated with motion of individual charges within atoms. In fact, as early as 1862, Faraday had placed a light source between the poles of a strong magnet in an attempt to detect changes in wavelength in the spectrum emitted. His apparatus was not sufficiently sensitive to detect changes, but in 1896 a similar experiment was performed by Zeeman, with the observation that measurable shifts of wavelength *do* occur. This lent further support to the model of vibrations of electric charge within atoms as the fundamental sources of light.

Aside from this qualitative picture, there was very little understanding of the phenomenon of the emission of light. It was known as early as 1752 that when substances in the gaseous state are excited by heating or by an electrical discharge they ordinarily emit light that contains only certain wavelengths, rather than a continuous spectrum. Because spectrometers used to observe spectra often employ a slit to define a narrow beam, which is then dispersed by a prism or diffraction grating, the various wavelengths appeared in the spectrometer as *lines* of various colors; hence such spectra came to be known as "line spectra." By 1823 it had been shown that each element has a characteristic spectrum and that elements can be identified by their spectra.

The phenomenon of *absorption spectra* was also observed early in the nineteenth century. When light passes through an element in the gaseous state, some wavelengths are absorbed much more strongly than others, and it was found that the wavelengths absorbed in such circumstances were the same as some of those *emitted* by the same element when thermally or electrically excited.

An enormous amount of effort was expended in searching for regularities or patterns in the observed spectra of elements. No real progress was made, however, until the work of Balmer, who in 1885 succeeded in finding an empirical rule governing the wavelengths of the visible spectrum emitted by hydrogen, the simplest atom. Even then, this rule had no real fundamental basis. This groping for schemes to correlate or systematize spectra reminds one of the long struggle of Kepler, culminating in his three empirical rules governing the motion of planets, and of the struggles of the chemists trying to find order among the chemical elements, culminating in the periodic table of Mendeleeff. Such groping is often a vital part of the advancement of scientific knowledge.

There were corresponding mysteries regarding the light emitted by solid matter. It was known in the nineteenth century that when solid bodies are heated very hot ("red hot" or "white hot") they usually emit light in a continuous spectrum, that is, a continuous distribution of wavelengths, rather than a line spectrum. It was observed that the frequency of the most intense radiation is directly proportional to the absolute temperature of the radiating body and that the total energy radiated is proportional to the fourth power of the absolute temperature. Some partially successful attempts were made to provide a theoretical basis for these observations, but full understanding had to wait until the first years of the twentieth century, when one of the key pieces of the puzzle was found by Max Planck.

There were a number of other phenomena that were difficult to understand on the basis of the classical theory of light. One of them was the photoelectric effect, discovered by Hertz in 1887 and investigated in detail by Hallwachs and Lenard, in which electrons are liberated from the surface of a material when it absorbs electromagnetic radiation. Another was the production of x-rays in cathode-ray tubes, first discovered by Roentgen in 1895.

Thus by the turn of the century it was clear that, while the electromagnetic theory of light was adequate for the treatment of phenomena concerned with *propagation* of light, it was completely inadequate for those involving *emission* and *absorption* of light. We can sense the excitement that must have pervaded scientific circles in those times. Only new ideas of major proportions could bring understanding into these diverse areas, and in 1900 the time was ripe for such ideas. The revolution in physical theory which took place in the 25 years following the turn of the century was undoubtedly one of the most significant in the entire history of scientific thought. This period witnessed the birth and flowering of the quantum theory and of the theory of relativity, both of which lie at the very heart of contemporary physical science.

It will be noted in the following pages that the development of new ideas does not always take place in a systematic and orderly way but sometimes seems to present the appearance of a partly assembled jigsaw puzzle. The reader may feel disappointment at the lack of a coherent, orderly scheme of development. The fact is, however, that physical theories, especially those representing as dramatic a departure from established tradition as we are discussing here, virtually never develop in an orderly manner. There is always considerable guesswork, much of which turns out to be wrong, following of blind alleys, and discarding of unsuccessful guesses in favor of more promising ones. By examining in detail the search for understanding at the beginning of the twentieth century, we gain a heightened appreciation of the conceptual basis of the new theories and of their significance.

5-2 *Photoelectric Effect*

The first hint of the photoelectric effect was discovered in 1887 by Hertz, quite by accident, in the course of his investigation of electromagnetic radiation. As a detector of radiation, Hertz used a rudimentary antenna made of a piece of wire with a small polished metal sphere on each end,

bent into a circle to form a narrow gap between the spheres. Electromagnetic waves induced a potential difference across the gap, as shown
by sparks jumping across it. Hertz observed that sparks jumped more
readily when the gap was illuminated by light from another spark gap
in the apparatus producing the waves. This suggested to Hertz that this
light facilitated the escape of charges from the metallic conductor of the
antenna.

This idea in itself was not revolutionary. It was already known
that mobile charges in electrical conductors are prevented from escaping
from the material of the conductor by potential-energy barriers at the
surface and that by various means the charged particles can gain enough
energy to surmount this barrier and escape. In thermionic emission,
first observed by Edison, the energy is supplied by heating the material
to a very high temperature. Figure 5-1 shows a possible scheme for
observing the flow of electrons from a heated filament to another electrode inside an evacuated tube as a result of thermionic emission from
the filament. Electrons may also be liberated from a surface by bombardment by other charged particles or by imposing very strong electric
fields at the surface to pull the particles away.

Although the basic idea of photoelectric emission of electrons was
not startling, the details of the phenomenon observed by Hallwachs and

Fig. 5-1 *An appa-
ratus for observing
thermionic emission of
electrons. The filament
is heated by an electric
current, liberating elec-
trons by a process
analogous to boiling a
liquid. The anode is
kept at a positive
potential with respect to
the filament, establish-
ing an electric field as
shown. The negatively
charged electrons are
pushed toward the
anode, and the result-
ing current is detected
by the galvanometer.*

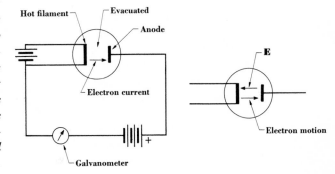

Lenard after detailed investigation were quite unexpected. A typical form of apparatus used to investigate the photoelectric effect is shown in Fig. 5-2a. Two electrodes are sealed in an evacuated glass bulb and connected to a battery with voltage-dividing resistors or with some other means of providing an adjustable potential difference V between the two electrodes. Monochromatic light, perhaps provided by a continuous-spectrum source with a prism spectrometer, illuminates the cathode, liberating electrons, some of which travel to the anode and around the external circuit. The resulting current may be measured with a sensitive galvanometer in the circuit, as shown. As the potential difference between the plates is varied, the current is found to vary in the manner shown in Fig. 5-2b. This curve shows that, at sufficiently high potential difference, *all* the electrons liberated from the illuminated cathode are collected by the anode, and then the current is not increased by a further increase in potential difference. This maximum current is called the *saturation current.*

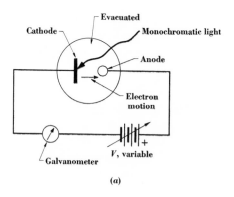

Fig. 5-2 (*a*) *An apparatus for observing photoelectric emission of electrons. The cathode is illuminated by monochromatic light, and the resulting current is measured with a galvanometer, as a function of the potential difference V. The intensity of illumination can also be varied.*
(*b*) *Graphs of current I as a function of voltage, for various intensities of incident light. Values of saturation current are directly proportional to the light intensity, but the stopping potential is independent of intensity.*

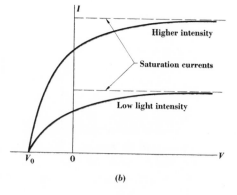

For smaller values of V not all the electrons are collected, but even for small *negative* values of V (corresponding to reversing the polarity of the battery in Fig. 5-2*b*), some current still flows, despite the fact that in this case the electrostatic force on the particles is toward the cathode rather than toward the collecting anode. This indicates that the electrons leave the cathode with a certain kinetic energy, and some have enough energy to reach the anode despite the repulsive force. When the potential difference V reaches a certain critical value, labeled V_0 in the figure, the current drops to zero, showing that no electrons leave the photocathode with kinetic energies greater than eV_0. This critical value of V is called the *stopping potential.*

Thus far the results are more or less as expected. But now let us change the *intensity* of the light, keeping its wavelength the same. When the intensity is increased, there is more energy available to liberate electrons, and so the saturation current should increase; this is, in fact, observed. Correspondingly, however, it might be thought that the electrons should leave the surface with more energy, and so a larger negative value of V_0 should be necessary in order to reduce the current to zero. Instead, it is found that the value of V_0 is, within experimental error, exactly the same and is in fact *independent* of the intensity of the radiation. This suggests that the maximum kinetic energy with which electrons leave the cathode depends only on the wavelength of the radiation and *not* on its intensity. When the experiment is repeated with different wavelengths, it is found that V_0 depends inversely on the wavelength. Specifically, it is found to be directly proportional to the *frequency* of the radiation. That is, the maximum kinetic energy of emitted electrons is a *linear* function of frequency. This relationship is illustrated in Fig. 5-3.

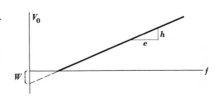

Fig. 5-3 *Graph showing stopping potential as a function of frequency of incident radiation. The intercept determines the work function W, and the slope determines the ratio h/e.*

In 1905 Albert Einstein showed that this relationship could be understood on the basis of a revolutionary hypothesis regarding the nature of light. Einstein hypothesized that the energy transported by electromagnetic radiation is composed of individual and indivisible bundles of energy, each having a quantity of energy proportional to the frequency of the corresponding radiation. If radiation of a given frequency is made more intense, *more* bundles of energy are transmitted, but the amount of energy in each individual bundle remains unchanged. In photoelectric emission, each electron absorbs only one such bundle. These bundles of energy were originally called *quanta* and are now more commonly known as *photons*. Expressing this hypothesis mathematically, we may say that the energy of one photon is

$$E = hf \tag{5-1}$$

where h is a proportionality constant.

The idea that the energy associated with electromagnetic radiation is packaged in units of a magnitude proportional to the frequency (usually called the *quantum hypothesis*) was not entirely original with Einstein. It had been proposed 5 years earlier by Max Planck in connection with attempts to understand the nature of the continuous spectrum emitted by very hot solid objects. Planck, however, tended to regard it as a calculational technique without any real fundamental physical significance. Einstein, characteristically, regarded it as a fundamental property of light. Revolutionary though this new concept was, it was in a sense a natural development, inasmuch as it introduced an "atomistic" aspect to the theory of electromagnetic radiation, which may be compared to the atomistic aspect of the structure of matter which had been introduced by Dalton a hundred years earlier.

Returning to the experimental situation, we now consider the energy relationships in somewhat greater detail. As already mentioned, in order for an electron to leave the surface of a conductor it must surmount a potential-energy barrier. The amount of energy necessary for an electron to be removed from the surface is usually called the *work function* for the material and is denoted by W. Thus when an electron absorbs a photon of energy $E = hf$, its kinetic energy just outside the surface is $hf - W$. Recalling that electrical potential is potential energy per unit charge, we see that, when the anode is at a negative potential V with respect to the cathode, an electron with charge e which travels from cathode to anode undergoes an *increase* in potential energy of eV, with a corresponding *decrease* in kinetic energy. If this potential difference is greater than the kinetic energy with which electrons leave the cathode, they can never reach the anode. Thus the critical potential difference V_0 to just stop the flow of current from cathode to anode is given by

$$eV_0 = hf - W \qquad (5\text{-}2)$$

By measuring this critical potential for various frequencies, one can draw a graph of V_0 versus f, as in Fig. 5-3; from this graph both h and W can be determined. The constant h is called *Planck's constant;* its value is found to be

$$h = 6.62 \times 10^{-34} \text{ joule sec} \qquad (5\text{-}3)$$

Work functions for common conductors typically are the order of 10^{-19} joule.

In many calculations involving energy relationships for electrons, it is often convenient to measure energies not in joules but in a unit called the *electron volt,* abbreviated ev. By definition, 1 electron volt is the amount of energy acquired or lost by an electron (or any charged particle with charge equal to that of the electron) in moving through an electrical potential difference of 1 volt. Electrical potential is potential energy per unit charge, and 1 volt is equal to 1 joule/coul; thus the two units of energy are related simply by the fact that 1 ev = (1 electron charge)(1 volt). The charge of the electron has been found to be 1.602×10^{-19} coul; therefore

$$1 \text{ ev} = 1.602 \times 10^{-19} \text{ joule} \qquad (5\text{-}4)$$

The electron volt is a unit of *energy*, not of potential. Expressed in these units, work functions typically range from 0.5 to 5 ev. Similarly, the energy of a photon of visible light, for example, with a wavelength of 5,000 Å $= 5 \times 10^{-7}$ m, is

$$E = hf = \frac{hc}{\lambda} = \frac{(6.62 \times 10^{-34} \text{ joule sec})(3.00 \times 10^{8} \text{ m/sec})}{5 \times 10^{-7} \text{ m}}$$

$$= 3.98 \times 10^{-19} \text{ joule} = 2.48 \text{ ev}$$

In problems such as this it is often useful to express h in units of ev sec rather than joule sec; in these units its value is

$$h = 4.139 \times 10^{-15} \text{ ev sec}$$

In this section we have seen that quantitative observations of the photoelectric effect led to the concept of an atomistic or quantum aspect of the nature of electromagnetic radiation. Revolutionary though this hypothesis was in its day, it provided insight into a phenomenon which could not be understood on the basis of classical electromagnetic theory.

5-3   X-ray Production and Scattering

Several phenomena involving x-rays give additional support to the quantum hypothesis for electromagnetic radiation. We consider first the production of x-rays. X-rays were first produced in 1895 by W. K. Roentgen, using an apparatus similar in principle to that shown schematically in Fig. 5-4. Electrons released from the heated cathode by thermionic emission are accelerated toward the anode by a large potential difference, as shown. It is found that at sufficiently high potentials (several thousand volts) a very penetrating radiation is emitted from the surface of the anode. It was suspected early that this radiation was electromagnetic in nature, and further experiments confirmed this suspicion. In 1913 W. H. Bragg discovered the phenomenon of x-ray diffraction by crystals, discussed in Sec. 3-4. This technique permitted precise measurements of the wavelength of x-rays and thus became the basis for a study of x-ray spectra.

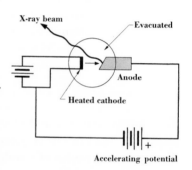

Fig. 5-4   *Apparatus used to produce x-rays. Electrons leave the heated cathode as a result of thermionic emission and are accelerated toward the anode; when they strike it, x-rays are produced.*

In subsequent investigations, several important observations emerged. Ordinarily, a continuous spectrum of frequencies of x-rays is emitted, but the maximum frequency was observed to be always directly proportional to the accelerating voltage between the electrodes. Furthermore, this maximum frequency was found to be very nearly independent of the material of which the electrodes were made. These observations can be understood on the basis of the quantum hypothesis. In its travel from cathode to anode, an electron acquires a kinetic energy equal to eV, where V is the potential difference between the electrodes. On striking the anode, it loses this kinetic energy, and a corresponding amount of energy is emitted as electromagnetic radiation. If one photon is produced in each collision, then it must be true that

$$eV = hf = \frac{hc}{\lambda} \tag{5-5}$$

For example, an accelerating voltage of 10,000 volts should lead to a photon energy of 10,000 ev and an x-ray wavelength of

$$\lambda = \frac{hc}{eV} = \frac{(6.62 \times 10^{-34} \text{ joule sec})(3.00 \times 10^8 \text{ m/sec})}{(1.601 \times 10^{-19} \text{ coul})(10^4 \text{ volts})}$$

$$\lambda = 1.24 \times 10^{-10} \text{ m} = 1.24 \text{ Å}$$

Such calculations agree with measured values of λ obtained by diffraction experiments and therefore lend strong support to the "quantum" picture of electromagnetic radiation.

Even more complete confirmation of the particle nature of x-rays is provided by the phenomenon of Compton scattering. In the course of some experimental investigations of x-ray scattering from matter, the American physicist A. H. Compton discovered in 1923 that some of the scattered radiation had longer wavelength and correspondingly smaller frequency than the incident radiation. This phenomenon cannot be understood on the basis of classical electromagnetic theory, in which the scattered radiation results from electron vibration induced by the incident radiation and therefore must have the same frequency as the incident radiation. Conversely, the quantum theory of radiation provides a beautifully clear and simple understanding of the basic features of Compton scattering. The scattering is described as a collision between two particles, the incident photon and an electron initially at rest. After the collision, the electron has energy and momentum, and the outgoing photon has less energy and smaller frequency than the incident one. Such a process is shown diagrammatically in Fig. 5-5.

Fig. 5-5 Diagram showing particle interpretation of Compton scattering. Wavy lines represent photons; the solid line, the electron, which is initially at rest. The particles are labeled according to their momenta.

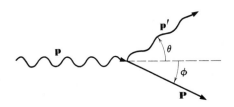

Compton scattering is so important and useful as an illustration of the properties of photons that we shall discuss it here in considerable detail. It is observed experimentally that the wavelength of the scattered radiation depends on the relative scattering angle, θ in Fig. 5-5. Using the familiar principles of conservation of energy and of momentum, we derive a relationship between the two wavelengths and the scattering angle θ. The analysis of this collision proceeds in exactly the same manner as the analysis of a collision between two billiard balls. Since the system is isolated, the total momentum must be the same before and after the collision. Furthermore, we assume that the collision is completely *elastic*, so that energy is also conserved.

For the electron we use the relativistic relationship between energy E and momentum $\mathbf{P}$,

$$E^2 = P^2c^2 + m^2c^4 \tag{5-6}$$

where E is the total electron energy, including the rest energy mc^2. Since photons always travel with the speed of light c, their rest mass must be zero, and the energy-momentum relationship for a photon is simply

$$E = pc \tag{5-7}$$

This relationship is also confirmed by measurements of radiation pressure, as discussed in Sec. 2-4.

Let $\mathbf{p}$ be the momentum of the photon before scattering and $\mathbf{p}'$ its momentum after scattering. Momentum is, of course, a vector quantity. We resolve each momentum into its components parallel and perpendicular to the direction of the incident photon and require that the sum of corresponding components be the same before and after the collision. Conservation of these two components of total momentum leads to the equations

$$\begin{aligned} p &= p' \cos \theta + P \cos \phi \\ 0 &= p' \sin \theta - P \sin \phi \end{aligned} \tag{5-8}$$

Since we are seeking a relationship which involves the direction θ of the scattered photon, it is useful first to eliminate the angle ϕ, which represents the direction of the final electron momentum. To do this, we solve Eqs. (5-8) for $P \cos \phi$ and $P \sin \phi$, respectively, square, and add, using the identity $\sin^2 \phi + \cos^2 \phi = 1$. The result is

$$P^2 = p^2 + p'^2 - 2pp' \cos \theta \tag{5-9}$$

Now, in order to obtain an expression involving only the photon frequencies or wavelengths, which are directly related to the momenta, we eliminate the electron momentum P. To do this we use the equation representing conservation of energy,

$$pc = p'c + T \tag{5-10}$$

where T represents the *kinetic* energy of the electron after the collision, which is directly related to its momentum. The most useful form of this relationship for our purposes is obtained as follows: The total energy and momentum are related by Eq. (5-6), and it is also true that the total energy E is equal to the sum of the kinetic energy T and the rest energy mc^2,

$$E = T + mc^2 \tag{5-11}$$

Combining Eqs. (5-6) and (5-11) to eliminate E, we find

$$P^2 = 2mT + \frac{T^2}{c^2} \tag{5-12}$$

Now all that remains is to put the pieces together. We equate the right sides of Eqs. (5-9) and (5-12), which eliminates P, and then use Eq. (5-10) to eliminate T. The result is

$$p^2 + p'^2 - 2pp' \cos \theta = 2m(pc - p'c) + \frac{(pc - p'c)^2}{c^2} \tag{5-13}$$

which may be simplified to

$$mc(p - p') = pp' (1 - \cos \theta)$$

or

$$mc\left(\frac{1}{p'} - \frac{1}{p}\right) = 1 - \cos \theta \tag{5-14}$$

This expresses the relationship between the momenta p and p' of the incident and scattered photons and the scattering angle θ. Finally, Eq. (5-14) can be written in terms of the *wavelengths* of the photons. Combining the basic relation $E = hf$ for the energy of a photon with the energy-momentum relation $E = pc$, we have $p = hf/c$. Since for any wave $c = \lambda f$, the momentum and wavelength of a photon are related simply by

$$p = \frac{h}{\lambda} \tag{5-15}$$

Using this relation in Eq. (5-14), we finally obtain

$$\lambda' - \lambda = \frac{h}{mc} (1 - \cos \theta) \tag{5-16}$$

In view of the somewhat involved derivation, this is a remarkably simple result, showing that the wavelength of the scattered photon is always longer than that of the incident photon by an amount that depends in a simple way on the scattering angle. Experiments with x-ray scattering, in which the wavelengths are measured directly by x-ray diffraction techniques, agree with Eq. (5-16) within the limits of the precision of the experiment.

The above analysis has assumed that the electron that scatters the photon is *free*. In actual fact, some of the electrons in any atom are rather tightly bound to the nucleus. When such electrons scatter x-rays, the recoil is not that of the electron alone, but of the entire atom. In such cases, Eq. (5-16) still gives the correct shift in wavelength, provided one uses for m not the mass of an electron but the mass of the entire atom, which is several thousand times larger. These wavelength shifts are so small as to be unnoticed in usual x-ray scattering experiments but are, in fact, the predominant events in most cases.

Thus we have seen that the phenomenon of Compton scattering provides additional strong support for the particle picture of electromagnetic radiation and also gives justification for the procedure of describing and analyzing electron-photon collisions in mechanical terms.

5-4   Line Spectra

The existence of line spectra gives further support to the particle picture of light and also provides valuable insight into an important aspect of atomic structure. In fact, atomic spectroscopy has been by far the most important experimental tool in investigating atomic structure in detail.

The existence of line spectra has been known for over 200 years, and in Sec. 5-1 we commented briefly on the characteristic emission and absorption spectra of elements. But as late as 1880, although line spectra were a familiar phenomenon, their basic nature was not understood. An enormous amount of effort went into searching for some pattern or orderly relationship among various lines in a spectrum, but no real progress was made until 1885, when a Swiss schoolteacher, Johann Balmer, succeeded, after a long period of groping, in finding an empirical formula relating various lines in the spectrum of hydrogen, the simplest atom.

Balmer's formula is most transparent when written in the following form:

$$\frac{1}{\lambda} = R \left(\frac{1}{2^2} - \frac{1}{n^2} \right) \qquad n = 3, 4, 5, \dots \tag{5-17}$$

The constant R is called the *Rydberg constant* after J. R. Rydberg, who, following Balmer, made considerable progress in the search for various spectral series. The currently accepted value of R is

$$R = 109{,}677 \text{ cm}^{-1}$$

As Table 5-1 shows, the predictions of Balmer's formula agree extremely well with observed wavelengths of lines in the hydrogen

Table 5-1   Data on Hydrogen Spectrum

n	Wavelength, Å	
	Balmer's formula	Ångström's measurements
3	6,562.08	6,562.10
4	4,860.8	4,860.74
5	4,340.0	4,340.1
6	4,101.3	4,101.2

spectrum. Balmer, in his original paper, also speculated on the possible existence of other series of spectrum lines corresponding to replacing the 2^2 in his formula by other numbers such as 1^2, 3^2, 4^2, and so forth, leading to possible spectral series given by

$$\frac{1}{\lambda} = R\left(\frac{1}{1^2} - \frac{1}{n^2}\right), \qquad \frac{1}{\lambda} = R\left(\frac{1}{3^2} - \frac{1}{n^2}\right), \qquad \text{etc.} \tag{5-18}$$

Calculation of numerical values shows that the first of these should lie in the far-ultraviolet region of the spectrum, 912 to 1,214 Å, while the others should be in the infrared region, $\lambda > 8{,}204$ Å. In the course of subsequent investigation, all these predicted spectral series were found to exist, and their wavelengths agreed extremely well with the predictions of Eqs. (5-18).

In the 25 years following Balmer's original paper, various physicists made some additional progress in systematizing the spectra of various elements. Ritz discovered that it is possible to represent the spectrum of an element by means of a set of characteristic numbers called *terms* such that the wave number of each of the observed spectrum lines is given by the difference of two terms. This scheme was called the *combination principle*. These terms and the corresponding spectrum lines were found to fall naturally into groups or series. These properties of spectra strongly suggested the existence of some simple underlying principle governing the emission of spectra, but there was as yet no inkling of what this principle could be.

Balmer's formula and the Ritz combination principle suffered from the same deficiency as Kepler's laws of planetary motion; they were empirical descriptions of phenomena without any fundamental basis. They provided no understanding of the mechanism of emission and absorption of light or of the basis of the observed regularities in spectra. A more complete understanding of the fundamental basis of spectra had to wait until the next generation. Two key pieces of the puzzle were missing; one was the idea of the quantization of electromagnetic wave energy, as described by the photon theory, and the other was a new and revolutionary picture of the structure of the atom.

The real key to the understanding of atomic spectra was provided in 1913 by Niels Bohr with an insight which, from a historical vantage point 50 years later, seems almost obvious; yet in its time it represented a bold and brilliant stroke. Bohr reasoned that if the atoms of a particular element can emit photons of only certain particular energies (corresponding to the spectrum of that element) then the atoms themselves must be able to possess only certain particular quantities of energy. That is, corresponding to the discrete spectrum of an element there must be a discrete series of possible energies that the atom can possess.

This bold hypothesis immediately shed new light on Balmer's formula. For the series of wavelengths given by Eq. (5-17) the corresponding photon energies are

$$E = \frac{hc}{\lambda} = hcR \left(\frac{1}{2^2} - \frac{1}{n^2} \right) \tag{5-19}$$

Thus if the hydrogen atom can exist only in states characterized by the series of possible energy levels

$$E_n = -\frac{hcR}{n^2} \qquad n = 1, 2, 3, \ldots \tag{5-20}$$

then all the spectral series of hydrogen predicted by the Balmer formula can be understood as originating from transitions between pairs of these allowed energy levels. Correspondingly, the *terms* in the Ritz combination principle are reinterpreted as representing corresponding energy levels.

Starting with the observed spectrum of an element, it is possible to reconstruct the energy-level scheme and to identify individual spectrum lines with particular transitions between energy levels. It is convenient to represent energy-level schemes graphically as in Fig. 5-6, which shows energy-level diagrams for two elements. In such a diagram, transitions accompanying emission or absorption of particular photons are indicated by arrows.

Although the above discussion has centered around emission spectra, it should be clear that the concept of atomic energy levels is equally

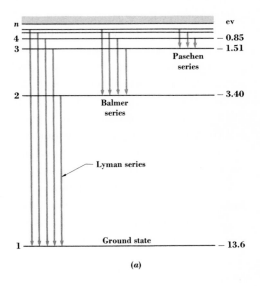

(a)

Fig. 5-6 *Energy-level diagrams.* (a) *Hydrogen. The series of transitions ending at the ground state* (n = 1) *give the Lyman series, in the ultraviolet. Those ending at n = 2 give the Balmer series, in the visible region, and at n = 3 the Paschen series in the infrared.* (b) *Sodium. Some energy levels are closely spaced doublets, and transitions involving these lead to doublet spectrum lines. The transitions leading to the* (5,890 Å, 5,896 Å) *doublet are shown.*

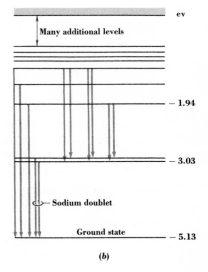

(b)

satisfactory in accounting for *absorption* spectra. The only difference is that the direction of energy transfer is opposite; the atom gains energy by absorption of a photon, rather than losing energy by emission. One remaining question in this picture is the mechanism by which atoms originally acquire the energy which they radiate away when they emit photons. In spectra emitted in flames or other hot gases, the mechanism is simply one of collision of one atom with another. In such a collision, some of the thermal energy corresponding to motion of the atoms is converted into internal energy of electrons in an atom. With electrical discharge in an arc or glow-discharge tube, the mechanism is usually collision with electrons or ions which acquire energy by being accelerated in an electric field.

A detailed study of conduction of electricity through gases provides additional and persuasive evidence for the existence of atomic energy levels. Such a study was made by J. Franck and G. Hertz starting in 1914. Using an apparatus shown schematically in Fig. 5-7, Franck and Hertz bombarded vapors of various elements with electrons emitted thermionically from the filament and accelerated toward the grid by the potential difference V. A smaller retarding potential V_0 slows the electrons somewhat as they approach the plate, and the current of electrons that reach the plate is measured by the galvanometer in this circuit.

As the accelerating potential V is increased, more and more electrons arrive at the plate and the current increases. But when a certain

Fig. 5-7 *Apparatus for the Franck-Hertz experiment. Electrons emitted thermionically from the heated filament are accelerated toward the grid by the potential difference V. They have enough energy to proceed on to the plate despite the smaller retarding potential V_0, unless they collide inelastically with atoms on the way. Measuring the potential differences V for which inelastic collisions set in gives a direct measurement of the excitation potentials, or energy levels.*

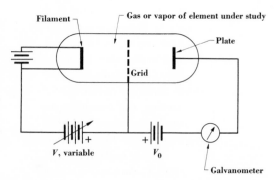

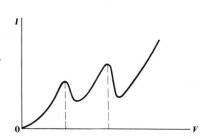

Fig. 5-8   *Galvanometer current as a function of accelerating voltage V in the Franck-Hertz experiment. The breaks in the curve indicate the onset of inelastic collisions, with corresponding energy loss eV, and thus give a direct measurement of energy levels, in electron volts.*

critical potential is reached, the plate current drops suddenly, as shown in Fig. 5-8. This is easily understood in terms of atomic energy levels. For small values of V, an electron collides elastically with atoms; since the electron is so much less massive, it loses practically no energy in such collisions and arrives at the grid with energy very nearly equal to eV. Then it can proceed to the plate, losing energy eV_0 in the process. But when the electron kinetic energy becomes as large as the energy difference between the two lowest levels in the atoms, electrons can then collide *inelastically* with atoms, giving up a certain fraction of their energy. When this happens, they may reach the grid with insufficient energy to proceed on to the plate, and the plate current is reduced. For example, with mercury vapor Franck and Hertz found that one of the breaks in the plate-current graph came at $V = 4.9$ volts (electron energy of 4.9 ev). This corresponds to the atoms being excited by collisions with electrons to an energy level of 4.9 ev above the lowest level. As V is increased further, the plate current again increases and then eventually drops sharply again, corresponding to excitation of a higher energy level. Thus a series of energy levels called *excitation potentials* is observed.

To check this interpretation, Franck and Hertz observed the spectra emitted by the vapors during this process. In the previous example, an atom excited to an energy level of 4.9 ev above the lowest state should emit a photon of corresponding energy when it returns to the lowest energy level, or *ground state*. This transition corresponds to a wavelength of 2,536 Å. This spectrum line was, in fact, observed, but only when V was greater than 4.9 volts. For smaller potentials, it disappeared. Similarly, by increasing V further, spectrum lines of other wavelengths could be excited. These experiments gave very direct and convincing confirmation of the existence of atomic energy levels and their relationship to line spectra.

The foregoing discussion cannot be considered a complete theory of atomic spectra because it has not provided a basis for *predicting* atomic energy levels. At the same time Bohr proposed his theory relating atomic spectra to energy levels, he also attempted to make an actual calculation of energy levels for the simplest atom, hydrogen, on the basis of a simple model which has come to be known as the *Bohr model*. Although this model has serious conceptual defects, it is important historically, for it was the first attempt to predict atomic energy levels that achieved any measure of success.

The Bohr theory comprises a *dynamic* model of the atom, in which the electron is pictured as moving in a circular orbit around the nucleus (a single proton) just as the planets move around the sun in nearly circular orbits. The electron is assumed to be subject to the classical laws of mechanics and electromagnetism, but an additional assumption is necessary in order to introduce a restriction as to the possible orbits in which the electron can move. Since the electron is so much less massive than the proton, we assume that the latter is stationary; the electron is attracted to it with a force given by Coulomb's law. Since each of the two particles has a charge of magnitude e, the attractive force has a magnitude

$$F = \frac{1}{4\pi\epsilon_0} \frac{e^2}{r^2} \tag{5-21}$$

where r is the radius of the orbit. This is the force responsible for the centripetal acceleration of the electron toward the center of its circle, which is v^2/r, where v is the electron's orbital speed. According to Newton's second law, this force equals the mass times the acceleration, and so we have

$$\frac{e^2}{4\pi\epsilon_0 r^2} = \frac{mv^2}{r} \tag{5-22}$$

This equation shows immediately that the kinetic energy T of the electron is inversely proportional to the radius of its orbit:

$$T = \frac{1}{2}mv^2 = \frac{e^2}{8\pi\epsilon_0 r} \tag{5-23}$$

The potential energy also depends on r. Taking the potential energy as 0 at $r = \infty$, it is easily shown, by integrating Eq. (5-21), that the potential energy $V(r)$ at any value of r is

$$V(r) = -\frac{e^2}{4\pi\epsilon_0 r} \tag{5-24}$$

OPTICAL SPECTRA

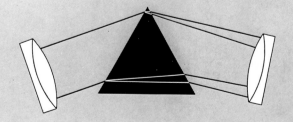

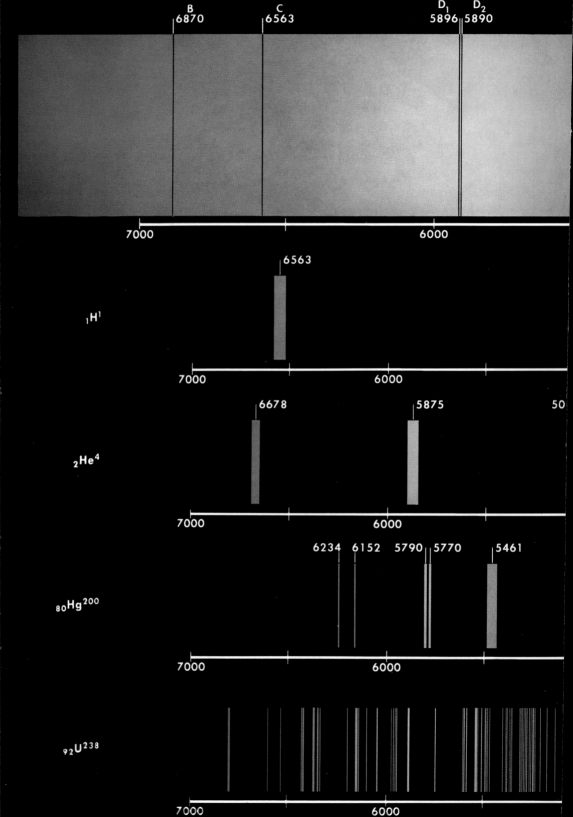

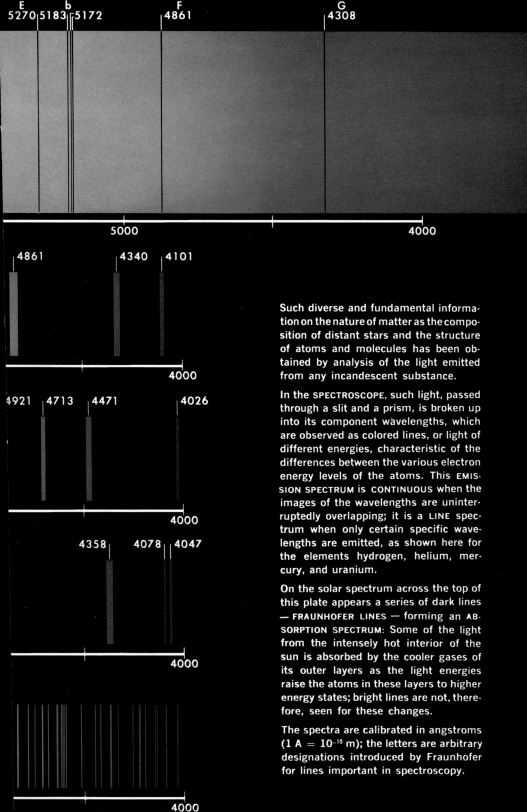

| E | b | | F | | G |
| 5270 | 5183 | 5172 | 4861 | | 4308 |

5000   4000

4861   4340   4101

4000

4921   4713   4471   4026

4000

4358   4078   4047

4000

4000

Such diverse and fundamental information on the nature of matter as the composition of distant stars and the structure of atoms and molecules has been obtained by analysis of the light emitted from any incandescent substance.

In the SPECTROSCOPE, such light, passed through a slit and a prism, is broken up into its component wavelengths, which are observed as colored lines, or light of different energies, characteristic of the differences between the various electron energy levels of the atoms. This EMISSION SPECTRUM is CONTINUOUS when the images of the wavelengths are uninterruptedly overlapping; it is a LINE spectrum when only certain specific wavelengths are emitted, as shown here for the elements hydrogen, helium, mercury, and uranium.

On the solar spectrum across the top of this plate appears a series of dark lines — FRAUNHOFER LINES — forming an ABSORPTION SPECTRUM: Some of the light from the intensely hot interior of the sun is absorbed by the cooler gases of its outer layers as the light energies raise the atoms in these layers to higher energy states; bright lines are not, therefore, seen for these changes.

The spectra are calibrated in angstroms (1 A = 10^{-10} m); the letters are arbitrary designations introduced by Fraunhofer for lines important in spectroscopy.

The total energy E of the electron is given by

$$E = T + V = -\frac{e^2}{8\pi\epsilon_0 r} \tag{5-25}$$

The new assumption which Bohr introduced in order to decide what particular values of r should be permitted is justified by more recent developments in quantum mechanics, but in Bohr's day it was a brilliant and remarkable guess. Bohr hypothesized that the *angular momentum* of the electron must be an integer multiple of the quantity $h/2\pi$, where h is the same Planck's constant which relates the energy and frequency of a photon. It may be remarked in passing that this is not a completely unreasonable guess, since h does have units of angular momentum, and since the condition that governs the possible radii of orbits must be related somehow to the existence of photons. The quantity $h/2\pi$ is now usually abbreviated $\hbar$, read "h-bar."

The angular momentum of the electron may be written as mvr, and Bohr's hypothesis therefore becomes

$$mvr = \frac{nh}{2\pi} = n\hbar \qquad n = 1, 2, 3, \ldots \tag{5-26}$$

Combining this with Eq. (5-22) to eliminate v, and solving the resulting equation for r, we find that the permitted radii, which we may call r_n, are

$$r_n = \frac{4\pi\epsilon_0 n^2 \hbar^2}{me^2} \tag{5-27}$$

Finally, inserting this expression into Eq. (5-25), we find that the allowed energies E_n are

$$E_n = -\left(\frac{e^2}{4\pi\epsilon_0}\right)^2 \frac{m}{2n^2\hbar^2} \qquad n = 1, 2, 3, \ldots \tag{5-28}$$

The form of this equation is identical to that deduced from the Balmer formula [Eq. (5-20)]; in both cases the energy levels are given by a certain constant divided by the square of an integer. Furthermore, Eq. (5-28) permits a theoretical prediction of the Rydberg constant. If Eqs. (5-20) and (5-28) are to agree, it must be true that

$$hcR = \left(\frac{e^2}{4\pi\epsilon_0}\right)^2 \frac{m}{2\hbar^2} \tag{5-29}$$

Thus this is the really crucial test of the Bohr theory. It turns out, in fact, that the value of R obtained from Eq. (5-29), using the measured values of m, e, c, and h, does agree with the value of R obtained directly from spectroscopic data and thus provides direct and rather astonishing confirmation of the Bohr theory.

This model also yields a prediction of the dimensions of the hydrogen atom. As Eq. (5-27) shows, the orbit radius depends on the energy level; for the lowest level, or *ground state*, corresponding to $n = 1$, the radius is given by $r_1 = 4\pi\epsilon_0\hbar^2/me^2$, which has the numerical value 0.527×10^{-10} m. This value agrees at least qualitatively with other estimates of the size of the hydrogen atom, such as those obtained from the density of solid hydrogen and from the deviations from ideal-gas behavior of gaseous hydrogen resulting from finite molecular size.

The Bohr theory was a remarkable combination of classical principles and of new postulates completely inconsistent with classical theory. Ordinarily it would be expected that an electron traveling in a circular orbit would continuously radiate energy, just as an oscillating dipole radiates, but this is not observed. Even worse, the frequencies of the emitted radiation are not the same as the frequencies of orbital motions predicted by the Bohr theory. The Bohr model achieved stability by simply *postulating* that radiation does not occur as long as an electron is in one of its permitted orbits, or "stationary states," as they came to be called. But this stability was bought at the expense of throwing away the only classical picture available at that time of the mechanism by which energy is radiated. That is, the Bohr theory provided no description of what happens during a transition from one stable orbit to another.

This hybrid character of the Bohr theory was felt by many physicists to be unsatisfactory, and it suffered from other equally serious deficiencies. It was not clear how it should be applied to atoms containing more than one electron, and all attempts to predict energy levels of more complicated atoms failed. Furthermore, later evidence accumulated from a variety of experiments with electrons showed that in many respects the classical picture of the electron as a charged particle with a definite position in space had to be modified drastically. The present-day concept of the electron, which will be discussed in considerable detail in later chapters, is of an *extended* entity which ordinarily is *not* localized at a particular point in space. Thus by present-day standards the Bohr theory was completely wrong conceptually. Still, it was an important milestone, inasmuch as it was the first successful attempt at predicting atomic energy levels, thus paving the way for more detailed understanding of the structure of atoms and the behavior of elementary particles.

5-5 *Continuous Spectra*

The discussion of the preceding section centered around the understanding of *line spectra* produced by elements in the gaseous state, when interactions between atoms are negligible. Similar and closely related problems arise in connection with the *continuous spectra* emitted by very hot materials in the solid and liquid states. By 1900 it was well known that the spectrum of radiation emitted by matter in condensed states (liquid or solid) is *continuous,* rather than a line spectrum, and that its details are nearly independent of the material emitting the radiation. Studies were made of the distribution of emitted energy among the various wavelengths and of the dependence of this distribution on the temperature of the radiating body. The results of such studies are conveniently represented graphically, as shown in Fig. 5-9. The significance of such a curve is that the area under the curve between any two values of λ represents rate of emission of energy in radiation having wavelengths in this interval.

Fig. 5-9 *Energy distribution in continuous-spectrum radiation. The area under the curve between any two wavelengths, such as the shaded area shown, represents the rate of energy radiation by waves with wavelengths in the corresponding interval. The total area under the curve represents the total rate of radiation of energy. The broken line shows the distribution for a lower temperature; the maximum is shifted in the direction of longer wavelengths, and the total area is decreased.*

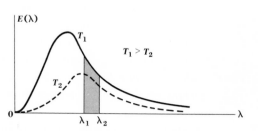

The empirical facts known in 1900 were these: First, the *total* rate of radiation of energy, represented by the total area under the curve, is proportional to T^4, where T is the absolute temperature; this relation is called the *Stefan-Boltzmann law.* Second, the wavelength at which the maximum rate of energy emission occurs (corresponding to the maximum point on the curve in Fig. 5-9) is inversely proportional to

T; that is, as the temperature of a body rises, its radiated energy is concentrated in shorter and shorter wavelengths. Thus a glowing body which appears yellow is hotter than one which appears red. This observation is called the *Wien displacement law*. Third, the *shape* of the energy-distribution curve does not change with temperature. A curve for one temperature can be made to fit any other temperature by simply changing the scales on the graph.

In the closing years of the nineteenth century, many attempts were made to understand this behavior of continuous spectra from hot solids and liquids. It was fairly well established by then that light is electromagnetic radiation, and it seemed natural to assume that it was produced by vibrations of elementary charges within a material. Several attempts were made to derive relationships for the energy radiated in various wavelengths in a continuous spectrum. Most of these regarded the electrons as harmonic oscillators with average energies determined by the equipartition theorem[1] of kinetic theory. That is, each oscillator was assumed to have an average kinetic energy of $\frac{3}{2}kT$, where k is Boltzmann's constant. None of these attempts was successful, but in 1900 Max Planck succeeded in deriving a formula by adding to the classical equipartition theorem the hypothesis that a harmonic oscillator with frequency f could gain or lose energy only in units of hf, where h is Planck's constant.

Planck himself, along with many other physicists of the time, tended to regard this *quantum hypothesis* more as a calculational trick than as a new fundamental principle. As we have already seen, however, evidence for the existence of "particles" of light accumulated to an impressive collection in the years following 1900, so that by 1920 there was no doubt of the validity of this concept. In a sense, the existence of microscopic energy levels may be said to have originated with Planck rather than with Bohr, since this concept is contained implicitly in his picture of the energy relationships of microscopic harmonic oscillators.

The details of Planck's derivation are somewhat involved and need not concern us here; the formula for the energy distribution which he derived with the aid of the quantum hypothesis is as follows:

$$F(\lambda) = \frac{2\pi hc^2}{\lambda^5} \frac{1}{e^{hc/\lambda kT} - 1} \tag{5-30}$$

This function represents the rate of energy radiation per unit surface

---

[1] See H. D. Young, "Fundamentals of Mechanics and Heat," sec. 16-4, McGraw-Hill Book Company, New York, 1964.

area of an ideal radiating substance. It agrees with experimental observations of the energy distribution in continuous spectra. It also contains the Wien displacement law and the Stefan-Boltzmann law as consequences. For the first of these, we take the derivative of Eq. (5-30) with respect to λ and set this derivative equal to zero to find the wavelength λ_m of maximum energy radiation. The details of this calculation are left as a problem; the result is

$$\lambda_m = \frac{hc}{4.965kT} \tag{5-31}$$

where the number 4.965 is a numerical constant, the root of the equation

$$5 - x = 5e^{-x} \tag{5-32}$$

which arises when the derivative of Eq. (5-30) is set equal to zero.

The particular combination of constants appearing in Eq. (5-31) and the dependence on $1/T$ are to be expected. Photons are emitted by microscopic oscillating charges, which, as we shall see in the next chapter, are usually individual electrons. They typically have energies of the order of a few times kT, as shown by the equipartition theorem. A photon whose energy is kT has a wavelength given by $\lambda = hc/kT$; correspondingly, a photon whose wavelength is given by Eq. (5-31) has energy of $4.965kT$.

The Stefan-Boltzmann law is obtained by integrating Eq. (5-30) over λ to find the *total* rate of radiation of energy per unit area. This calculation is also left as a problem; the result is

$$\int_0^\infty F(\lambda)\ d\lambda = \frac{2\pi^5 k^4}{15c^2 h^3}\ T^4 \tag{5-33}$$

which shows that the total rate of energy radiation is proportional to T^4, in agreement with experimental observations.

5-6   *Wave-Particle Duality*

We have now examined at some length a considerable variety of phenomena involving light and other electromagnetic radiation. One group of phenomena, comprising what is usually called classical optics, points to the *wave* nature of light, in accordance with the predictions of classical electromagnetic theory. Another class of phenomena, observed in more recent years, points with equal force to the *particle* nature of light. These two aspects of the behavior of electromagnetic radiation seem at first glance to be in direct conflict; nevertheless, the accepted viewpoint today is that they are not incompatible. The situation may be compared to that of several blind men trying to describe an elephant after touching various parts of its anatomy. By making various kinds of observations, the blind men can explore various parts of the elephant's structure, but it is difficult for any of them to get a correct overall picture. So it is with light. We have to accept the fact that light has both particle and wave properties and that different experiments reveal different aspects of its nature.

We have seen in Sec. 3-7 a hint that wave and particle descriptions of light are not necessarily incompatible. The simplest example, a superposition of two waves with slightly different wavelengths, results in a wave having a lumpy character not possessed by either separate wave. Similarly, by superposing a large number of waves having frequencies close to a given central frequency, it is possible to construct a wave pulse such as that shown in Fig. 5-10. This wave has regular spacing between successive maxima, equal to the wavelength of the central waves out of which it was constructed, but at any instant of time it is localized in a finite region of space. Such a wave packet clearly partakes of both wave and particle characteristics.

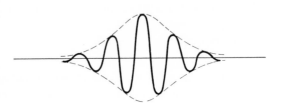

Fig. 5-10   *A wave pulse, or wave packet, which has a more or less definite wavelength but which is localized in a finite region of space. Such a wave packet can be constructed as a linear superposition of sinusoidal waves with wavelengths close to that corresponding to successive maxima of the pulse.*

It would be a considerable oversimplification to state that Fig. 5-10 is an illustration of a photon, for various reasons. In the first place, the fact that various wavelengths were used to construct this wave packet indicates a corresponding spread of energies, and this clearly is incompatible with the concept of a photon as having a definite energy. Furthermore, such a simplified picture gives no indication of why the *energy* of such a wave packet should be restricted to the value $E = hf$, as has been observed experimentally. Nevertheless, this picture is useful as an illustration of a phenomenon having both wave and particle aspects.

As an example of the difficulties that arise from attempts to picture a photon too specifically as a particle localized in space or as a wave spread out over a large region, one may consider the quantum interpretation of the two-slit interference experiment discussed in Sec. 3-2. The intensity-distribution pattern corresponds to varying numbers of photons emerging in various directions; the intensity at any point is directly proportional to the number of photons per unit area, per unit time, in the vicinity of that point; this quantity is sometimes called the *photon flux*.

In the two-slit situation it is tempting to suppose that each individual photon must pass through either one or the other of the slits. But if this is the case it should be possible to produce a two-slit interference pattern on a photographic film by opening one slit for a certain time interval, then closing it and opening the other slit for the same time. Experiment shows, however, that this procedure does *not* result in a two-slit interference pattern but rather in two superposed single-slit patterns, in general quite different from the two-slit pattern. In the wave picture it is easy to see why this procedure fails, since in two-slit interference it is essential for the radiation from the two sources to be *coherent* in order to produce the characteristic two-slit pattern.

The only way to reconcile this apparent paradox in the photon picture of light is to assume that *every* photon goes partly through *both* slits; only then can the radiation from the two slits be coherent. We must recognize that there is nothing conceptually wrong with this point of view. The photon is not a single point in space, and there is no reason it should have to pass through one slit or the other.

Additional features of the photon interpretation of interference phenomena emerge when we consider what happens when the incident intensity is made extremely small. Suppose we record the interference pattern not with photographic film but with a device which detects individual photons. Such devices actually exist; the most common type is called a *photomultiplier*, and its details need not concern us. To observe the interference pattern, we place the photomultiplier at various positions for equal time intervals and count the numbers of photons emerging in various directions, as shown in Fig. 5-11. *On the average,* over a sufficiently long time interval, the photon distribution obtained agrees with the prediction of the two-slit pattern. But if the intensity is reduced to the point where there are only a few photons per second, there is no way of predicting precisely where any individual photon will go.

The interference pattern now emerges as a *statistical distribution*

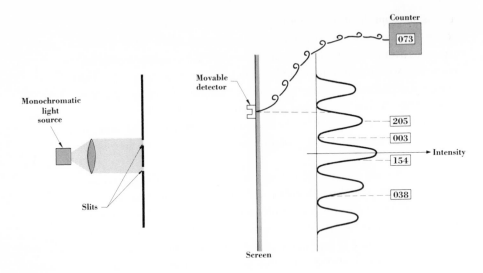

Fig. 5-11 *Two-slit interference pattern observed with photomultipliers. The curve shows the intensity distribution predicted by the wave picture, and the photon distribution is shown schematically by the numbers of photons counted at various positions.*

of photons, describing how many photons go in each direction, or alternatively the *probability* for an individual photon to go in each direction, but *not* where any individual photon will go.   Thus the photon picture reveals an intrinsically statistical aspect of the description of interference phenomena.   The idea of describing radiation in statistical language is an important concept, and as we shall see in the following chapters this concept reappears in the quantum-mechanical description of particles.

A really thorough understanding of the nature of light, with the formulation of a theory that treats adequately both its wave and particle aspects, has come only in the past 15 years, in that branch of physics called *quantum electrodynamics.*   It is not possible to summarize in a few paragraphs the enormous amount of work that has gone into this field.   We remark only that quantum electrodynamics embodies an extension of the concepts of energy levels of an atomic system so that they are applied also to electromagnetic fields.   That is, just as an atom is pictured as existing only in certain definite energy states, so the electromagnetic field has certain well-defined energy states, which can be described as corresponding to the presence of various numbers of photons having various energies.   Present-day quantum electrodynamics is capable of making extremely precise predictions of energy levels of atoms and of other phenomena involving interaction of matter with electromagnetic radiation. But this subject came to full flower 50 years after the conceptual birth of quantum mechanics in 1900 with Planck's original quantum hypothesis.

PROBLEMS

5-1   Roughly how many photons does a 100-watt light bulb emit per second? At what distance is the photon flux equal to 100 per square centimeter of surface per second?

5-2   A certain radio station broadcasts at a frequency of 1,000 kc with an average power output of 5,000 watts.
   a.   What is the energy of a photon in electron volts?
   b.   How many photons does the station emit per second?
   c.   Why are no quantum effects observed in radio transmission at frequencies such as this?

5-3   A γ-ray photon emitted in a certain nuclear reaction has an energy of 1 Mev. Find its wavelength and frequency. How does the wavelength compare with typical nuclear sizes (the order of 10^{-15} m)?

5-4   What minimum accelerating voltage is needed in an x-ray tube in order to produce x-rays with a wavelength of 1 Å?

5-5   A radioactive isotope of cobalt, Co^{60}, emits a γ ray with a wavelength of about 0.932×10^{-12} m. The nucleus contains 27 protons and 33 neutrons.
   a.   If the nucleus is at rest before emission, what is its speed afterward?
   b.   Is it necessary to use the relativistic expression for momentum to find this speed?

5-6   Suppose that the cobalt atom of Prob. 5-5 is in a metallic crystal containing 0.01 mole of cobalt (about 6.02×10^{21} atoms) and that the crystal recoils as a whole, rather than only the single nucleus. Find the recoil velocity. (This recoil of the whole crystal rather than a single nucleus is called the Mössbauer effect, in honor of its discoverer, who first observed it in 1958.)

5-7   In a photoelectric-effect experiment, it is observed that for light with a wavelength of 4,000 Å a stopping potential $V_0 = 2$ volts is needed, and for light with a wavelength of 6,000 Å, a stopping potential of 1 volt. From these data, calculate the work function for the material, and Planck's constant.

5-8   What energy (in electron volts) must a photon have so that its wavelength is of the order of magnitude of nuclear diameters (10^{-15} m)?

5-9   Why is the Compton effect not observed for visible light?

5-10   For what wavelength photon does Compton scattering produce a 1 percent increase in wavelength, at a photon scattering angle of 45°? In what region of the electromagnetic spectrum does such a photon lie?

5-11   For what wavelength photon does Compton scattering result in a photon whose energy is one-half that of the original photon, at a photon scattering angle of 45°? In what region of the electromagnetic spectrum does such a photon lie?

5-12   Compton scattering has been observed from protons (in targets containing hydrogen) as well as from electrons. For what order of magnitude of photon energy (in electron volts) would this effect be observable? For example, for what photon energy would the energy loss be of the order of 1 percent?

5-13   Why are the energy levels of the hydrogen atom less than zero?

5-14   A certain atom has the following energy-level scheme: $-8, -5, -2, -1, -0.5$ ev. Calculate the wavelengths corresponding to all possible transitions between these levels. Which ones lie in the visible spectrum? The ultraviolet? The infrared?

5-15   A certain atom emits spectrum lines at 3,000, 4,000, and 12,000 Å. Assuming that three energy levels are involved in the corresponding transitions, calculate the spacing of these levels, in electron volts.

5-16   An electron with mass m collides inelastically with an atom of mass M, initially at rest, and excites it to an energy E above the ground state. By applying the principles of conservation of energy and momentum, show that the initial energy of the electron must be at least $(1 + m/M)E$.

5-17   What minimum electron energy (in electron volts) is necessary for an electron to excite a hydrogen atom from $n = 1$ to $n = 2$? Is the effect illustrated by Prob. 5-16 significant in this case?

5-18   A proton collides with a hydrogen atom and excites it from $n = 1$ to $n = 2$. What minimum energy must the proton have if the hydrogen atom is initially at rest? Compare your result with that of Prob. 5-17.

5-19   A hydrogen atom makes a transition from $n = 3$ to $n = 1$, with emission of a photon.   If it is initially at rest, what is its recoil velocity after emission?

5-20   In a hydrogen glow discharge tube, the atoms are in motion with various velocities, according to the kinetic theory of gases.   As a result of the corresponding Doppler frequency shifts, spectrum lines appear not as perfectly sharp lines but as somewhat spread-out distributions of wavelengths.   Make a rough estimate of the spread of wavelengths corresponding to Doppler broadening for the $n = 3$ to $n = 2$ transition in hydrogen, for a temperature $T = 1000°$K.

5-21   For the ground state of the hydrogen atom, as described by the Bohr model, find the radius of the orbit, the speed of the electron, its angular velocity, and angular momentum, in the usual mechanical units.

5-22   How do the various mechanical quantities mentioned in Prob. 5-21 depend on the quantum number n?

5-23   A helium atom with one of its two electrons removed (a "singly ionized atom," denoted as He$^+$) resembles a hydrogen atom in its electron configuration.   How are the energy levels and the orbit radii related to the corresponding quantities for the hydrogen atom?

5-24   A *positron* is a particle having the same mass as an electron but opposite charge.   A positron and an electron can form a bound state in much the same manner as an electron and a proton form a hydrogen atom.   This "atom" is called *positronium*.   Make an analysis like that of the Bohr model to find the energy levels and orbit radii of the positronium atom.   Hint: Neither particle is at rest, but if the distance between them is d, then each particle travels in a circle of radius $d/2$, with its center midway between the particles.

5-25   Derive Eq. (5-31), using the root of Eq. (5-32) given in the text.

5-26   Integrate Eq. (5-30) to obtain the Stefan-Boltzmann law [Eq. (5-33)].   In the integral, make the change of variable $x = hc/\lambda kT$ and use the following fact:

$$\int_0^\infty \frac{x^3\,dx}{e^x - 1} = \frac{\pi^4}{15}$$

which can be derived by mathematical trickery.

5-27   What is the total rate of radiation per unit area from:
   a.   A frying pan at $300°$C
   b.   A tungsten lamp filament at $3000°$C
   if each behaves as an ideal radiator in accordance with Eqs. (5-30) and (5-33)?

5-28   Calculate the numerical value of the Stefan-Boltzmann constant, which is the constant σ in the relation $P = \sigma T^4$ for the total rate of radiation of energy per unit area for an ideal radiating body at absolute temperature T.

5-29   A 100-watt light bulb operates at a temperature of $3000°K$. Assuming it loses energy only by radiation, what must be the total surface area of the filament? Is your result reasonable, considering actual light bulbs?

5-30   Roughly, what temperature is necessary for "red heat," according to the Wien displacement law?

5-31   The temperature in the gaseous outer layers of the sun is about $6000°K$. At what wavelength is the maximum radiated intensity? In what range of the electromagnetic spectrum does this wavelength lie?

CORRESPONDING TO THE wave-particle duality for electromagnetic radiation, the fundamental "particles," such as electrons, exhibit wave properties in some situations. This dual nature of material particles was first predicted theoretically and then observed experimentally a few years later. The discovery of the wave properties of particles necessitates sweeping changes in the fundamental concepts of the description of particles. In general, it is not possible to specify the position of a particle precisely, nor its velocity. Instead the particle is described as a wave function which is not localized in space and which moves with time. The wave function describing a particle is found to be a solution of a certain equation, analogous to the wave equation for classical waves.

6-1 De Broglie Waves

In the year 1924 a young French graduate student, Louis de Broglie, put forth a revolutionary hypothesis which was to shake the very foundations of mechanics and open the door to solution of many of the baffling problems concerning the structure of the atom and its interaction with electromagnetic radiation.

De Broglie's hypothesis was approximately as follows: Nature loves symmetry and simplicity in physical phenomena. The two great classes of entities which seem to be basic to the structure of matter are electromagnetic radiation and material particles. The first of these, electromagnetic radiation, has been demonstrated conclusively to have a dual wave-particle nature. Therefore, it is reasonable to suppose that particles also have a dual nature and that in some circumstances they may behave like waves rather than particles.

De Broglie drew an analogy to the various branches of optics. It is well known that geometrical optics, with its description of light in terms of rays, is an approximation of the more general wave analysis of optics, an approximation which is valid whenever interference and diffraction phenomena can be neglected. Perhaps the particle description of electrons and other particles and the description of their motion in terms of line trajectories are approximations which are valid under certain circumstances, but perhaps there are other conditions under which a more general description is necessary, embodying a wave description of electrons and other particles.

If an electron behaves like a wave, what determines the wavelength and frequency of this wave? The two fundamental dynamical qualities involved in the motion of a particle are its energy and its momentum, and these presumably should determine the wavelength and frequency. Pursuing the analogy with electromagnetic radiation, de Broglie proposed that the wavelength and frequency should be determined by the momentum and energy, respectively, in exactly the same way as for photons. That is, the wavelength and frequency should be given by

$$\lambda = \frac{h}{p} \qquad f = \frac{E}{h} \tag{6-1}$$

which may be compared with Eqs. (5-1) and (5-15). There was some uncertainty in de Broglie's mind as to whether the energy in the last expression should be the total energy of the particle, which would include potential energy and, in the case of relativistic dynamics, the rest energy, or whether it should be just kinetic energy. In the present discussion, we confine our attention to the nonrelativistic case with free particles, so that there is no energy other than kinetic energy, and E is therefore the kinetic energy.

The wave hypothesis has an interesting consequence in connection with the Bohr theory of the hydrogen atom. We recall that it was necessary for Bohr to introduce the somewhat artificial restriction that the angular momentum of the electron must be an integer multiple of $h/2\pi$, expressed by Eq. (5-26) as

$$mvr = \frac{nh}{2\pi} \qquad n = 1, 2, 3, \ldots$$

(6-2)

Now mv is just the momentum of the electron, $mv = p$, and according to de Broglie this is related to its wavelength by Eq. (6-1). Therefore, $(h/\lambda)r = nh/2\pi$, and

$$2\pi r = n\lambda \qquad n = 1, 2, 3, \ldots$$

(6-3)

That is, the orbit circumference $2\pi r$ must be an integral number of wavelengths. This result seems somehow to be reasonable and suggests that some sort of standing wave is associated with a circular orbit. This is, to be sure, a rather vague and not very satisfactory picture, but the relationship is much too remarkable to be regarded as a coincidence and must, instead, be an indication that de Broglie's hypothesis does indeed have something to do with the description of electrons in atoms.

To appreciate the magnitude of de Broglie's work, we must remind ourselves that at the time there was no direct experimental evidence that particles have wave characteristics. It is one thing to suggest a new hypothesis to explain experimental observations; it is quite another thing to propose such a radical departure from established concepts on theoretical grounds alone. But it was clear that a radical idea was needed; the dual nature of electromagnetic radiation had forced just such a revolutionary proposal in that area, and the relatively complete lack of success in understanding atomic structure and spectra indicated that a similar revolution was needed in the mechanics of particles. Thus, in a sense, the time was ripe for de Broglie's hypothesis, and so it was that in the following year he and other physicists developed it into a detailed theory, even before there was any direct experimental verification of the wave properties of particles.

6-2 Diffraction of Particles

Three years after de Broglie first advanced his theory about the wave nature of particles, Davisson and Germer obtained, by a method discovered quite by accident, direct experimental confirmation of the de Broglie hypothesis. During 1926 and 1927 Davisson and Germer, working at the Bell Telephone Laboratories, were studying the scattering of electrons from the surface of a solid. Electrons emitted from a heated filament were accelerated by electrodes, and the resulting beam of electrons was directed at a block of nickel. The numbers of elec-

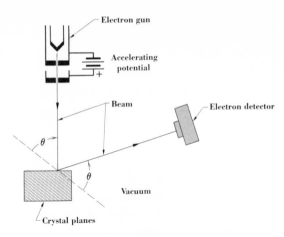

Fig. 6-1 Apparatus for the Davisson-Germer experiment. Electrons emitted from the heated filament are accelerated by the electrodes in the electron gun and directed at the crystal, and the electrons in the scattered beam are observed by a suitable detector. The relative orientation of the electron gun, crystal, and detector can be varied. The entire apparatus is enclosed in an evacuated chamber.

trons scattered in various directions were then measured. The experimental setup is shown schematically in Fig. 6-1.

In the midst of the experiments, an accident occurred which permitted air to enter the vacuum chamber enclosing the apparatus. This resulted in the formation of a film of oxide on the surface. To reduce this oxide the target was baked in a high-temperature oven; unknown to Davisson and Germer, this had the effect of *annealing* the sample, which had originally been a polycrystalline specimen, so that after the heat treatment it became a large single crystal. After the accident the experimental results were quite different. At certain particular angles there were sharp maxima and minima in the intensity of scattered electrons, in contrast to the smooth variation with angle which had been observed before the accident. Furthermore, the angular positions of these maxima and minima depended on the electron energy. Typical results from these experiments are shown in the polar graphs of Fig. 6-2. The similarity of these results to corresponding results from x-ray diffraction experiments, especially in the light of the de Broglie hypothesis, suggested to Davisson and Germer that the electrons were being *diffracted*. If so, this experiment would provide a direct test of the de Broglie hypothesis.

In one particular measurement, using an electron energy of 54 ev, an intensity maximum was observed when both the incident beam and the detector for the scattered beam made an angle of 65° with a particular family of crystal planes (cf. Sec. 3-4) whose spacing had been measured by x-ray diffraction techniques and found to be 0.91×10^{-10} m. As shown in Sec. 3-4, the Bragg relation for constructive interference of waves scattered at an angle θ from planes spaced a dis-

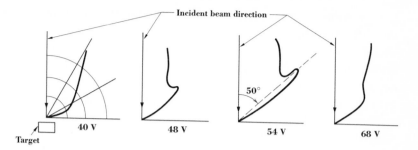

Fig. 6-2 *Polar plots of the intensity of a scattered electron beam as a function of angle between incident and scattered beams, showing an intensity maximum in a particular direction for certain electron energies.*

tance d apart is

$$2d \sin \theta = n\lambda \qquad n = 1, 2, 3, \ldots \tag{6-4}$$

Thus the electron scattering in this particular experiment is characteristic of a wave whose wavelength is given (with $n = 1$) by

$$\lambda = 2(0.91 \times 10^{-10} \text{ m}) \sin 65° = 1.65 \times 10^{-10} \text{ m}$$

This value is to be compared with the wavelength obtained from the de Broglie hypothesis. The momentum of the particle can be expressed in terms of its energy, which in turn is equal to eV, where V is the potential difference through which the electron was accelerated. That is,

$$E = \frac{p^2}{2m} = eV \tag{6-5}$$

Solving this equation for p and inserting the result in the de Broglie relation [Eqs. (6-1)], we find

$$\lambda = \frac{h}{p} = \frac{h}{\sqrt{2meV}} \tag{6-6}$$

Inserting the appropriate numerical values,

$$\lambda = \frac{6.62 \times 10^{-34} \text{ joule sec}}{\sqrt{2(9.11 \times 10^{-31} \text{ kg})(1.60 \times 10^{-19} \text{ coul})(54 \text{ volts})}}$$

$$= 1.67 \times 10^{-10} \text{ m}$$

in remarkable agreement with the direct determination from the electron diffraction data.

The following year a similar experiment was performed by the British physicist G. P. Thomson, who used a thin film of metal consisting of many microscopic crystals with random orientation. A similar technique had been developed some years earlier by Debye and Sherrer to observe x-ray diffraction with powdered specimens. Again the results were in agreement with the de Broglie hypothesis. It is of interest to note that G. P. Thomson was the son of J. J. Thomson, who 30 years previously had performed the definitive experiment to establish the *particle* nature of electrons.

Further investigation of the wave properties of particles was carried out by many physicists throughout the world. In Germany, Estermann and Stern diffracted ionized helium atoms (α particles) from a lithium fluoride crystal, establishing that they too had wavelike properties. More recently, neutron diffraction experiments have been performed. Thus the wave properties of particles have become well established.

To the extent that an electron or other elementary particle behaves as a wave, it should be possible to describe it with a *wave function*. We recall that waves on a vibrating string are described by a function which represents the displacement of each point on the string in terms of its equilibrium position and the time, and in the description of an electromagnetic wave, each component of the electric and magnetic fields is represented as a function of the space coordinates and time.

The nature of this wave function for a particle needs to be clarified. For the vibrating string, the function represents a displacement, and for electromagnetic waves it is an electric or magnetic field at a point. But what is it for a "matter wave"? It is appropriate to remark first that there is some doubt about whether this is even a proper question. Just as the concept of electric field is an abstraction introduced to describe the interaction between electrical charges, the concept of a wave function associated with a particle is an abstraction introduced to describe the motion of the particle. It would not be appropriate to ask what an electric field is made of, and one may question whether it is proper to ask similar questions about the wave function for a particle. Perhaps we should just accept the fact that using a wave function provides a description of phenomena, and let it go at that.

Nevertheless, it is possible to discuss the meaning of the wave function in somewhat more definite terms. First, to the extent that a particle behaves as a wave, it can no longer be regarded as localized at a single point, as in the classical conception of a particle. Thus the question whether the particle lies in a specified region of space at a particular instant of time cannot, in general, have a definite yes-or-no answer. As we shall see in detail later, the wave function provides an answer to such questions in terms of the *probability* of finding the particle in a given region, in an experiment which measures position. Thus we are led naturally to a *statistical* description of the particle's position, quite analogous to the statistical interpretation of interference patterns discussed in Sec. 5-6 in connection with the photon concept. This interpretation helps to round out the symmetry between the description of radiation and that of particles, in the spirit of de Broglie's original hypothesis; it will be discussed in greater detail in Sec. 7-1.

A somewhat easier question to resolve is the apparent inconsistency of the wave and particle points of view. It has already been mentioned in Secs. 3-7 and 5-6 that by superposition of sinusoidal waves with various wavelengths it is possible to construct a wave pulse, or wave packet, which has a more or less definite wavelength and yet is localized in a finite region of space. Such a wave will show interference or diffraction effects only in experiments whose scale is of the same order of magnitude as the wavelength; in any experiment of grosser scale it will appear as a particle, not a wave. For example, electrons accelerated in a television picture tube have to pass through apertures in the accelerating electrodes, and, in principle, diffraction effects should be observed. But the electron wavelength is exceedingly small compared with the size of the aperture, and the resulting diffraction pattern on the fluorescent screen of the picture tube is so small as to be unobservable.

6-3 Wave Packets

The key to understanding the relationship between the wave and particle properties of electrons and other particles is found in the consideration of wave packets. We now consider in detail how sinusoidal waves can be superposed to form a wave packet which has a characteristic wavelength and yet is localized in a finite region of space. In order to illustrate principles in as simple a context as possible, the present discussion will be limited to waves in one space dimension.

It is convenient to characterize sinusoidal waves by means of the *wave number k* and the *angular frequency ω*, related to the wavelength λ and frequency f, respectively, just as in Sec. 1-4:

$$k = \frac{2\pi}{\lambda} \qquad \omega = 2\pi f \tag{6-7}$$

As in Sec. 1-4, the wave speed u is related to k and ω by

$$\omega = uk \tag{6-8}$$

Sinusoidal waves corresponding to wave number k and frequency ω have the following functional forms:

$$\sin (kx \pm \omega t)$$
$$\cos (kx \pm \omega t) \tag{6-9}$$
$$e^{i(kx \pm \omega t)}$$

In all these, the negative sign corresponds to a wave propagating in the $+x$ direction, and conversely. In each case, the wave speed is the coefficient of t divided by the coefficient of x, that is, ω/k, in agreement with Eq. (6-8). For mechanical or electromagnetic waves it is necessary to rule out the complex exponential functions or to combine them in such a way as to obtain *real* functions, since mechanical displacements and electric and magnetic fields are always real quantities. Since at this stage in our discussion the wave function for particles is of completely unknown nature, there is no *a priori* reason for ruling out complex functions. We shall find, in fact, that the last functional form above is often the most convenient with which to work.

It is not clear how any of the above functions can represent a particle, since they are not localized in space but rather extend over all possible values of the coordinate x. But, as pointed out earlier, it is possible to superpose several waves of this form having different values of k and ω so as to obtain a composite wave which *is* localized in space. The simplest example is a wave obtained by superposing two sinusoidal waves with slightly different wave numbers, say k_1 and k_2, with equal amplitudes A. This case was discussed in detail in Sec. 3-7, and it would do no harm for the reader to review that discussion. The result, we recall, is an interference pattern resembling a series of pulses. Even superposition of only two waves has the effect of "bunching" the resultant wave in some regions of space. Furthermore, as mentioned in Sec. 3-7, there is nothing to prevent our constructing a wave function $\Psi(x,t)$ which is a more general superposition of waves such as

$$\Psi(x,t) = \sum_n A_n e^{i(k_n x - \omega_n t)} \tag{6-10}$$

in an effort to construct a wave which is more localized. We can even add waves with a continuous distribution of wave numbers and frequencies, in which case the sum in Eq. (6-10) becomes an integral:

$$\Psi(x,t) = \int A(k) e^{i(kx - \omega t)} \, dk \tag{6-11}$$

The amplitude function $A(k)$ gives the amplitude of each component wave and is thus a function of k; ω is also a function of k.

It turns out, not surprisingly, that by using an appropriate function $A(k)$ we can construct a wave pulse, or packet, with any desired shape. The process of representing an arbitrary function as a superposition of sinusoidal functions is called *Fourier analysis,* and the representations themselves are called Fourier series or Fourier integrals.

Of particular interest are wave pulses constructed with sinusoidal waves having wave numbers in the vicinity of some central wave number k_0. For example, suppose the amplitude function describing the distribution of amplitudes as a function of the wave number k has the form shown in Fig. 6-3. One function $A(k)$ having this general shape is

$$A(k) = Ce^{-a^2(k-k_0)^2}$$

(6-12)

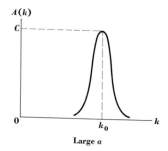
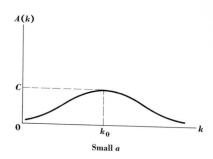

Fig. 6-3 *Graphs of Eq. (6-12). The central wave number is k_0, and the maximum height C. Curves for two different values of a are shown; the width of the curve is inversely proportional to a.*

The constant C represents the maximum value of the function in Eq. (6-12); the corresponding function of x and t is proportional to C. The constant a characterizes the *width* of the curve; when a is large, the curve is sharply peaked, dropping away rapidly from its maximum at the central wave number k_0, but when a is small the curve is broader and flatter. Thus a characterizes the range or spread of values of k used.

The analytical expression for the resulting wave function is obtained by substituting Eq. (6-12) into Eq. (6-11) and performing the integration. That is,

$$\Psi(x,t) = \int_{-\infty}^{\infty} Ce^{-a^2(k-k_0)^2}e^{i(kx-\omega t)}\,dk$$

(6-13)

To see the general shape of the wave function it is sufficient to consider only one instant of time; at the particular time $t = 0$, the wave function is given by

$$\Psi(x,0) = \int_{-\infty}^{\infty} Ce^{-a^2(k-k_0)^2}e^{ikx}\, dk \tag{6-14}$$

The evaluation of this integral is straightforward but somewhat involved. The details are given in Appendix C; the result is

$$\Psi(x,0) = \frac{C\sqrt{\pi}}{a}e^{-x^2/4a^2}e^{ik_0x} \tag{6-15}$$

This expression represents a sinusoidal wave e^{ik_0x} modulated by the envelope function $e^{-x^2/4a^2}$. The real part of this function is plotted in Fig. 6-4.

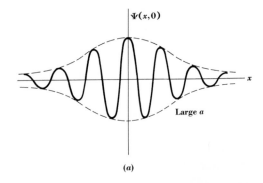

(a)

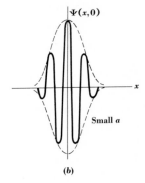

(b)

Fig. 6-4 Graphs of the real part of Eq. (6-15) for one value of k_0 but two different values of a. The width of the curve is directly proportional to a.

Thus by superposing an infinite number of sinusoidal waves, all with wave numbers in the vicinity of k_0, we have succeeded in producing a localized wave pulse having successive maxima and minima characteristic of a wave number k_0, but with a decreasing amplitude so that the wave pulse is localized in space.   Again we see that the constant a characterizes the width of the envelope function $e^{-x^2/4a^2}$ but that its role is just the inverse to that in Eq. (6-12).   In the function of x, when a is small the exponent quickly becomes large and negative when x becomes different from zero, while when a is large the envelope is less peaked.   Thus we see that a sharply peaked function $A(k)$ corresponds to a rather flat function $\Psi(x,0)$, while if $A(k)$ is broader, corresponding to a wider range of component wave numbers, $\Psi(x,0)$ is more sharply peaked.   This reciprocal relationship has an important significance which will be explored in the next section.

The preceding discussion is designed to persuade the reader that perhaps an electron can be a particle and a wave at the same time.   Wave properties are clearly visible in the structure of the packet, and to the extent that it is a particle, its position is determined by the position of the envelope of the wave packet.

We now come to a crucial question.   How does the particle *move?* That is, how does the envelope of the wave packet move?   It is clear that we should identify the change in position of this envelope with time as the *velocity* of the particle, in the classical sense, and we must now investigate how to calculate this motion of the packet.   If we were dealing with electromagnetic radiation in vacuum, there would be no difficulty. All the individual waves would propagate with a speed c, independent of the wave number k, and any superposition of such waves would also move with speed c; as a result the entire picture in Fig. 6-4 would move with the speed of light.

When the speeds are different for the various component waves, the situation is somewhat different, as shown in Sec. 3-7 for the superposition of two sinusoidal waves with slightly different wave numbers and different speeds.   In that case, as Eq. (3-60) shows, the sinusoidal wave itself moves with speed $u = \omega_0/k_0$, the speed corresponding to the *average* wave number and frequency, but the *envelope* of the wave moves with a speed called the *group velocity*, given by

$$v = \frac{\Delta\omega}{\Delta k} \tag{6-16}$$

which, if ω is not directly proportional to k, is not at all the same thing. In the limit as the difference between the two wave numbers becomes very small, the group velocity approaches the value

$$v = \frac{d\omega}{dk} \tag{6-17}$$

A similar calculation may be performed for the wave packet described by Eq. (6-13). The details of the calculation are somewhat more complicated than in the simple case considered in Sec. 3-7, but the end result is precisely the same; it can be shown that the peak of the envelope of the wave packet moves with a speed given by Eq. (6-17). In fact, it is possible to prove this relationship quite generally for any wave packet constructed of sinusoidal waves with wave numbers in the vicinity of a central value k_0; it is understood always that the derivative in Eq. (6-17) is evaluated at k_0. A proof of the general validity of this relation is given in Appendix D.

Now let us see how all this applies to waves describing particles. We recall the de Broglie hypothesis, which states that the energy and momentum of a particle are related to the frequency and wavelength, respectively, by Eqs. (6-1). It is convenient to express these in terms of k and ω. Introducing the notation $\hbar = h/2\pi$ and using Eqs. (6-7), we find

$$p = \frac{h}{\lambda} = \frac{h}{2\pi}\frac{2\pi}{\lambda} = \hbar k$$

$$E = hf = \frac{h}{2\pi}2\pi f = \hbar\omega$$

(6-18)

The energy and momentum are also related to each other by the familiar expression from classical mechanics, $E = p^2/2m$. Therefore,

$$\hbar\omega = \frac{\hbar^2 k^2}{2m}$$

(6-19)

from which we immediately obtain

$$u = \frac{\omega}{k} = \frac{\hbar k}{2m} = \frac{p}{2m}$$

(6-20)

showing that the wave velocity of a matter wave is directly proportional to its wave number, unlike the situation for light, for which c is independent of k.

Equation (6-20) may seem a little alarming, inasmuch as this velocity is exactly *one-half* the classical velocity $v = p/m$ of a particle. But we remember that the significant velocity in the description of a particle in terms of waves is the *group* velocity, or the velocity of the envelope of the wave. This, as we have just discussed, is given by Eq. (6-17). Applying this to Eq. (6-19), we find for the group velocity of matter waves

$$v = \frac{d\omega}{dk} = \frac{\hbar k}{m} = \frac{p}{m} \qquad (6\text{-}21)$$

which agrees with the definition of momentum $p = mv$ familiar from classical mechanics.

We have learned from this consideration of the wave description of particles that the classical concept of velocity of a particle has meaning in this picture only when it is redefined in terms of the motion of the envelope of a wave packet. Still, this is a natural extension of the classical concepts of kinematics, and it is helpful in understanding how a single basic entity can exhibit wave properties in certain experiments and particle properties in others.

The thoughtful reader has probably observed, however, that there is a serious difficulty in this description, at least from the point of view of classical mechanics. In constructing wave packets having a finite extension in space, we have had to superpose waves having a spread of values of k. This implies that the particle does not have a definite momentum but rather is a mixture of states having different momenta, corresponding to the different values of k. From the point of view of classical mechanics, dealing as it does with point masses having definite positions and velocities at each instant, this is clearly nonsense. But as we shall see in the following sections, it is necessary in the more general wave description of the behavior of matter to accept the possibility that, just as a particle described by a wave packet does not have a precisely defined position, it also need not have a definite momentum.

If this idea seems strange and even contrary to common sense, it is because of the prejudices created by newtonian mechanics. Common sense certainly tells us that every object which we can see must move with a definite, well-defined velocity at any instant of time and must therefore at that instant have a definite momentum. But common sense is based to a large extent on everyday observations, and these do not include looking directly at the motions of electrons and atoms. Thus we must be prepared to abandon some of the prejudices founded on everyday experience when dealing with situations and phenomena that are far removed from everyday experience, in areas where intuition may be misleading. In the next section we shall explore in more detail the concepts of *uncertainty* of momentum and position of a particle and the relationship between them.

6-4   Uncertainty Principle

As we have seen in the previous section, a wave packet that is localized in space can be obtained only by using a spread of wave numbers. A wave corresponding to a single wave number k is a sine wave with no beginning or end, spreading throughout space. In mechanical language, a particle described by such a wave may have a definite momentum $p = \hbar k$ only if its position is completely *indefinite*. Conversely, description of a particle that is even partly localized in space by means of a wave packet with a finite extension requires a spread of values of k, which means in turn a spread of values of momentum, such as the super-position given by Eq. (6-11). In particular, the amplitude function of Eq. (6-12) leads to the wave packet of Eq. (6-15). Let us now exam-ine these equations in more detail, particularly the role of the constant a in these equations.

As observed in Sec. 6-3, when a is large, the function $A(k)$ is sharply peaked, as in Fig. 6-5a; conversely, when a is small, the graph of $A(k)$ is relatively flat, without a sharp maximum, as shown in Fig. 6-5b. The shape of the envelope of the resulting wave packet, given by Eq. (6-16), depends on a in a similar manner. Here, however, a

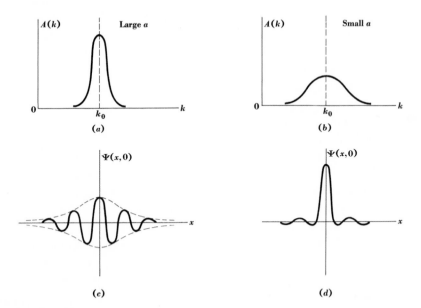

Fig. 6-5   *Two different functions $A(k)$ and the corresponding functions $\Psi(x,t)$, at time $t = 0$. The width of $\Psi(x,0)$ is inversely proportional to that of $A(k)$.*

appears in the *denominator* of the fractional exponent, rather than the *numerator*, so that the dependence is just opposite to the situation for the function $A(k)$. Thus a large value of a gives a rather broad, flat envelope, as in Fig. 6-5c, while a small value of a gives a sharply peaked envelope, as in Fig. 6-5d.

We are now on the brink of an extremely important discovery. Clearly, the extent to which the position or momentum of a particle is undetermined depends on the width of the functions $\Psi(x,0)$ or $A(k)$, respectively. A particle with relatively little uncertainty in its momentum has correspondingly great uncertainty in position, as in Fig. 6-5a and 6-5c, and a particle with great uncertainty in momentum can have relatively small uncertainty in position, as in Fig. 6-5b and 6-5d. The momentum can be completely definite only if the position is completely indefinite. Correspondingly, it can be shown that a particle whose position is completely well determined requires a uniform distribution of all possible wave numbers, so that the momentum is completely indefinite.

This whole situation is in sharp contrast to that of classical mechanics, in which it is possible in principle to determine the position and momentum of a particle precisely. Here we find instead what seems to be a fundamental limitation, inasmuch as we can define the position precisely only if the momentum is uncertain to a high degree, and conversely. Thus it becomes necessary to readjust our entire conception of the description of motion of a particle; it is necessary to abandon the classical notion of specifying position and velocity with arbitrarily great precision and, instead, to be content with a somewhat less precise description including uncertainties in both position and momentum, which appear in a complementary way.

The relationship between the uncertainty in position and that in momentum can be put in a more quantitative form by first defining more precisely what we mean by "uncertainty." To do this, we consider again the particular wave packet described by Eqs. (6-12) and (6-15). Both the amplitude function $A(k)$ and the envelope of $\Psi(x,0)$ have the general form

$$f(y) = (\text{const})\, e^{-y^2/2\sigma^2} \tag{6-22}$$

where the general variable y is identified as $k - k_0$ in one case and as x in the other.

Figure 6-6, which is a graph of Eq. (6-22), suggests a general scheme for characterizing the width of this function. We note that when $y = \pm\sigma$, corresponding to a value of the exponent of $-\frac{1}{2}$, the curve

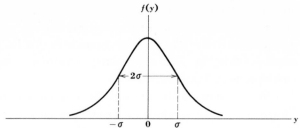

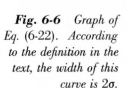

Fig. 6-6 *Graph of Eq. (6-22). According to the definition in the text, the width of this curve is 2σ.*

has dropped to about 0.61 of its maximum height and that about as much area under the curve is contained inside these limits as outside. Therefore we define the width of the curve, or more properly the *halfwidth*, as the interval in the variable y in which the function drops from maximum to $e^{-1/2}$ of maximum; thus in Eq. (6-22) the halfwidth is simply σ.[1]

The halfwidth does not represent the *maximum* possible departure of position or momentum from the central peak, but it does represent typical or characteristic deviations from it; therefore it is reasonable arbitrarily to *define* the uncertainty in x or k as the halfwidth of the corresponding curve. Applying this definition to Eq. (6-12), we see that the exponent is equal to $-\frac{1}{2}$ when

$$-a^2(k - k_0)^2 = -\tfrac{1}{2}$$

or

$$k = k_0 \pm \frac{1}{a\sqrt{2}} \tag{6-23}$$

Thus the uncertainty in k, which for brevity we denote simply as Δk, is given by

$$\Delta k = \frac{1}{a\sqrt{2}} \tag{6-24}$$

Similarly, considering the factor of Eq. (6-15) which represents the envelope of the wave packet, we find

$$\frac{-x^2}{4a^2} = -\tfrac{1}{2} \qquad \text{when} \qquad x = \pm a\sqrt{2} \tag{6-25}$$

Thus the uncertainty in x, which we denote as Δx, is

$$\Delta x = a\sqrt{2} \tag{6-26}$$

---

[1] This quantity is also equal to the *standard deviation* of the function, a concept widely used in statistics.

Although each of the uncertainties Δk and Δx depends on a, as we have already pointed out, their *product* is independent of a:

$$\Delta x\, \Delta k = 1$$

(6-27)

The fact that Δx is inversely proportional to Δk is no surprise; Fig. 6-5 and the accompanying discussion strongly suggest such a relationship. The simplicity of the result we have just derived is, however, pleasing.

A more fundamental relation is obtained by expressing Eq. (6-27) in terms of dynamical quantities, using $p = \hbar k$. The result is

$$\Delta x\, \Delta p = \hbar$$

(6-28)

Although we have developed this equation only with reference to one specific wave packet, it is possible to prove a much more general result. The derivation will not be discussed in detail here, but the result is as follows: No matter what amplitude function $A(k)$ is used in the construction of a wave packet, it is always true that

$$\Delta x\, \Delta p \geq \hbar$$

(6-29)

The physical content of Eq. (6-29) is as follows: If the position of a particle is known to within an uncertainty Δx, its momentum must necessarily be uncertain by an amount Δp which is *at least* as great as $\hbar/\Delta x$, and conversely. This statement is one form of a famous principle first enunciated by Werner Heisenberg in 1927 and is known as *Heisenberg's uncertainty principle*. Although the original derivation used reasoning somewhat different from the above, we see that this principle is a natural outgrowth of the description of particles in terms of waves.

Additional insight into this important principle can be gained by considering it from a purely particle point of view. In studying the motion of a classical particle, such as a rifle bullet, we have no difficulty in determining the position and velocity with great precision. (For example, we can use multiple-flash stroboscopic photography.) But, as Heisenberg pointed out, this is possible only because, on the scale of observation used in such measurements, the uncertainty required by Eq. (6-29) is so minute that it is much smaller than the experimental errors. On an atomic scale, things are quite different. Suppose we were to try to determine the position of an electron with a precision of 10^{-10} m, the order of magnitude of the dimensions of an atom, by scattering light from it. In order to have sufficient resolving power, the light would have to have a very small wavelength and correspondingly large energy and momentum per photon. If we are to "see" the electron, at least one photon must bounce off it and enter the microscope or other optical instrument we are using. But associated with the scattering of this photon, which occurs in an unpredictable direction, there is a corresponding unpredictable recoil momentum of the electron. The more closely we look, the shorter wavelength and therefore higher-energy photons we must use, and the uncertainty introduced in the electron's momentum becomes correspondingly larger. Clearly, this argument can be made more quantitative, and the result is in agreement with Eq. (6-29).

Arguments such as that in the preceding paragraph can be somewhat misleading, however, inasmuch as they imply that the particle under discussion *has* a definite position and that because of the inadequacy of our measuring instruments we are not able to determine this position precisely. But the difficulty is more fundamental than this. As the discussion of wave packets has shown, the electron or other particle is *not* a point with a definite position and momentum, but rather a wave packet, and it is not correct to say that it *has* precisely a certain position or momentum. Thus we are forced to revise our fundamental model for describing what we are accustomed to call *particles*. Although we continue to use the term *particle*, it must now be understood in this more general sense.

Consideration of attempts to measure the position of a particle with precision greater than the spatial spread of its wave packet leads to a somewhat more specific interpretation of the meaning of the wave function $\Psi(x,t)$. For the wave packet shown in Fig. 6-7, suppose we per-

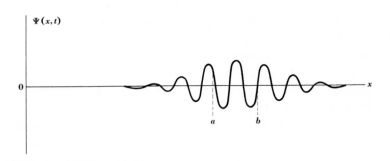

Fig. 6-7   *A wave packet. In an experiment designed to determine whether the "particle" is in the interval a to b, the probability that the measuring apparatus will interact with the particle so as to produce a wave which is localized in this interval is determined by values of the initial wave function in the interval.*

form an experiment, the details of which need not be specified, designed to determine whether the particle is in a small region of x, say between $x = a$ and $x = b$. As we have seen, this is fundamentally an improper question; a particle can be "found" in the interval between a and b only if the measuring instruments interact with the wave function in such a way as actually to localize it in this interval. Such a localization of position must be accompanied by a corresponding increase in uncertainty of momentum.

Before the measurement, it is perfectly correct to say that the particle is *partly* in the interval between a and b and partly outside this interval. After the measurement, it must be for the moment *entirely* within the interval, or else not at all, by the nature of the experiment. Clearly, the interaction is most likely to take place in such a way that the final wave function lies entirely within the interval if a substantial part of the initial wave function is in the interval. That is, in such an experiment the "particle" is most likely to be "found" at intervals where the initial wave function is large. More specifically, the probability of "finding" the particle in any interval is proportional to the square of the magnitude of the wave function in that interval. Thus we arrive at a more direct interpretation of the wave function in terms of probability of finding a particle in certain regions of space.

This last statement is subject to the danger of a variety of misinterpretations. There is a temptation to take it as implying erroneously that the particle really does have a definite position but that at various times there are various probabilities for finding it in various places. By "probability of finding a particle in a given region" we must mean the probability that, as a result of the interaction of the initial wave function with the measuring apparatus, the final wave function is localized in the interval a to b.

Thus we are led to a fundamental revision of the concept of the *state* of a system. In classical mechanics, the state of motion of a point particle is described completely by specifying its position and velocity at any instant of time, and a complete description of motion consists in specifying the position at all times. In terms of wave mechanics, this is, in general, not possible. Rather, a complete description of the state of a particle at one instant of time consists in specifying the wave function of the particle. Correspondingly, a complete description of its state of motion consists in specifying the wave function for every instant of time. In some respects this is a less precise and complete description than that of classical mechanics, but the nature of the physical world is such that this is as complete a description as it is possible to give. Thus, just as in classical mechanics the goal of a problem is frequently to find the position and velocity of a particle as functions of time, in the new *quantum mechanics* the goal is frequently to find the wave function describing a particle as it varies with time. The final section of this chapter and most of Chap. 7 will deal with this general problem.

6-5 Schrödinger Equation

In the various examples of wave phenomena discussed in Chaps. 1 and 2, it is possible to derive from basic principles a differential equation which the possible wave functions for the system concerned must obey. In the case of transverse waves on a stretched string, for example, the wave function $y(x,t)$ must satisfy the wave equation

$$\frac{\partial^2 y}{\partial x^2} = \frac{\mu}{T} \frac{\partial^2 y}{\partial t^2} \tag{6-30}$$

which is derived from Newton's laws of motion. Similarly, in the case of electromagnetic radiation, we derived from Maxwell's equations a wave equation that must be satisfied by each component of the electric and magnetic fields. For the one-dimensional waves considered in Chap. 2, the equation is

$$\frac{\partial^2 F}{\partial x^2} = \mu\epsilon \frac{\partial^2 F}{\partial t^2} \tag{6-31}$$

where F may denote any component of the electric field **E** or the magnetic field **B**.

Although we have discussed wave functions for particles in considerable detail, we have no corresponding *wave equation* governing such functions. Worse than that, we have no general principle corresponding to Newton's laws or Maxwell's equations from which to *derive* such an equation. Nevertheless, it seems reasonable that a wave equation should exist. The publication of de Broglie's wave hypothesis stimulated a great deal of discussion at various European centers of activity in research in theoretical physics. At one of these, Zurich, the eminent physical chemist Peter Debye suggested to a young German physicist named Erwin Schrödinger that he make a careful study of de Broglie's theory and present it for discussion in a seminar at Zurich. In the course of this study, Schrödinger developed the wave equation which now bears his name and which we shall now discuss. Our development will not precisely parallel Schrödinger's original work, but the principles are identical.

In searching for a wave equation, we are tempted to try an equation having the classical wave-equation form, as in Eqs. (6-30) and (6-31), which contain second derivatives with respect to both the space coordinates and time. But a little thought shows that this cannot be the correct form, inasmuch as the solutions of these equations represent waves propagating with a speed which is independent of wavelength, whereas we have already seen that for a wave representing a particle the speed of propagation *does* depend on wavelength, as shown by Eq. (6-20). However, the *form* of this dependency suggests a possible form of the wave equation. The simplest periodic wave is a sinusoidal wave, which may be written in the complex exponential form as

$$\Psi(x,t) = Ae^{i(kx-\omega t)}$$

(6-32)

in the one-dimensional case. For such a function, taking the derivative with respect to x yields the same result as multiplying by ik, while taking the derivative with respect to time is equivalent to multiplying by the factor $-i\omega$.

Now the energy relationship $E = p^2/2m$ leads, as Eq. (6-19) shows, to the wave number–frequency relation $\hbar\omega = \hbar^2 k^2/2m$. Thus for the sinusoidal wave just mentioned it must be true that

$$\hbar\omega e^{i(kx-\omega t)} = \frac{\hbar^2 k^2}{2m} e^{i(kx-\omega t)}$$

(6-33)

This relationship suggests that perhaps the differential equation which we seek contains a *first* derivative with respect to time and a *second* derivative with respect to the space coordinate, corresponding to the appearance of ω and k^2, respectively, in Eq. (6-33). This equation is made even more suggestive by rearranging it as follows:

$$-\frac{\hbar^2}{2m}(ik)^2 e^{i(kx-\omega t)} = i\hbar(-i\omega)e^{i(kx-\omega t)}$$

(6-34)

As just pointed out, this is equivalent to

$$-\frac{\hbar^2}{2m}\frac{\partial^2}{\partial x^2} e^{i(kx-\omega t)} = i\hbar\frac{\partial}{\partial t} e^{i(kx-\omega t)}$$

(6-35)

In other words, in the particular case where the wave function $\Psi(x,t)$ is a sinusoidal wave, it must satisfy the differential equation

$$-\frac{\hbar^2}{2m}\frac{\partial^2\Psi}{\partial x^2} = i\hbar\frac{\partial\Psi}{\partial t}$$

(6-36)

We have already discussed at length the representation of a wave of arbitrary shape as a superposition of sinusoidal waves. If each sinusoidal wave separately is a solution of Eq. (6-36), it is easy to show that any *sum* of such solutions is also a solution. Thus it is reasonable to surmise that Eq. (6-36) must be satisfied by *every* wave function that represents a physically possible state of the particle. All this is, of course, conjecture, and the conjecture must stand or fall by the test of experiment. It is already clear that this equation passes one experimental test, inasmuch as it is consistent with the observed relationship between energy, momentum, and wavelength for particle waves. In following chapters we shall see much more detailed evidence for the correctness of this equation. The appearance of the imaginary unit i in Eq. (6-36) is significant; it shows that in general the solutions of this equation can be expected to contain complex quantities, and it corroborates the suspicion expressed at the beginning of Sec. 6-3 that wave functions for particles need not be *real* quantities but may sometimes be *complex*.

Equation (6-36) is the *Schrödinger wave equation*. In the form presented here, it applies only to a free particle. That is, its solutions describe a particle that is the quantum-mechanical analog of a classical particle moving in a straight line with constant velocity, in the absence of interactions with any other particle. Thus this equation plays a role in quantum mechanics analogous to that of Newton's first law in classical mechanics. Most of the really crucial problems to which quantum mechanics must address itself involve interactions among particles. The electron in the hydrogen atom, for instance, moves under the action of the electrical attraction toward the nucleus. Our next task will be to understand how interactions can be introduced into the wave equation, in order to provide a means for determining the possible wave functions for a particle interacting with a force field. This area is the principal subject for discussion in the next chapter.

PROBLEMS

6-1   A "thermal neutron" is a neutron that has come to thermal equilibrium with its surroundings and therefore has, according to the equipartition principle, an average energy $\tfrac{3}{2}kT$, where k is Boltzmann's constant and T is the absolute temperature. For $T = 300°K$,

   a. What is the energy of such a particle, in electron volts?

   b. What is the wavelength of such a particle?

6-2 Scattering of high-energy electrons is used as a means of investigating the structure of nuclei. For this purpose the electrons must have a wavelength smaller than nuclear diameters (of the order of 10^{-15} m). What energy (in electron volts) must an electron have for its wavelength to be 10^{-16} m? Note that this energy is in the "extreme relativistic" range; i.e., the energy is much larger than mc^2, and so the energy and momentum are related approximately by $E = pc$.

6-3 Find the wavelength of a bullet with a mass of 5 g traveling at 300 m/sec. Do you think diffraction effects have anything to do with marksmanship?

6-4 Find the energy (in electron volts) corresponding to a wavelength of 1 Å for:
  a. A photon
  b. An electron
  c. A neutron

6-5 Plot graphs showing wavelength as a function of energy, up to about 10^4 ev, for:
  a. Photons
  b. Electrons

6-6 In the Davisson and Germer experiment, for the particular numerical data given, what electron energy would be needed to observe the second-order diffraction maximum at the same angle as the first-order maximum described?

6-7 What order-of-magnitude energy of α particles would be appropriate for crystal diffraction experiments?

6-8 Find the wave velocity and the group velocity for a wave packet described by the wave function

$$\Psi(x,t) = \frac{1}{4 + (2x - 4t)^2} \sin (\tfrac{1}{2}x - 2t)$$

6-9 For particles moving at relativistic speeds, $E^2 = p^2c^2 + m^2c^4$, and the corresponding relation for ω and k for the associated waves is $\omega^2 = c^2(k^2 + \mu^2)$, where $\mu = mc/\hbar$. Show that the wave velocity $\mu = \omega/k$ is always greater than c but that the group velocity $v = d\omega/dk$ is always less than c, and that $uv = c^2$ always.

6-10 A wave packet is constructed using the function

$$A(k) = Ae^{-b|k-k_0|} \qquad \text{where } |k - k_0| = k - k_0 \quad \text{if } k > k_0$$
$$|k - k_0| = k_0 - k \quad \text{if } k < k_0$$

Find the corresponding function $\Psi(x,0)$ at time $t = 0$ and the envelope of the function. To evaluate the integral, divide the interval of integration into two regions, $k < k_0$ and $k > k_0$. Make estimates of the "widths" of $A(k)$ and $\Psi(x,0)$ and show that $\Delta x \, \Delta k \simeq 1$.

6-11 A wave packet is constructed using for $A(k)$ a function which has the value A (a constant) when $k_0 - a < k < k_0 + a$ and is zero for values of k outside this interval. Find the corresponding function $\Psi(x,0)$ and the envelope of the function. Estimate the widths of $A(k)$ and $\Psi(x,0)$, and show that $\Delta x \, \Delta k \simeq 1$.

6-12 For the wave pulse given by Eq. (6-14) at time $t = 0$, find the general wave function $\Psi(x,t)$ for any x and t, if the wave speed is $c = \omega/k$ and is independent of k. By examining the resulting wave function, show that in this case the wave and group velocities are equal.

6-13 Show that the wave function obtained in Prob. 6-12 is a solution of the wave equation

$$\frac{\partial^2 \Psi}{\partial x^2} = \frac{1}{c^2} \frac{\partial^2 \Psi}{\partial t^2}$$

6-14 Find the uncertainty in momentum for an electron with energy of 10 ev and an uncertainty of position of 10^{-10} m, quantities characteristic of electrons in atoms. Compare this momentum uncertainty with the momentum of an electron in a hydrogen atom in the $n = 1$ state.

6-15 An electron in a television picture tube emerges from a hole of 1.0-mm diameter with an energy of 10^4 ev. Calculate the uncertainty in the transverse component of momentum, and from this find the uncertainty of the point where the electron strikes the screen, 0.25 m away. Is this uncertainty likely to have significant effects on the quality of the picture?

6-16 For a particle which has an uncertainty in position equal to its de Broglie wavelength, find the corresponding uncertainty in velocity, and compare with the magnitude of the velocity.

6-17 The minuteness of detail that can be seen with a microscope is limited by the wavelength of the radiation used. To "see" the internal structure of an atom one would have to use "light" with a wavelength of the order of 0.1 Å. If an electron is "seen" by using this method, find the uncertainty of momentum of the electron:
a. By using the uncertainty principle directly
b. By considering the momentum transfer to the electron in a head-on collision with a photon of the specified wavelength

6-18 Repeat Prob. 6-17, using an electron instead of a photon.

6-19 Show that any function in the form

$$\Psi(x,t) = A e^{i(kx - \omega t)}$$

is a solution of Eq. (6-36), provided ω is given by $\hbar\omega = \hbar^2 k^2/2m$.

6-20 Show that if $\Psi_1(x,t)$ and $\Psi_2(x,t)$ are solutions of Eq. (6-36) then the sum $\Psi_1 + \Psi_2$ is also a solution. This important result shows that "matter waves" obey the principle of superposition, so useful in calculations of optical phenomena.

6-21 Show that Eq. (6-36) has solutions in the form

$$\Psi(x,t) = e^{at} f(x)$$

Find the function $f(x)$. Do you think such solutions are likely to be physically meaningful? Explain.

IN THE NEW system of mechanics known as quantum mechanics, the fundamental description of the state of a system is given in terms of a wave function for the system. Some wave functions describe a state corresponding to a mixture of values of momentum, or energy, or other dynamical quantities. For any given system, Schrödinger's equation, together with some auxiliary conditions, determines the possible wave functions that can describe this system and, at the same time, determines the possible energy states. We examine solutions of Schrödinger's equation for two specific systems, a particle in a box and the harmonic oscillator. Finally, we discuss the fact that in some cases other dynamical quantities such as angular momentum are "quantized," and we discuss briefly the general operator formalism by which allowed values of these quantized quantities can be determined. This chapter provides the foundation for the discussion of atomic structure in the following chapters.

7-1   State of a System
For the sake of simplicity in the exposition of general principles, we shall consider in this chapter only systems that would be described

classically as a particle moving in one dimension, as, for example, a bead sliding along a straight wire. Correspondingly, the quantum-mechanical description of such a system makes use of a wave function $\Psi(x,t)$ which is a function of one space coordinate and time. In accordance with the basic concepts presented in Chap. 6, we regard $\Psi(x,t)$ as a complete description of the state of the system. That is, this wave function contains all the information that it is in principle possible to know about the system. We have already remarked that in some respects this information is somewhat less specific than the classical description of the motion of a particle, in which it is possible to describe the position and velocity at every instant of time. Nevertheless, it is now recognized that the nature of the physical world is such that this more detailed description is not always possible; this is a fact of life which must be accepted.

It is already clear that the spatial dependence of the function $\Psi(x,t)$ shows how the particle is distributed in space. More specifically, since $\Psi(x,t)$ may be positive or negative, real or complex, it is reasonable to suppose that the quantity $\Psi^*\Psi = |\Psi|^2$ at a given point in space represents the extent to which the particle is localized in the vicinity of that point. This dependence on the square of the absolute value of the wave function is analogous to the situation in optics, where the *intensity* of a wave, which determines the rate of energy transmission, is proportional to the square of the electric-field amplitude.

The statement is often made that, when one performs an experiment designed to ascertain whether or not a particle is in a particular small interval of space Δx, the *probability* that the particle will be found in this interval is given by

$$\Psi^*\Psi \, \Delta x \tag{7-1}$$

This statement requires further explanation. First, in the course of any such experiment, the wave function is disturbed so that after the experiment, if the particle has been found in the interval, the final wave function describing the system *is* concentrated entirely in the interval Δx. This does *not* mean that the particle was in this interval before the experiment. As we have already seen, the particle had no definite location before the experiment. The point is that, in the interaction between the system and the measuring apparatus, the wave function describing the system is most likely to be transformed into one concentrated in the interval Δx if the quantity $\Psi^*\Psi$ was initially large in that interval. It is in this sense that Eq. (7-1) represents the probability that the particle will be found in this interval.

The wave function can also be used to obtain information about the *momentum* of the particle in a certain state. As we have seen, a wave function with a mixture of different values of momentum can be represented as

$$\Psi(x,t) = \int_{-\infty}^{\infty} A(k) e^{i(kx-\omega t)}\, dk \tag{7-2}$$

Clearly, the function $A(k)$ represents the extent to which the particle's momentum is in the vicinity of that corresponding to the wave number k, that is, $\hbar k$. In fact, in the same sense that the term probability was used above, $A^*(k)A(k)\,\Delta k$ represents the probability that, in a measurement of the momentum of the particle, it will be found to have a momentum in the interval corresponding to the wave-number interval Δk. Again, this is not to say that the particle actually *has* this momentum before the experiment is made; before the experiment it has, in general, a mixture of values of momentum, and it is given a definite momentum in the course of the experiment only because the measuring apparatus changes the wave function.

Equation (7-2) shows how the wave function $\Psi(x,t)$ is represented in terms of the momentum distribution $A(k)$; conversely, if $\Psi(x,t)$ is known, $A(k)$ can be found. In the language of Fourier analysis, each of these is the Fourier transform of the other. The inverse relation to Eq. (7-2), which we state here without proof, is

$$A(k) = \frac{1}{2\pi} \int_{-\infty}^{\infty} \Psi(x,0) e^{-ikx}\, dx \tag{7-3}$$

Later in this chapter we shall see how other kinds of information can be extracted from the wave function, such as information concerning the angular momentum of the particle.

As we have seen in Chap. 6, some wave functions correspond to states having definite energy; for free particles without interactions such states are described by sinusoidal waves which are not localized at all in space. Correspondingly, when one uses a mixture of values of k to construct a wave packet that *is* localized in space, such a packet does *not* have a definite momentum or energy. With particles which are *bound*, such as electrons in atoms, we expect the situation to be quite different. Atoms certainly have fairly definite sizes; at least they are not spread over all space. There is also conclusive evidence that atoms have definite energy levels. Therefore, we expect that for a particle attracted toward a center of force, such as an electron in an atom, there are wave functions describing possible states of the system which correspond to definite energies and which are nonetheless *bounded* in space.

We now summarize the general problems that lie ahead. Pursuing the idea that wave functions describing possible states of a system are solutions of a certain differential equation, we first evolve a wave equation that includes interactions of the particle with a force field. This equation is the quantum-mechanical analog of Newton's second law, whereas the Schrödinger equation for a free particle, as already observed, is the analog of Newton's first law. Having developed this equation, we must then find functions that are solutions and therefore represent possible states of the system. In the process, we hope to be able to predict the energy levels of the possible states. Finally, we shall use the wave functions so obtained to develop whatever additional information is needed concerning particular states of the system.

7-2   *Particle in a Box*

As is often the case with physical theories, the problems of greatest real physical interest are not always those which are easiest to deal with. Often, in a first encounter with new principles, it is profitable to consider a few particularly simple applications as illustrations of the principles. The following simple problem is a useful illustration of some new ideas not found in the discussion of wave functions for a free particle. We consider a particle which moves along the x axis and is restricted to the interval $-L \leq x \leq L$ by rigid walls at $x = \pm L$, as shown in Fig. 7-1. This situation could be a model for a bead sliding along a perfectly

Fig. 7-1   Particle in a one-dimensional box of width 2L. The particle is confined to the region $-L < x < +L$; the wave function must become zero at $x = \pm L$. An alternative statement of the problem is a particle in a force field such that the potential energy is zero for $-L < x < +L$ but is infinite outside these limits. Such a potential-energy function is called a potential well.

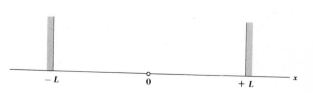

smooth straight wire with rigid barriers at $x = \pm L$. What are the wave functions for the possible states of this system, and what are their characteristics?

We begin by searching for states having a definite energy E. As we have seen, any such state is represented by a wave function whose time dependence consists of a sinusoidal variation with frequency ω related to the energy by $E = \hbar\omega$. Such a function may therefore be expressed as

$$\Psi(x,t) = e^{-i\omega t}\psi(x) \tag{7-4}$$

where the function $\psi(x)$ does not contain the variable t. Substituting Eq. (7-4) into the Schrödinger equation (6-36), we obtain

$$-\frac{\hbar^2}{2m}\frac{\partial^2\psi}{\partial x^2}e^{-i\omega t} = i\hbar\psi\frac{\partial}{\partial t}e^{-i\omega t}$$

$$= \hbar\omega\psi e^{-i\omega t} = E\psi e^{-i\omega t} \tag{7-5}$$

That is, $\Psi(x,t)$ is a solution of the Schrödinger equation if and only if $\psi(x)$ satisfies the equation

$$-\frac{\hbar^2}{2m}\frac{\partial^2\psi}{\partial x^2} = E\psi \tag{7-6}$$

which is usually called the *time-independent Schrödinger equation*. In the following discussion the capital letter Ψ is always used for the complete wave function, which contains both x and t, and the lowercase letter ψ for the corresponding time-independent function.

Equation (7-6) may be rewritten

$$\frac{\partial^2\psi}{\partial x^2} = -\frac{2mE}{\hbar^2}\psi \tag{7-7}$$

from which it is evident that the possible solutions have the form

$$\psi(x) = A\begin{Bmatrix}\sin\\\cos\end{Bmatrix}\sqrt{\frac{2mE}{\hbar^2}}\,x \tag{7-8}$$

where A is a constant. Furthermore, these are solutions of the equation for every possible value of E, and so this does not yet tell us anything about permissible values of E.

There is, however, a new consideration which did not enter the discussion of the completely free particle in Sec. 6-5. Since in the present case the particle is confined between the limits $x = \pm L$, the wave function must be zero whenever $x > L$ or $x < -L$. Furthermore, it is reasonable to require that the wave function should be a *continuous* function of x. The necessity of this requirement is perhaps not completely obvious at this point, and in fact the continuity requirement must be regarded as an additional assumption. Continuity of wave function will be discussed in more detail in the following sections; meanwhile, we make use of this requirement in the present problem. To satisfy this continuity condition, the function must become zero at the points $x = \pm L$. That is, we have the additional requirements that

$$\psi(L) = \psi(-L) = 0 \tag{7-9}$$

These requirements are analogous to the boundary conditions for a vibrating string with fixed ends, which lead to the normal modes of vibration.

Clearly, Eqs. (7-9) will not be satisfied in general for all the possible functions given by Eq. (7-8). We must next find the particular values of E such that Eqs. (7-9) are satisfied. Considering first the sine functions, we must have

$$\sin \frac{\sqrt{2mE}}{\hbar} L = 0 \tag{7-10}$$

and this is true only when

$$\frac{\sqrt{2mE}}{\hbar} L = n\pi \qquad n = 1, 2, 3, \ldots \tag{7-11}$$

There is an additional possibility when $E = 0$, but that leads to a wave function that is zero everywhere and therefore has no physical meaning. Solving Eq. (7-11) for E, we find that the possible energies E_n are given by

$$E_n = \frac{1}{2m} \left(\frac{\pi \hbar}{L} \right)^2 n^2 \qquad n = 1, 2, 3, \ldots \tag{7-12}$$

and the corresponding wave functions, which we may call $\psi_n(x)$, are given by

$$\psi_n(x) = A \sin \frac{n\pi}{L} x \tag{7-13}$$

Writing the wave function in this form makes it easy to see that Eq. (7-9) is satisfied.

This whole development can be repeated for the cosine functions. The resulting energy levels and corresponding wave functions are

$$E_n = \frac{1}{2m}\left(\frac{\pi\hbar}{L}\right)^2 (n - \tfrac{1}{2})^2 \qquad n = 1, 2, 3, \ldots$$

$$\psi_n(x) = A \cos \frac{(n - \tfrac{1}{2})\pi}{L} x$$

(7-14)

Development of these results is left as a problem.

Several wave functions in each of these series are shown in Fig. 7-2. We note that in each series there is a direct relationship between the integer n and the number of nodes in the corresponding wave functions. This figure illustrates graphically the analogy with the vibrating string mentioned earlier.

We discussed in Sec. 7-1 the interpretation of the quantity $\Psi^*\Psi \, dx$ as the probability of finding the particle in the interval dx. Referring

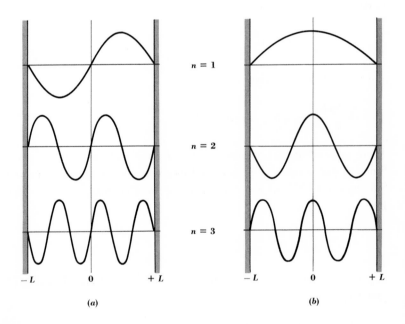

$n = 1$

$n = 2$

$n = 3$

$-L$ 0 $+L$

(a)

$-L$ 0 $+L$

(b)

Fig. 7-2 *Wave functions for a particle in a box. (a) Sine functions; (b) cosine functions. For each value of n, the sine function has higher energy than the cosine function, as shown by Eqs. (7-12) and (7-14).*

to Eq. (7-4), we see immediately that $\Psi^*(x,t)\Psi(x,t) = \psi^*(x)\psi(x)$, which shows that for any state having definite energy the probability distribution is independent of time. It is customary to define probabilities in such a way that the *total* probability for all possible events is unity. This corresponds to saying that the probability of finding the particle *somewhere* in the region $-L \leq x \leq +L$ is unity. Thus it is convenient to choose the constant A in Eq. (7-8) in such a way that

$$\int_{-L}^{L} \psi^*(x)\psi(x)\, dx = 1 \tag{7-15}$$

Since we are dealing here with functions that are real numbers, the functions $\psi^*(x)$ and $\psi(x)$ are equal, and for Eq. (7-13) the requirement given by Eq. (7-15) becomes

$$\int_{-L}^{L} A^2 \sin^2 \frac{n\pi}{L} x\, dx = 1 \tag{7-16}$$

This integral may be evaluated by standard methods, the details of which need not be given here. The result is that Eq. (7-16) is satisfied by choosing $A = L^{-1/2}$; this also turns out to be the correct choice for the wave functions given by Eq. (7-14).

A wave function that satisfies Eq. (7-15) is said to be *normalized*. For a variety of reasons, it is usually convenient to deal with normalized wave functions wherever possible, and we shall do so in all future discussions. Thus, the normalized wave functions corresponding to possible states for a particle moving according to the conditions of this problem are

$$\psi_n(x) = \frac{1}{\sqrt{L}} \sin \frac{n\pi}{L} x \qquad n = 1, 2, 3, \ldots$$

$$\psi_n(x) = \frac{1}{\sqrt{L}} \cos \frac{(n - \tfrac{1}{2})\pi}{L} x \qquad n = 1, 2, 3, \ldots \tag{7-17}$$

To summarize the above procedure, we obtained a doubly infinite set of solutions for the differential equation governing wave functions for this problem. From this infinite set, we selected two series of functions satisfying not only the differential equation but also the *boundary conditions* resulting from the continuity condition. While the differential equation itself is satisfied for *any* value of E in the solutions, only for a certain discrete set of values of E is it possible to satisfy *both* the differential equation and the boundary conditions. This situation is typical of those found in solutions of Schrödinger's equation. In Sec. 7-5 we shall consider a similar problem but one in which the boundary condition is of a somewhat more subtle nature. The problem discussed there is the harmonic oscillator, in which there is a potential-energy function $\frac{1}{2}kx^2$, and the boundary condition is simply that the wave function should *approach* zero at distances very far away from the center of force, rather than that it should be zero at some finite distance. Before discussing this problem, however, we need to develop methods for finding the differential equation corresponding to any given force field. This is the subject of the next section.

7-3 *Schrödinger Equation with Interactions*

The preceding sections have been devoted to the development of a wave equation that governs the possible wave functions for a free particle, the quantum-mechanical analog of a classical particle moving with uniform velocity, in the absence of forces. Now we shall generalize this equation to include the possibility of interaction of the particle with its surroundings by means of a force field. As mentioned previously, this more general equation corresponds to Newton's second law in classical mechanics, just as the free-particle wave equation already discussed corresponds to Newton's first law.

It should be pointed out that the experimental evidence on which this new equation is based is of a rather indirect nature, consisting mostly of data on energy levels of atoms, together with the observation that free particles behave like waves with a wavelength related directly to their momentum and energy. From such data it is not possible to *derive* the general dynamical law without making a bold guess at some point, just as 300 years ago it required the genius of Newton to make the leap from a mass of empirical data on planetary and terrestrial motion to a compact set of dynamical laws. Equipped with the hindsight provided by the 40-year history of quantum mechanics, we can try to make this new dynamical law look reasonable, but it would be misleading to pretend that it can be rigorously derived. Rather, it must be regarded basically as a brilliant intuitive guess that is justified by the correctness of the results derived from it.

As with the free-particle discussion, we restrict our attention for the present to motion in only one space dimension with coordinate x. In addition, we consider only an interaction which can be described as a conservative force field,[1] that is, a force $F(x)$ which is a function only of position and can be represented in terms of a potential-energy function

[1] See H. D. Young, "Fundamentals of Mechanics and Heat," sec. 9-6, McGraw-Hill Book Company, New York, 1964.

$V(x)$, where $F(x) = -dV/dx$. A familiar example from classical mechanics is the spring force in a harmonic oscillator, $F = -kx$, with corresponding potential energy $V = \frac{1}{2}kx^2$. The restriction to conservative force fields is justified at least in part by the fact that many of the important interactions between particles, including electrical and gravitational interactions, are represented by conservative force fields.

In general, a particle does not have a definite position, and so neither will it have a definite potential energy V at any instant. But the particle's momentum and thus its kinetic energy are also uncertain, and so perhaps it is possible to have a state with definite *total* energy, despite the fact that kinetic or potential energy separately may not have a definite value. Thus the classical concept of potential energy can be taken over into quantum-mechanical problems without difficulty.

Because a particle has both kinetic and potential energies, it is not obvious which of these, if either, should be used to determine the *frequency* of the wave function. In making the choice we are guided by the analogous situation in classical wave propagation; when a wave in one medium enters another medium in which the wave speed is different, its wavelength changes but its frequency is the same in both media. It is not entirely unreasonable to expect a similar state of affairs with "matter waves." At each point x the wave function is some periodic function of time, and in analogy with the classical wave situation we expect the *frequency* of this time dependence to be the same at various points even though the potential energy is, in general, different. For this to be true, the frequency must be determined by the *total* energy of the system. This observation provides an important clue to the development of the generalized wave equation.

In developing the free-particle wave equation in Sec. 6-5 we wrote the energy-momentum relation $p^2/2m = E$ as a wave number–frequency relation $\hbar^2 k^2/2m = \hbar\omega$. Then associating ik with the operation $\partial/\partial x$ and $-i\omega$ with the operation $\partial/\partial t$ led to the wave equation

$$-\frac{\hbar^2}{2m}\frac{\partial^2 \Psi}{\partial x^2} = i\hbar\frac{\partial \Psi}{\partial t} \tag{7-18}$$

We now retrace this path; the energy-momentum relation is

$$\frac{p^2}{2m} + V(x) = E \tag{7-19}$$

expressing the fact that for a conservative system the sum of kinetic and potential energies is the constant E. The corresponding wave number–frequency relation, associating frequency with total energy as discussed above, is

$$\frac{\hbar^2 k^2}{2m} + V = \hbar\omega \tag{7-20}$$

Making the same associations $ik \leftrightarrow \partial/\partial x$ and $-i\omega \leftrightarrow \partial/\partial t$ as before, we obtain the equation

$$-\frac{\hbar^2}{2m}\frac{\partial^2\Psi}{\partial x^2} + V\Psi = i\hbar\frac{\partial\Psi}{\partial t} \tag{7-21}$$

which differs from the free-particle Schrödinger equation, Eq. (6-36), in having the additional term containing the potential energy. In Eq. (7-21) the functional dependence of $V(x)$ and $\Psi(x,t)$ is not shown explicitly.

Equation (7-21) is thus a more general form of *Schrödinger's equation*. With one further generalization, to be discussed in Sec. 7-6, it provides the key to the application of the ideas of quantum mechanics to a wide variety of systems. Solutions for this equation contain, in principle, all there is to know about the structure of atoms, including electron configurations, energy levels, and so on. To be sure, applications of this equation to some problems pose formidable mathematical difficulties, but as far as *principles* are concerned, we are now well on our way to an understanding of atomic structure.

We now return briefly to the continuity condition introduced in Sec. 7-2. Clearly, for any physically possible state of the system, Eq. (7-21) must be satisfied at every value of x and at every instant of time. Thus it is necessary for the derivatives $\partial^2\Psi/\partial x^2$ and $\partial\Psi/\partial t$ to *exist* for all x and t; a sufficient condition for the existence of these derivatives is for Ψ to be a *continuous* function of x and t, and for $\partial\Psi/\partial x$ also to be a continuous function. The only exception to this requirement occurs when $V(x)$ has an infinite discontinuity; at such a point it can be shown that it is sufficient for Ψ itself to be continuous.

Any wave function corresponding to a state having definite total energy E has a definite frequency $\omega = E/\hbar$; the time dependence of such a wave function is contained in a factor

$$e^{-i\omega t} = e^{-iEt/\hbar} \tag{7-22}$$

just as for a free particle. Thus any wave function $\Psi(x,t)$ representing a state with a definite, constant total energy E can be written in the form

$$\Psi(x,t) = e^{-iEt/\hbar}\psi(x) \tag{7-23}$$

where the function $\psi(x)$ must satisfy the differential equation

$$-\frac{\hbar^2}{2m}\frac{d^2\psi(x)}{dx^2} + V(x)\psi(x) = E\psi(x) \tag{7-24}$$

in which the factor $e^{-iEt/\hbar}$ has been divided out from the previous equations. This equation is usually called the *time-independent Schrödinger equation.* It is less general than Eq. (7-21) because it is valid only for states that have constant total energy. Nevertheless, one of the important problems in atomic structure is to predict energy levels, and so this is a useful equation.

7-4   *Solutions of Schrödinger Equation*

Many of the most important problems of quantum mechanics are concerned directly with finding and interpreting the solutions of Eq. (7-24) or a similar equation for problems in three dimensions. Solving such equations often involves considerable mathematical complexity, and we shall consider only a few particularly simple examples. First, however, it is instructive to make a qualitative study of properties of solutions corresponding to certain simple kinds of potential-energy functions. In this preliminary discussion the relation between classical and quantum-mechanical descriptions of motion will be emphasized.

First, as already shown in the "particle-in-a-box" problem, in any region where the potential energy V is *constant,* the solution of Eq. (7-24) is a sinusoidal function; the equation then takes the form

$$-\frac{\hbar^2}{2m}\frac{d^2\psi}{dx^2} + V\psi = E\psi$$

or

$$\frac{d^2\psi}{dx^2} + \frac{2m(E-V)}{\hbar^2}\psi = 0 \tag{7-25}$$

The solutions of this equation can be written

$$\psi(x) = A\begin{Bmatrix} \sin \\ \cos \end{Bmatrix}kx \tag{7-26}$$

where k is the wave number, related to the wavelength λ as usual by $k = 2\pi/\lambda$, and A is a constant amplitude factor. Substitution of Eq. (7-26) into Eq. (7-25) shows that the wave number is given by

$$k^2 = \frac{2m(E-V)}{\hbar^2} \tag{7-27}$$

and the corresponding wavelength is

$$\lambda = \frac{h}{\sqrt{2m(E - V)}} \tag{7-28}$$

We note that this result agrees with the de Broglie relation $\lambda = h/p$, with the momentum p determined from the energy relation $p^2/2m + V = E$.

Using this result, we can predict some general features of wave functions corresponding to a potential-energy function, such as that shown in Fig. 7-3. In each of the two regions the potential energy is constant; the constant total energy E is also shown. According to Eq. (7-28), the wave function for $x > 0$ should have a longer wavelength than in the region $x < 0$. Furthermore, since the particle's *speed* is greater in the region where $V = 0$ than in the region where it is V_0, it spends a relatively smaller time on the left side than the right; hence we expect the *amplitude* of the wave function to be smaller on the left than the right. The general behavior of the wave function is shown in Fig. 7-3b. We also note that different amplitudes for the two sides are necessary in order for the two functions to join smoothly at $x = 0$, as required by the continuity condition that the function and its first derivative must be continuous at $x = 0$.

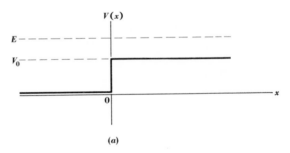

(a)

Fig. 7-3 (a) A two-level potential-energy function. The broken line labeled E represents the constant total energy, and the distance between this and the potential-energy line represents the kinetic energy. (b) A possible wave function. The left side is a region of larger kinetic energy and correspondingly shorter wavelength and smaller amplitude than the right side; the two functions must join smoothly at $x = 0$.

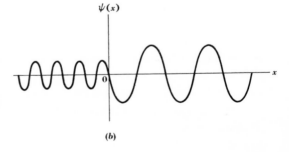

(b)

When the total energy E is *less than* V_0, a new consideration enters. In classical mechanics, for the potential energy to be greater than the total energy, the kinetic energy would have to be negative; this is impossible, and so classically a particle can never enter such a region. But Eq. (7-25) still has solutions in this region; the coefficient of ψ is now negative, so that the solutions are not sinusoidal but rather real exponential functions. The reader can verify that the appropriate solutions are

$$\psi(x) = Ae^{\pm \gamma x}$$

with

$$\gamma^2 = \frac{2m(V_0 - E)}{\hbar^2} \tag{7-29}$$

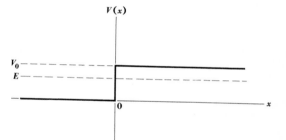

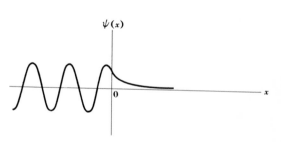

Fig. 7-4 *A possible wave function for the two-level potential energy function of Fig. 7-3a for the case $E < V_0$. The function is sinusoidal in the region of positive kinetic energy and exponential in the region of negative potential energy; the two functions must join smoothly at $x = 0$.*

In the present problem, the function with the positive exponent is not physically reasonable since it grows large without bound in the classically forbidden region $x > 0$. Thus the wave function for $x > 0$ must be a decaying exponential function. According to the continuity condition, this must join smoothly onto the sinusoidal solution for $x < 0$, so that the solutions have the general form shown in Fig. 7-4. As this figure shows, there is some penetration of the wave function into the region of negative kinetic energy, a phenomenon which has no analog in classical mechanics.

An even more striking situation occurs when two regions of positive kinetic energy are separated by a potential-energy barrier of height greater than the total energy, as shown in Fig. 7-5. In the central region the wave function is exponential, and in the side regions sinusoidal; at each boundary the function and its first derivative are continuous. Such a function, representing a state of definite total energy, is not localized in

Fig. 7-5 (a) A potential-energy barrier. A particle whose energy E is less than the height V_0 of the barrier can move from one side to the other even though they are separated by a region of negative kinetic energy. (b) A possible wave function. This function is sinusoidal on each side and exponential in the middle. The functions must join smoothly at each boundary.

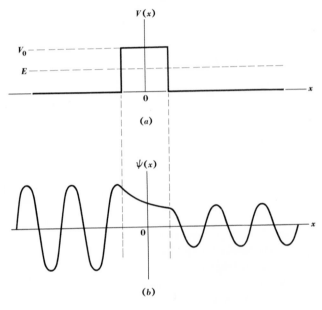

space. However, just as for free particles, a wave packet can be constructed by superposing several wave functions with slightly different energies and a corresponding spread of wavelengths. As we have seen, these functions are not precisely zero in the classically forbidden region. Thus if such a wave packet approaches a potential barrier, there is a finite probability that it will appear at a later time on the opposite side of the barrier! This behavior, which again has no analog in classical mechanics, has been described as "tunneling through a potential hill" which could not be surmounted classically. Although this phenomenon makes no sense in the context of classical mechanics, it is a very real quantum-mechanical phenomenon. It is by this mechanism that α particles are emitted by radioactive nuclei despite the potential-energy barriers that bind the particles to their nuclei.   In the electronic circuit device called the *tunnel diode,* electrons traverse a region of negative kinetic energy in traveling from one region of the device to another.

For the potential-energy functions considered thus far in this section, the particle is not *bound* in the sense of being localized permanently in a certain region of space.   Correspondingly, there are no restrictions on the possible energy states of the particle, since the continuity conditions for the wave function can be satisfied for any choice of energy.   Conversely, however, the particle-in-a-box problem of Sec. 7-2 showed that there are problems in which the particle *is* localized or "bound" and in which the appropriate boundary conditions can be satisfied only with certain particular values of total energy.   To illustrate this situation further, we consider the potential-energy situation shown in Fig. 7-6a and the corresponding wave functions for total energy E less than V_0.

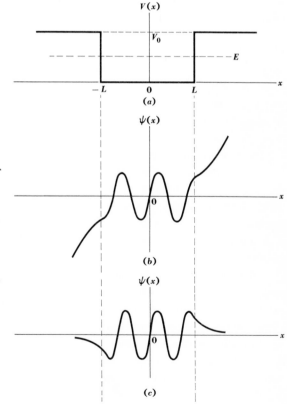

Fig. 7-6   (a) *A potential well of finite depth.   (b) An impossible wave function.   For the energy chosen, boundary conditions require growing exponentials in the end regions, which have no physical meaning.   Hence this energy is not one of the permitted energy levels for the system.   (c) A possible wave function. The function is sinusoidal in the central region and a decaying exponential on each end.   The functions must join smoothly at the boundaries.*

Just as before, the solution of the Schrödinger equation is sinusoidal in the region $-L < x < +L$ and exponential in the other two regions. One can think of constructing the wave function graphically or numerically by the following procedure. We pick a value of $\psi(x)$ at $x = 0$; this determines the value of the second derivative and therefore of the curvature at this point. We draw a short segment of curve corresponding to this curvature, and from this we determine the value of $\psi(x)$ at a neighboring point. This value in turn determines the curvature at this point, and so the curve may be extended another small interval. Repeating this procedure, we can construct the entire function. Just such a procedure is often used in solutions of differential equations by digital computer. The Schrödinger equation shows that in the central region where $E - V_0 > 0$ the function is concave downward whenever it is positive, and concave upward whenever it is negative. At each point where it crosses the x axis the second derivative is zero; such points are therefore points of inflection.

For points outside the central region the situation is reversed. When ψ is positive the function is concave upward. Thus it is entirely possible that the continuation of the function generated according to the above procedure will increase without bound for $x > L$, as shown in Fig. 7-6b. But it has already been pointed out that such a function is not physically reasonable. The only way out of this dilemma is to conclude that when such a result occurs the original choice of the total energy E was incompatible with the physically possible states of the system. We should choose a different E, repeat the construction of the wave function, and continue this procedure until we find a value of E for which the function and its slope have at $x = L$ just the right values for the function to approach zero asymptotically for large x, as in Fig. 7-6c. By the trial-and-error method, it is possible in principle to discover the energy levels of a system, and this procedure shows explicitly the role the boundary conditions play in determining these levels. Of course, it is often possible to arrive at the same results by more analytical methods.

It is easy to see how this general discussion can be extended to problems in which the potential-energy function $V(x)$ is a continuously varying function rather than a series of steps. It is still true that in the vicinity of any given point the function behaves like a segment of a sinusoidal function with a wavelength characteristic of the kinetic energy at that point, according to Eq. (7-28). For some functions the potential energy may vary sufficiently rapidly compared with a wavelength so that the resulting wave function bears little resemblance to a sinusoidal function. Still, the concept of a "locally sinusoidal" wave often is a useful one; this viewpoint is helpful in understanding the properties of the wave functions for the quantum-mechanical harmonic oscillator to be discussed in the next section.

7-5   *Harmonic Oscillator*

To illustrate some additional principles and techniques in finding solutions of the Schrödinger equation, we now consider a quantum-mechanical analysis of the harmonic oscillator. In classical mechanics, we recall, the idealized harmonic oscillator consists of a point mass m attracted to a center of force at the origin ($x = 0$) with a force given by $F = -kx$, where x is the displacement from the origin and k is the force constant. Correspondingly, the potential energy of the particle at point x is $V(x) = \frac{1}{2}kx^2$. Application of Newton's second law leads to the differential equation

$$\frac{d^2x}{dt^2} + \frac{k}{m}x = 0 \tag{7-30}$$

whose solutions are

$$x = A \cos(\omega t + \phi) \qquad \omega = \sqrt{\frac{k}{m}} \tag{7-31}$$

where A and ϕ are constants, and ω is the usual angular frequency, determined by the mass and force constant as shown. In the quantum-mechanical discussion which follows, we continue to use ω as an abbreviation for the quantity $(k/m)^{1/2}$ even though this quantity does not have the direct significance of a frequency that it has in the classical case.

Just as in newtonian mechanics, the harmonic oscillator in quantum mechanics is of considerable importance, not only because situations involving harmonic motion occur frequently, but also because there are a great many situations in which the harmonic oscillator provides a simplified model of a more complicated phenomenon. Planck, in his original work on radiation, represented the sources of radiation as harmonic oscillators with various frequencies. In connection with this work, we recall that energy is emitted by these oscillators in bundles of size $hf = \hbar\omega$. Thus it would not be surprising if the energy levels of a quantum-mechanical harmonic oscillator turned out to have energy levels separated by spacing $\hbar\omega$ between adjacent levels. Indeed, it would be somewhat surprising if the result were otherwise.

In accordance with the discussion of Sec. 7-3, the wave functions representing states of definite total energy should be solutions of the time-independent Schrödinger equation, which for the present problem takes the form

$$-\frac{\hbar^2}{2m}\frac{d^2\psi}{dx^2} + \frac{1}{2}kx^2\psi = E\psi \tag{7-32}$$

This equation becomes considerably easier to handle if we make two changes of variable. To accomplish this, we multiply the entire equation by the factor

$$\frac{2}{\hbar\omega} = \frac{2}{\hbar}\sqrt{\frac{m}{k}} \tag{7-33}$$

obtaining the following result:

$$-\frac{\hbar}{\sqrt{mk}}\frac{d^2\psi}{dx^2} + \frac{\sqrt{mk}}{\hbar}x^2\psi = \frac{2E}{\hbar\omega}\psi \tag{7-34}$$

The form of this equation suggests the following substitutions:

$$y^2 = \frac{\sqrt{mk}}{\hbar}x^2 \qquad \alpha = \frac{2E}{\hbar\omega} \tag{7-35}$$

This step has the advantage that the new variables y and α are *dimensionless* quantities. Proof of this statement is left as a problem. The change of variable from x to y simply corresponds to changing the scale of measurement of length, and changing from E to α corresponds to measuring energy in different units.

In terms of the new variables, the wave equation becomes

$$\frac{d^2\psi}{dy^2} = (y^2 - \alpha)\psi \tag{7-36}$$

There are well-known, although not elementary, techniques for solving this equation. Before we discuss the solutions, however, let us discuss their general nature, especially with respect to the question whether the solutions represent particles that are localized in space.

First, we consider only positive values of y and observe that the *sign* of the second derivative tells whether the function is concave upward or downward. When the second derivative is greater than zero the function is concave upward, and conversely. The equation shows that, whenever $y^2 > \alpha$, the second derivative has the same sign as the function itself, while for $y^2 < \alpha$ the two have opposite signs. The critical point $y^2 = \alpha$ has a special significance; reference to Eqs. (7-35) shows that at this point

$$\frac{\sqrt{mk}}{\hbar} x^2 = \frac{2E}{\hbar \omega}$$

Since $\omega = (k/m)^{1/2}$, this can be rewritten

$$\tfrac{1}{2} kx^2 = E$$

That is, at this point, or rather at these two points, since x can be positive or negative, the potential energy $\tfrac{1}{2}kx^2$ is equal to the total energy; this therefore represents the classical limit of motion.   The regions $y^2 > \alpha$ correspond to the classically forbidden regions of negative kinetic energy.   If the function is to represent a particle localized in space, it must approach zero in these regions.   Thus it is instructive to examine the behavior in the region $y^2 > \alpha$.

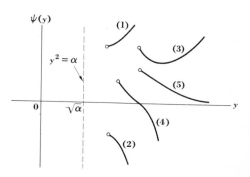

Fig. 7-7 *Behavior of solutions of Eq. (7-36) in the region $y^2 > \alpha$, in which the function and its second derivative always have the same sign.   In general, the function is unbounded for large values of y; only in the special cases where the function approaches the y axis asymptotically does a bounded solution exist.*

Figure 7-7 illustrates several possibilities:

1. If at a given point in this region the function is positive and has a positive slope, the slope increases with y because the second derivative is positive, and the function increases without bound.   Clearly, such a function cannot describe a particle bound as a harmonic oscillator.

2. A similar catastrophe occurs if the function is negative and has a negative slope, as shown in the figure.

Next, suppose that at some point in the region $y^2 > \alpha$ the function is positive but has a negative slope.   Then there are several possible kinds of behavior; the magnitude of the constant α determines which of them occurs.

3. If the rate of change of slope is sufficiently *large*, the function may turn back up and again increase without bound.
4. If it is sufficiently *small*, the function will cross the axis, then turn downward, and increase in the negative direction without bound.
5. Between these is a special case in which the curve approaches the axis asymptotically, and as y increases the function becomes sufficiently close to zero so that the second derivative also approaches zero. Clearly, this behavior represents the only possible hope of describing a particle which is bound in the vicinity of $y = 0$. We see that this is a very special case and can be expected to occur only for very specific values of the constant α.

Thus, just as for the particle in a box, the admissible wave functions and corresponding energies are those which satisfy not only the wave equation but also the *boundary conditions*. For the particle in a box, the boundary condition was simply that the wave function should become zero at the walls of the box. In this case, we must require instead that the wave function *approach* zero at large values of y. Solutions of the differential equation having this property exist only for certain specific values of the constant α, and they are therefore the values corresponding to the possible states.

The admissible solutions of Eq. (7-36) and the corresponding values of α are rather simple in form. The functions all have the form $e^{-y^2/2}$ multiplied by a polynomial in powers of y which contains either only even-power terms or only odd-power terms. These polynomials are known as *Hermite polynomials*, and the functions, each consisting of a polynomial multiplied by the exponential factor, are called *Hermite functions*. For reference, the first few Hermite functions and the corresponding values of α are listed in Table 7-1. These are customarily

Table 7-1   Hermite Functions, Solutions of the Equation

$$\frac{d^2\psi}{dy^2} = (y^2 - \alpha)\psi$$

n	$\psi_n(y)$	$\alpha_n = 2n + 1$
0	$e^{-y^2/2}$	1
1	$2ye^{-y^2/2}$	3
2	$(4y^2 - 2)e^{-y^2/2}$	5
3	$(8y^3 - 12y)e^{-y^2/2}$	7
4	$(16y^4 - 48y^2 + 12)e^{-y^2/2}$	9
5	$(32y^5 - 160y^3 + 120y)e^{-y^2/2}$	11

labeled according to the maximum power of y that appears in the polynomial, which is n in the table. The corresponding functions are then called $\psi_n(y)$ and the corresponding values of α are $\alpha_n = 2n + 1$. As the table shows, it is customary to define the Hermite functions so that the coefficient of the highest power of y in the polynomial is equal to 2^n in each case. When defined in this way, the functions are not normalized in the sense of Sec. 7-2. To normalize them it is necessary to multiply each function $\psi_n(y)$ by a numerical factor, but this is a mathematical detail. Graphs of the first few Hermite functions are shown in Fig. 7-8. For each, the corresponding "classical limits" of motion are shown as broken lines. As discussed earlier, these are points of inflection of the curve.

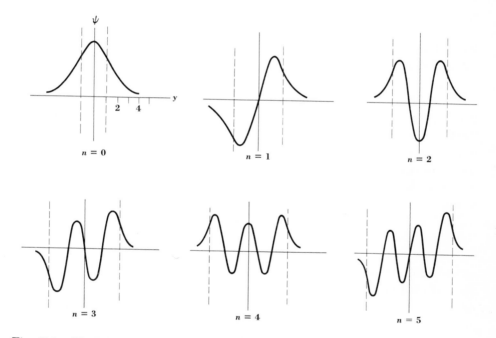

Fig. 7-8   *The first six harmonic-oscillator wave functions. These are graphs of the Hermite functions in Table 7-1. The number of nodes in each function is equal to the quantum number n. The scale for y is the same for all functions, but the vertical scales are different. The classical limits of motion are shown as broken lines; these correspond to inflection points on the curves, and are determined in each case by the condition $y^2 = \alpha = 2n + 1$.*

Table 7-1 also shows another important result. The permissible values of α are given by the expression $\alpha_n = 2n + 1$. Returning to the second of Eqs. (7-35) we see that the corresponding energies are given by

$$E_n = (n + \tfrac{1}{2})\hbar\omega \qquad n = 0, 1, 2, 3, \ldots \tag{7-37}$$

As anticipated, the energy-level scheme consists of a series of equally spaced levels, with a separation of adjacent levels given by $\hbar\omega$. This result confirms Planck's original hypothesis, which preceded the solution of the Schrödinger equation for the harmonic oscillator by 25 years. The number n is called a *quantum number;* just as for the hydrogen-atom energy levels predicted by the Bohr theory, it is an integer that labels the possible quantum-mechanical *states* and their corresponding energies.

Equation (7-37) shows another interesting feature. The lowest energy level is not zero but rather $E_0 = \tfrac{1}{2}\hbar\omega$. This suggests that it is not possible for a harmonic oscillator to exist in a state with zero energy but rather that there is a minimum energy of $\tfrac{1}{2}\hbar\omega$. This energy is, of course, unobservable, since in interactions of the oscillator with an external system only *changes* in energy would be observed. But the fact that the energy cannot be zero corresponds to the fact that, in a quantum-mechanical sense, the particle can never exist in a state in which it has zero velocity and lies precisely at the origin. Such a state would be a clear violation of the uncertainty principle, and so it is not surprising to find that such a state is also forbidden by the Schrödinger equation.

It is instructive to examine a wave function corresponding to a *very large* value of n. We might expect that when the energy of the oscillator is very much larger than the spacing between any two adjacent levels (corresponding to very large n) the behavior might begin to resemble that predicted by classical mechanics. Figure 7-9 shows the square of the wave function for $n = 10$. For comparison, the same graph shows the "probability distribution" for a classical particle. In the classical case, the probability of finding the particle in a certain interval is proportional to the fraction of the total cycle during which it is in that interval. Thus, this function is greatest near the end points of the motion, where the particle moves relatively slowly and therefore spends more time than near the center. We see that for sufficiently large N the function $|\psi|^2$ begins to take on the general shape of the classical probability function. This graph also shows that the wavelength of the wave function is longer in the end regions of small kinetic energy and correspondingly small

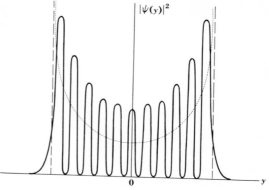

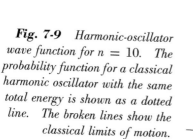

Fig. 7-9 *Harmonic-oscillator wave function for n = 10. The probability function for a classical harmonic oscillator with the same total energy is shown as a dotted line. The broken lines show the classical limits of motion.*

momentum than in the central region where the momentum is larger. This effect is also discernible in some of the functions shown in Fig. 7-8, but it becomes more conspicuous with increasing n.

As already mentioned, the solutions of the Schrödinger equation for a harmonic oscillator provide a detailed verification of the Planck quantum hypothesis. The usefulness of this development does not end here, however. Just as the classical harmonic oscillator is useful as an idealized model to describe vibrating systems which are more complicated but which can be approximated by the oscillator model, so it is in the quantum-mechanical case. Molecular vibrations provide an important example. The potential energy associated with the interaction of atoms in a diatomic molecule may behave in a manner similar to that shown in Fig. 7-10, where r is the spacing between atoms. Just as in the classical case, when the separation is close to its equilibrium value r_0, the potential

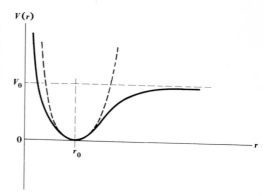

Fig. 7-10 *A potential-energy curve describing the attractive force for atoms in a diatomic molecule. The potential energy has been chosen to be zero at the equilibrium separation r_0 and as a result has the value V_0 at large separations. The approximation given by Eq. (7-38) is equivalent to approximating a section of this curve near $r = r_0$ by a parabola, as shown by the broken curve.*

energy in the vicinity of this region may be approximated, in terms of the distance $x = r - r_0$ from the equilibrium position, as[1]

$$V(x) = \frac{1}{2}\left(\frac{d^2V}{dr^2}\right)_{r=r_0} x^2 \qquad (7\text{-}38)$$

Thus the foregoing development can be applied directly to finding energy levels associated with vibrations of diatomic molecules. Even the vibrational motions of more complicated molecules can be represented as combinations of simple harmonic motions, and there is a corresponding simplicity of energy levels for such vibrations. We shall return to the subject of molecular energy levels in Chap. 9 in connection with the discussion of molecular spectra.

7-6 *Schrödinger Equation in Three Dimensions*

For the sake of simplicity in presenting fundamental concepts, the discussion of the Schrödinger equation and its solutions has thus far been restricted to systems that correspond to a classical particle moving in one dimension. The entire formulation can readily be extended to three dimensions, and this extension is in fact necessary for an analysis of even the simplest atoms. The wave function in general is a function of three space coordinates and time; in rectangular coordinates it may be written as $\Psi(x,y,z,t)$. The interpretation of the wave function in terms of the probability of finding the particle is generalized so that $\Psi^*\Psi\,dV$ represents the probability of finding the particle in a small element of volume dV.

As in Sec. 7-3, we are guided by the correspondence between terms in the classical energy relation and terms in the Schrödinger equation. The momentum of the particle is now a vector quantity and may be represented in terms of its rectangular components p_x, p_y, p_z in a specified coordinate system. The magnitude p of the momentum is given by $p^2 = p_x^2 + p_y^2 + p_z^2$. Similarly, the potential energy is, in general, a function of the three space coordinates and is written as $V(x,y,z)$. The energy relation in three dimensions is

$$\frac{p_x^2 + p_y^2 + p_z^2}{2m} + V(x,y,z) = E \qquad (7\text{-}39)$$

Following the same reasoning as in Sec. 7-3, we conclude that the Schrödinger equation in three dimensions is

[1] See, for example, *ibid.*, sec. 10-5.

$$-\frac{\hbar^2}{2m}\left(\frac{\partial^2\Psi}{\partial x^2} + \frac{\partial^2\Psi}{\partial y^2} + \frac{\partial^2\Psi}{\partial z^2}\right) + V(x,y,z)\Psi = i\hbar\frac{\partial\Psi}{\partial t} \tag{7-40}$$

where the wave function $\Psi(x,y,z,t)$ is a function of the three space co-ordinates and time.

For states of definite total energy we again represent the time-dependent wave function $\Psi(x,y,z,t)$ as in Eq. (7-23); the generalization to three dimensions is clearly

$$\Psi(x,y,z,t) = e^{-iEt/\hbar}\psi(x,y,z) \tag{7-41}$$

where $\psi(x,y,z)$ must satisfy the three-dimensional time-independent Schrödinger equation

$$-\frac{\hbar^2}{2m}\left(\frac{\partial^2\psi}{\partial x^2} + \frac{\partial^2\psi}{\partial y^2} + \frac{\partial^2\psi}{\partial z^2}\right) + V\psi = E\psi \tag{7-42}$$

For a free particle, corresponding to $V(x,y,z) = 0$ everywhere, there are sinusoidal solutions of Eq. (7-42) analogous to the functions $\psi = Ae^{ikx}$, with $p = \hbar k$ for the one-dimensional problem. We introduce a wave vector $\mathbf{k}$, the three-dimensional generalization of the wave number k in one dimension, such that the momentum of the particle is given by $\mathbf{p} = \hbar\mathbf{k}$; $\mathbf{k}$ may be represented in terms of its components k_x, k_y, k_z, just as the position vector $\mathbf{r}$ is represented by its components x, y, z. The reader can verify that the functions

$$\psi = Ae^{i\mathbf{k}\cdot\mathbf{r}} \tag{7-43}$$

are solutions of the three-dimensional Schrödinger equation (7-42) and that they represent states of definite energy and momentum, with completely undefined position. The functions of Eq. (7-43) have the additional feature that each can be written as a product of three functions, each of which contains only one of the three coordinates, as follows:

$$Ae^{i\mathbf{k}\cdot\mathbf{r}} = Ae^{i(k_x x + k_y y + k_z z)} = Ae^{ik_x x}e^{ik_y y}e^{ik_z z} \tag{7-44}$$

This decomposition of a wave function into functions of one variable is a logical extension of the separation of the factor containing t, exhibited by Eq. (7-41), and is a very useful procedure in many problems.

There is nothing particularly sacred about rectangular coordinates; for some problems other coordinate systems are more convenient. A simple example of great importance is the hydrogen atom, to be discussed in detail in Chap. 8. In this problem, the electron is attracted to a fixed center of force (the nucleus) by the Coulomb force, with corresponding potential energy

$$V = -\frac{e^2}{4\pi\epsilon_0}\frac{1}{r} = -\frac{e^2}{4\pi\epsilon_0}\frac{1}{\sqrt{x^2 + y^2 + z^2}} \tag{7-45}$$

Clearly, this potential-energy function is represented more simply in spherical coordinates than rectangular because it depends on only one of the three spherical coordinates r, θ, ϕ. The derivatives with respect to x, y, and z can be expressed in terms of derivatives with respect to r, θ, and ϕ shown in Fig. 7-11 by means of the transformation equations

$$
\begin{aligned}
x &= r\sin\theta\cos\phi \\
y &= r\sin\theta\sin\phi \\
z &= r\cos\theta
\end{aligned} \tag{7-46}
$$

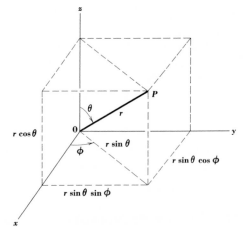

Fig. 7-11 *A spherical-coordinate system. From this diagram the coordinate transformation given by Eqs. (7-46) can be derived.*

The resulting expressions, which we shall discuss in detail in Chap. 8, are more complicated, but the simplification of the potential-energy function more than compensates, making the problem much more tractable in spherical coordinates than in rectangular.

7-7 Operators and Eigenvalues

The energy levels for a quantum-mechanical system are determined by the solutions of the time-independent Schrödinger equation for the system. The solutions of this equation, therefore, represent in every case states with definite total energies. The time-independent Schrödinger equation can be restated in an illuminating form. We define an *operator* H, as follows:

$$H = -\frac{\hbar^2}{2m}\frac{d^2}{dx^2} + V(x) \tag{7-47}$$

The significance of this operator is that the indicated operations, multiplication or differentiation, are to be performed on any function that follows the operator in an algebraic expression. That is,

$$H\psi(x) = \left[-\frac{\hbar^2}{2m}\frac{d^2}{dx^2} + V(x)\right]\psi(x) = -\frac{\hbar^2}{2m}\frac{d^2\psi}{dx^2} + V(x)\psi \tag{7-48}$$

With this operator, Schrödinger's equation becomes simply

$$H\psi(x) = E\psi(x) \tag{7-49}$$

That is, the states of definite total energy have the property that when the operator H is applied to any one of them the result is the same function multiplied by a constant equal to the total energy. For other functions, which are *not* solutions of this equation, there is no reason to expect that the quantity $H\psi(x)$ should be a multiple of the original function $\psi(x)$, but for functions that satisfy the equation, it is.

Mathematicians describe this situation by saying that $\psi(x)$ is a *characteristic function* of the operator H. The corresponding constant E for each function is called the *characteristic value*. Actually, these terms are not as common as their German equivalents, which are *eigenfunction* and *eigenvalue*, respectively. Using this language, we say that every wave function that represents a state of definite total energy is an eigenfunction of the energy operator, and the corresponding eigenvalue is equal to the total energy.

This observation gives a clue to how to proceed in order to find states with a definite value of some other dynamical quantity such as momentum or angular momentum rather than definite total energy. Perhaps there is an *operator* corresponding to each dynamical quantity, so that a state that has a definite value of that quantity is represented by an eigenfunction of the corresponding operator. To test this hypothesis, we consider states having definite total momentum. We have already seen in Chap. 6 that such states, at least for a free particle, are sinusoidal waves. For a momentum $p = \hbar k$, the time-dependent wave function is

$$\Psi(x,t) = Ae^{i(kx - \omega t)} = Ae^{i(px/\hbar - \omega t)} \tag{7-50}$$

This wave function has the property that

$$\frac{\hbar}{i}\frac{\partial \Psi}{\partial x} = p\Psi \tag{7-51}$$

Therefore, it is reasonable to conclude that the operator corresponding to momentum is

$$p \rightarrow \frac{\hbar}{i} \frac{\partial}{\partial x} \tag{7-52}$$

Checking this with Eq. (7-47), we see that the two are consistent, since if we start with the classical expression for total energy, $E = p^2/2m + V$, and make the substitution suggested by Eq. (7-52), the result is precisely the energy operator of Eq. (7-47).

We can now state the principles of quantum mechanics in a considerably more general form than previously. _For every observable physical quantity, there is a corresponding operator. The states of the system corresponding to definite values of that physical quantity are represented by eigenfunctions of the operator, and the corresponding eigenvalues are the possible values of the physical quantity._ Thus if A is an operator corresponding to a physical quantity and a is one of the permissible values of that quantity, the states of the system having a definite value of that physical quantity are represented by wave functions that are solutions of the equation

$$A\Psi = a\Psi \tag{7-53}$$

where A may be a differential operator, or a function of the space coordinates, or both, and a is a constant.

This more general formalism paves the way for the "quantization" of other physical quantities. In this chapter we shall consider only one example, that of angular momentum. As we have seen, angular momentum played a central role in the early attempts to predict energy levels of the hydrogen atom; Bohr's quantum hypothesis is essentially the assumption that the angular momentum of the electron in the hydrogen atom must be an integer multiple of $\hbar$. Furthermore, there is now a variety of direct experimental evidence that angular momentum and its components are *quantized.* That is, in any experiment that measures angular momentum or a component in a specified direction, the result is never a continuous distribution of values but rather a discrete set.

Just as atomic spectra provided the first experimental evidence of the existence of quantized energy levels in atoms, spectroscopy also helped to establish the quantization of angular momentum. We consider here only one particular class of phenomena, the Zeeman effect. This effect, mentioned briefly in Sec. 5-1, concerns the changes in atomic spectra that result from placing the emitting atoms in a magnetic field. It would be premature to analyze this effect in detail at this stage of our introduction to quantum mechanics, but a qualitative description will illustrate its importance in connection with quantization of angular momentum.

In any dynamic model of the atom, whether it be the Bohr model or the improved description provided by the Schrödinger equation, the electrons have various dynamical properties, including energy, momentum, and angular momentum. In the Bohr picture it is evident that the angular momentum must be accompanied by a magnetic moment, since the electron travels in a circle and is therefore equivalent to a current loop. In classical electromagnetism a plane loop of area A carrying a current I has a magnetic moment $\boldsymbol{\mu}$ whose magnitude is $\mu = IA$ and whose direction is determined by the right-hand rule, as shown in Fig. 7-12. In the presence of a magnetic field this magnetic moment experiences a torque $\boldsymbol{\tau}$ given by

$$\boldsymbol{\tau} = \boldsymbol{\mu} \times \mathbf{B} \tag{7-54}$$

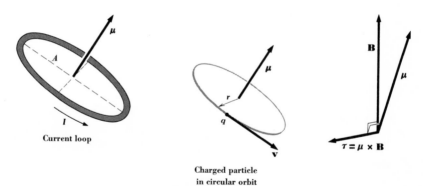

Current loop

**Charged particle
in circular orbit**

$$\boldsymbol{\tau} = \boldsymbol{\mu} \times \mathbf{B}$$

Fig. 7-12 *A current loop or a charged particle in a circular orbit possesses a magnetic moment $\boldsymbol{\mu}$. In the presence of a magnetic field $\mathbf{B}$ the loop experiences a torque $\boldsymbol{\tau} = \boldsymbol{\mu} \times \mathbf{B}$ tending to orient the magnetic moment parallel to $\mathbf{B}$. The potential energy of this interaction is minimum when $\boldsymbol{\mu}$ and $\mathbf{B}$ are parallel, maximum when they are antiparallel, and zero when they are perpendicular.*

Correspondingly, the potential energy associated with the interaction of the magnetic moment with the magnetic field is given by

$$V = -\boldsymbol{\mu} \cdot \mathbf{B} \tag{7-55}$$

The existence of a magnetic moment is less easy to visualize in the wave-mechanical picture, but it is not unreasonable to surmise that the relationship between angular momentum **L** and magnetic moment μ holds here as well as in the Bohr model and that, in fact, μ is directly proportional to **L**, as can be shown directly for the Bohr model.

An atom placed in a magnetic field should have its energy levels shifted by an amount given by Eq. (7-55), which depends on the orientation of the magnetic moment relative to the field and is proportional to the component of μ in the direction of **B**. If there were no restrictions on the orientation of the atom relative to the field, an energy level with the value E in the absence of a field might have any value between $E - \mu B$ and $E + \mu B$ in a magnetic field. Correspondingly, any spectrum line resulting from a transition to or from this level would become smeared out by the corresponding amount.

Fig. 7-13 *Photographs of spectrum lines, illustrating the Zeeman effect. When the source of radiation is placed in a magnetic field, some individual lines split into sets of lines, as shown, as a result of the interaction of the magnetic moments of the atoms with the magnetic field. The fact that discrete lines appear rather than a continuous smear demonstrates the quantization of the component of magnetic moment, and thus of angular momentum, in the direction of the magnetic field.*

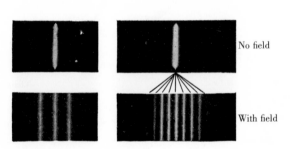

No field

With field

This smearing out is not observed experimentally. Instead, individual spectrum lines are split into two or more distinct lines which are displaced various amounts from the zero-field positions, as shown in Fig. 7-13; this indicates corresponding splitting in energy levels. But the fact that the energy shifts are discrete rather than a continuous smear shows that only certain values of the interaction energy given by Eq. (7-55) actually occur; correspondingly, only certain values of the component of μ in the direction of **B** are allowed, and finally we conclude that the component of angular momentum in the direction of **B** is quantized.

Observation of this effect in a wide variety of spectra leads to the conclusion that this component of angular momentum is *always* an integral or half-integral multiple of $\hbar$. Many other experimental results, including molecular-beam and magnetic-resonance experiments, are also consistent with this conclusion.

The above discussion of operators shows, at least in principle, how to find the permitted values of angular momentum for any system. We first develop an angular-momentum *operator*. The classical definition of angular momentum is

$$\mathbf{L} = \mathbf{r} \times \mathbf{p} \qquad \text{or} \qquad \begin{aligned} L_x &= yp_z - zp_y \\ L_y &= zp_x - xp_z \\ L_z &= xp_y - yp_x \end{aligned} \tag{7-56}$$

The corresponding operators for the components of angular momentum are

$$\begin{aligned} L_x &\rightarrow \frac{\hbar}{i}\left(y\frac{\partial}{\partial z} - z\frac{\partial}{\partial y} \right) \\ L_y &\rightarrow \frac{\hbar}{i}\left(z\frac{\partial}{\partial x} - x\frac{\partial}{\partial z} \right) \\ L_z &\rightarrow \frac{\hbar}{i}\left(x\frac{\partial}{\partial y} - y\frac{\partial}{\partial x} \right) \end{aligned} \tag{7-57}$$

Correspondingly one can develop an operator for the square of the total angular momentum, L^2. For many systems of physical interest, including electrons in atoms, the permitted values of angular momentum are given by

$$L^2 = l(l + 1)\hbar^2 \qquad l = 0, 1, 2, 3, \ldots \tag{7-58}$$

and the possible values for the *component* of angular momentum in the direction corresponding to any particular measurement are integral multiples of $\hbar$. Thus if we design an apparatus which measures the component of momentum along the z axis, the possible values are

$$L_z = m\hbar \tag{7-59}$$

where m is an integer which can take any value between $-l$ and $+l$. It is interesting to note that while the magnitude of the total angular momentum is

$$L = \sqrt{l(l + 1)}\,\hbar \tag{7-60}$$

its *component* in any direction cannot be quite as large as this. This corresponds to a basic uncertainty in angular momentum associated with the uncertainties of position and momentum already discussed. That is, the *direction* of the angular-momentum vector is never completely well defined. It is often useful to classify states of atomic systems according to angular momentum and its components. Such classifications will be discussed in considerable detail in Chap. 8.

We have now developed several important general principles which can be applied to a variety of problems associated with the microscopic structure of matter. In the following chapters, we shall see that these principles, along with a few additional ones, provide the key to understanding of the structure of atoms, molecules, and solids. These areas are the principal subjects of the next four chapters.

PROBLEMS

7-1 A certain particle has a wave function

$$\psi(x) = \frac{1}{\sqrt{2\pi}\,\sigma}\,e^{-x^2/2\sigma^2}$$

Estimate roughly the probability that, in an experiment to determine its position, the particle will be found between $x = \sigma$ and $x = 2\sigma$. This estimate is made most easily by plotting the appropriate function on graph paper and counting squares to find the relevant areas.

7-2 For the wave packet of Prob. 6-11, find the probability that, in an experiment which measures momentum, the particle's momentum will be found to lie between $\hbar(k_0 - a/2)$ and $\hbar(k_0 + a/2)$.

7-3 For a particle in a box, discussed in Sec. 7-2, find the probability that in the lowest energy state the particle is in the interval $-L/2$ to $+L/2$.

7-4 For a particle in a box, find the energy of the lowest energy state, and from this find the magnitude of momentum of the particle. The *direction* of the momentum is indefinite. Show that the corresponding uncertainty in momentum and the uncertainty of position given by the size of the box are consistent with the uncertainty principle.

7-5 Find the lowest energy for a neutron in a box with a width of 5×10^{-15} m, the order of magnitude of the nuclear diameter for heavy elements.

7-6   Verify that Eq. (7-14) is a solution of the Schrödinger equation that satisfies the boundary conditions and that the energy levels E_n are correct.

7-7   Show that the wave functions in Eqs. (7-17) are normalized.

7-8   For the wave functions in Eqs. (7-17), show that for any two functions $\psi_n(x)$ and $\psi_{n'}(x)$

$$\int_{-L}^{L} \psi_n(x)\psi_{n'}(x)\, dx = 0$$

unless $n = n'$, and the integral is also zero when $n = n'$ unless both functions are sines or both cosines.

7-9   Show that for a particle in a two-dimensional box the Schrödinger equation for states with definite energy is

$$-\frac{\hbar^2}{2m}\left(\frac{\partial^2\psi}{\partial x^2} + \frac{\partial^2\psi}{\partial y^2}\right) = E\psi$$

7-10 Show that the solutions of the two-dimensional Schrödinger equation for a particle in a box (Prob. 7-9) have the form

$$\psi = A\begin{Bmatrix}\sin\\\cos\end{Bmatrix}mx\begin{Bmatrix}\sin\\\cos\end{Bmatrix}ny$$

Find the energy levels for a box of length L and width W by using the same boundary conditions as for the one-dimensional box. Also find the normalized wave functions.

7-11 Show that the variables y and α defined by Eqs. (7-35) are dimensionless.

7-12 Show by direct substitution that the first two functions in Table 7-1 are solutions of Eq. (7-36).

7-13 Estimate the width of the harmonic-oscillator wave function for the $n = 0$ state, in terms of k, m, and $\hbar$, and compare this with the amplitude of a classical (non-quantum-mechanical) harmonic oscillator having the same energy.

7-14 Find the constant factors needed to normalize the harmonic-oscillator wave functions for $n = 0$ and $n = 2$. The following integral will be useful:

$$\int_{-\infty}^{\infty} e^{-x^2}dx = \sqrt{\pi}$$

This is derived by mathematical trickery. The normalization integrals for all values of n can be reduced to this integral by successive integrations by parts.

7-15 Find the constant factor needed to normalize the harmonic-oscillator wave function for $n = 1$.

7-16 Show that the harmonic-oscillator wave functions $\psi(y)$ can all be written in the form

$$\psi(y) = e^{-y^2/2}H_n(y)$$

where $H_n(y)$ is a polynomial of the nth degree in y. By substituting this expression into Eq. (7-36), show that $H_n(y)$ must satisfy the differential equation

$$H''(y) - 2yH'(y) + (\alpha_n - 1)H_n(y) = 0 \qquad \text{with } \alpha_n = 2n + 1$$

Taking the polynomials $H_n(y)$ from the functions in Table 7-1, show by direct substitution that they satisfy this equation for $n = 2$ and $n = 4$. These polynomials are called the Hermite polynomials.

7-17 Show that the Hermite polynomials $H_n(y)$ satisfy the relation

$$H_{n+1}(y) = 2yH_n(y) - 2nH_{n-1}(y)$$

That is, if $H_n(y)$ and $H_{n-1}(y)$ satisfy the equation in Prob. 7-16 with $\alpha = 2n + 1$ and $2(n - 1) + 1$, respectively, then $H_{n+1}(y)$ satisfies the same equation with $\alpha = 2(n + 1) + 1$. Hence a table of Hermite polynomials can be constructed by starting with $H_0(y)$ and $H_1(y)$. Check several functions in Table 7-1 to see that this relation is followed.

7-18 For the $n = 1$ harmonic-oscillator wave function, find the probability that, in an experiment which measures position, the particle will be found within a distance $\frac{1}{2}\hbar^{1/2}(mk)^{-1/4}$ of the origin.

7-19 Show that, in transitions between energy states of a harmonic oscillator, the frequency of the emitted or absorbed radiation is always an integer multiple of the classical oscillator frequency $(k/m)^{1/2}$.

7-20 For a harmonic oscillator whose mass is that of a hydrogen atom and whose spring constant is typical of interatomic forces in molecules (say $k = 50$ nt/m), how does the spacing of adjacent energy levels compare with typical energies associated with thermal motion at ordinary temperatures (say kT at $300°$K, where k is Boltzmann's constant)?

7-21 In the Bohr model, calculate the magnetic moment of the electron in the $n = 1$ state. From this, calculate the energy-level splitting in a magnetic field $B = 1.0$ weber/m². Into how many levels is the original level split, and how are their positions related to that of the original level?

7-22 The *gyromagnetic ratio* of a system is defined as the ratio of the magnitude of magnetic moment to the magnitude of angular momentum. For a charged particle in a circular orbit, such as an electron in the Bohr model, show that the gyromagnetic ratio is given by $e/2m$, where e is the charge and m the mass, and that this result is independent of orbit speed or radius.

7-23 Using the transformations given by Eqs. (7-46), show that, in terms of the spherical coordinates, the operator L_z corresponding to the z component of angular momentum, Eq. (7-57), is given simply by

$$L_z = \frac{\hbar}{i}\frac{\partial}{\partial\phi}$$

This is accomplished most simply by starting at the end and going backward, beginning with the observation that

$$\frac{\partial}{\partial\phi} = \frac{\partial x}{\partial\phi}\frac{\partial}{\partial x} + \frac{\partial y}{\partial\phi}\frac{\partial}{\partial y} + \frac{\partial z}{\partial\phi}\frac{\partial}{\partial z}$$

7-24 Suppose a particle whose position is described by spherical coordinates has a wave function which can be represented as a product of three functions:

$$\psi(r,\theta,\phi) = R(r)\Theta(\theta)\,\Phi(\phi)$$

Using the result of Prob. 7-23, show that, in any such function having a definite value of L_z, the function $\Phi(\phi)$ has the form $e^{im\phi}$. Furthermore, since the coordinates (r,θ,ϕ) and $(r,\theta,\phi+2\pi)$ represent the same point, it must be true that

$$\Phi(\phi + 2\pi) = \Phi(\phi)$$

Hence, show that the permissible values for L_z are $m\hbar$, where m is a positive or negative integer.

THE THREE PRECEDING chapters have introduced some of the most important concepts of *quantum mechanics*.   As we have seen, various
phenomena associated with the emission and absorption of radiation exhibit a discrete or quantum aspect of electromagnetic radiation which cannot be understood on the basis of classical electrodynamics.   Correspondingly, there are phenomena associated with
the behavior of particles which cannot be understood adequately
on the basis of newtonian mechanics but rather suggest a *wave*
aspect of particle behavior.

More generally, both particles (in the old sense) and radiation
exhibit *both* wave and particle aspects.   As we have seen, these two
kinds of behavior are not mutually exclusive but rather are *complementary*; an entity which may seem to have wave characteristics
in one kind of experiment may exhibit particle characteristics in
another, and both can be understood as aspects of a more general

kind of description. Thus the wave concept has the happy effect of bringing *unity* into the description of both particles and radiation; it is on this basis that we have claimed that wave concepts are central and essential to contemporary theories of matter and radiation and their interaction.

In developing a language for describing this dual wave-particle nature of matter, we have found that in quantum mechanics the *state* of a particle or of a system of particles is not described by the position and velocity of a point but rather is given in terms of a wave function which depends on spatial coordinates and time. Furthermore, some systems, especially those associated with "bound states" of particles, can exist only in states with certain discrete energy levels. When such a system interacts with an electromagnetic field, the emission or absorption of radiation is to be understood on the basis of a transition from one energy state to another, with emission or absorption of a photon of electromagnetic energy of corresponding magnitude. Thus this analysis provides the key for an understanding of the characteristic spectra of elements, in terms of the structure of their atoms.

Our next task is to pursue further the analysis of atomic structure and its relation to the spectra and other properties of atoms. The logical place to begin is with the simplest atom, hydrogen. It is found that the solutions of the Schrödinger equation for the hydrogen atom predict correctly the energy levels of hydrogen already established from spectrum analysis and also describe the electron configurations in the various quantum states.

We then proceed to the analysis of more complicated atoms containing several electrons. When more than one electron is present, the analysis immediately becomes much more complicated because of the interactions between electrons, but it is found that with the help of certain approximations we can still make some progress in the analysis of the structure of more complicated atoms. Central to this analysis is a "zoning ordinance" called the *exclusion principle*, which forbids two electrons in an atom from occupying the same quantum state. This principle is responsible for the periodically recurring properties of elements exhibited by the periodic table of the elements.

The same principles used to understand the structure of individual atoms can be extended to an analysis of systems containing several interacting atoms. In particular, the various kinds of molecular binding and the structure of complex molecules can be understood on the basis of the electron configurations of the constituent atoms. Thus quantum mechanics provides the fundamental basis for the phenomenon of *valence*. With systems containing several atomic nuclei, there are additional effects associated with relative motion of the nuclei, commonly called *molecular vibrations*. The energy levels associated with these vibrations and with rotational motion of molecules lead to additional interesting features in the spectra of molecules.

Next, we consider systems containing such a large number of atoms, molecules, or other subsystems that it is impractical to describe the state of each subsystem in detail. In such cases, it is helpful to employ a *statistical* description of the state of the system, in which one abandons hope of describing individual constituents in detail and instead describes the statistical distribution of states of individual atoms or molecules. The classical counterpart of this description is the kinetic theory of gases, which relates the macroscopic behavior of a gas to a statistical description of its microscopic constituents. By extending this analysis to quantum-mechanical systems, we are able to formulate a statistical description of the states of electrons in a solid, the quantum states of molecules in a gas, and similar problems. The methods of statistical mechanics provide very useful and powerful tools for the analysis of complex systems containing many interacting subsystems.

THE CONCEPTS OF quantum mechanics are applied to a detailed analysis of the structure and behavior of the simplest atom, hydrogen.   The Schrödinger equation is applied to the hydrogen atom, and it is shown that solution of this equation with the appropriate boundary conditions leads naturally to the energy levels of the atom and its possible angular-momentum states.   Transitions from one quantum state to another during emission or absorption of radiation are discussed.   The changes in energy levels resulting from the application of a magnetic field are discussed, and it is shown that this behavior and other details of the hydrogen spectrum point to the existence of an intrinsic angular momentum and magnetic moment of the electron, conveniently pictured as "spin."

8-1   *The Nuclear Model*
In order to understand the conceptual context within which we shall analyze the structure of the hydrogen atom, we review briefly the nuclear model of the atom.   By the beginning of the twentieth century it was well established that the constituent parts of atoms carry electrical

charges and that the negative charges, electrons, can be removed from atoms. In 1897 the English physicist J. J. Thomson, by observing the trajectories of electrons in electric and magnetic fields, measured the charge-to-mass ratio (e/m) for electrons and thereby established that the electron mass accounts for only a small fraction of the total mass of the atom, about $1/2,000$ for the hydrogen atom.

There were several independent bits of evidence concerning the order of magnitude of atomic dimensions. These included the van der Waals correction to the ideal-gas equation (associated with finite molecular sizes), observations on density of matter in the solid state, and a variety of experiments on diffusion and mean free paths of molecules in the gaseous state. All these indicated atomic diameters of the order of 10^{-10} m or about 1 Å.

There were a number of proposals regarding the *internal structure* of atoms. Of particular prominence in 1900 was a model proposed by J. J. Thomson, in which the positive charge was pictured as being spread out over the entire volume of the atom, with the negative electrons embedded in it like raisins in a custard pudding or seeds in a watermelon. This model had certain advantages; by ascribing elastic properties to the positive charge, one could imagine the electrons as being elastically bound and therefore possessing the ability to vibrate about their equilibrium positions. Thus this model seemed to offer some hope of providing a mechanism for absorption and emission of electromagnetic waves, in terms of electron vibrations. There was, however, no basis on which to account for the existence of particular series of spectrum lines, such as the Balmer series.

Starting in 1909, Ernest Rutherford and his collaborators at the University of Manchester (England) obtained experimental evidence showing conclusively that the Thomson model was in need of drastic revision. Rutherford's experiments consisted in observing the deflections in the trajectories of α particles (emitted by radioactive elements such as uranium) as they passed through thin films of metal. It was known by then that α particles have positive charges and a mass about 8,000 times that of the electron. Because of this much greater mass, the electrons should have relatively little effect on the motion of an α particle, just as a truck can drive through a hailstorm without having its motion altered appreciably by collisions with the hailstones. Any significant deflection of the particles would have to be produced by interaction with the more massive *positively* charged constituents of the atoms. Thus the extent of the deflections provided valuable information regarding the distribution of the positive charge.

Calculation of the electric field produced by a uniform distribution of charge throughout a sphere of radius R is a straightforward problem in electrostatics.   Application of Gauss' law shows that for points outside the sphere the field has the same $1/r^2$ behavior as though all the charge were concentrated at the center, and for points inside the sphere the field is directly proportional to r, as shown in Fig. 8-1.   Clearly, the maximum field occurs just at the surface $(r = R)$ of the spherical charge distribution, and the magnitude of this maximum value is proportional to $1/R^2$.

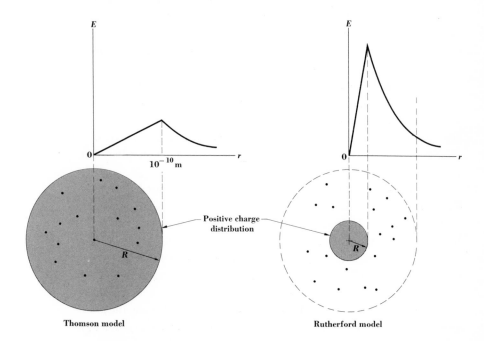

Fig. 8-1   *Electric field produced by a uniform distribution of charge throughout a sphere of radius R. The maximum value of E occurs at the surface of the sphere and is greater for small R than for larger R.*

Rutherford's calculations[1] showed that, if the positive charge extends over a sphere of radius $R = 10^{-10}$ m, the maximum electric field is sufficient to deflect an α particle only a few degrees, at most.   Instead, he found that some particles were scattered through rather large angles, and a few almost exactly backward.   Since the scattering targets were

[1] For a more detailed discussion of the dynamics of Rutherford scattering, see H. D. Young, "Fundamentals of Mechanics and Heat," sec. 12-3, McGraw-Hill Book Company, New York, 1964.

very thin foils, it was very unlikely that this resulted from multiple collisions; Rutherford was forced to conclude that these scatterings were the result of forces much larger than predicted by the Thomson model and that the positive charge must be concentrated in a much smaller region. Quantitative observations of the number of particles scattered through various angles showed that the positive charge of the atom is concentrated in a region no larger than 10^{-14} m in radius, 10,000 times smaller than the overall size of the atom itself.

Although the Rutherford nuclear model shed important new light on the internal structure of atoms, it left a number of questions unanswered. Most important of these was the difficulty in understanding the *stability* of an atom. If the electrons are stationary, what holds them in place? Why are they not pulled into the nucleus by the electrostatic attraction? On the other hand, if they move in orbits about the nucleus, why do they not emit electromagnetic radiation continuously as a result of this accelerated motion, eventually losing energy and spiraling into the nucleus? Also unexplained were the phenomena of line spectra. Why does an atom emit only certain frequencies of radiation rather than a continuous spectrum?

The Bohr theory of the hydrogen atom, introduced just 4 years after Rutherford's discoveries, provided the means for a successful prediction of the spectrum of hydrogen and a partial explanation of the stability of the hydrogen atom. As pointed out in Chap. 5, however, this model had a number of important shortcomings. The most important *conceptual* defects were the artificial nature of the assumption necessary to achieve discrete energy levels and the mixing of classical and quantum-mechanical concepts in a seemingly inconsistent way. Among the *practical* disadvantages was the fact that the Bohr theory failed completely for atoms more complicated than hydrogen. Thus, although the Bohr theory achieved a certain measure of success in understanding the properties of the hydrogen atom, it was by no means a complete theory.

With the introduction of the wave concept of electrons by de Broglie in 1925 and its subsequent development into a detailed theory by Schrödinger, Heisenberg, and others, an important new tool for the analysis of atomic structure became available. In the next section we shall see how the Schrödinger equation can be applied to an analysis of the structure of hydrogen. In pursuing this analysis and in evaluating its success, we must keep in mind that a successful prediction of the energy levels of hydrogen is not in itself conclusive evidence of the correctness of the new wave picture. The Bohr theory, after all, did predict the energy levels successfully. But we shall see that the discreteness of energy levels appears in a natural way in the solutions of the Schrödinger equation, rather than having to be inserted artificially as in the Bohr theory. Furthermore, the Schrödinger equation also gives new insight into a number of other phenomena associated with the hydrogen atom and into the structure of more complicated atoms.

8-2   Spherically Symmetric Wave Functions

We now proceed to the Schrödinger equation for the hydrogen atom and its solutions. We consider first the time-independent Schrödinger equation, which is the basis for calculation of energy levels. The application of this equation to three-dimensional problems was discussed in Sec. 7-6. In rectangular coordinates the wave function and the potential energy are functions of the three space coordinates x, y, and z, and the Schrödinger equation for a particle in three dimensions is

$$-\frac{\hbar^2}{2m}\left(\frac{\partial^2\psi}{\partial x^2} + \frac{\partial^2\psi}{\partial y^2} + \frac{\partial^2\psi}{\partial z^2}\right) + V\psi = E\psi \tag{8-1}$$

in which ψ and V are functions of x, y, and z.

The potential energy is associated with the electrostatic attraction of the electron and the nucleus. As in the case of the Bohr model, we take advantage of the fact that the nucleus is almost 2,000 times as massive as the electron, and we regard it as a stationary center of force, with the electron moving around it. Each of the particles has a charge of magnitude e, and so when they are separated a distance r the attractive force is given by Coulomb's law:

$$F = \frac{1}{4\pi\epsilon_0}\frac{e^2}{r^2} \tag{8-2}$$

The corresponding potential energy, which we define to be zero when the particles are separated an infinite distance, is

$$V(r) = -\frac{1}{4\pi\epsilon_0}\frac{e^2}{r} = -\frac{1}{4\pi\epsilon_0}\frac{e^2}{\sqrt{x^2 + y^2 + z^2}} \tag{8-3}$$

As pointed out in Sec. 7-3, the electron does not have a definite position, and therefore it does not have a definite potential energy, even in a state where the *total* energy has a definite value. Nevertheless, we may still say that, to whatever extent the particle is localized in the vicinity of the point (x,y,z), it has the potential energy given by Eq. (8-3).

Because the potential-energy function depends only on the distance r between the two particles, finding solutions of Eq. (8-1) with the

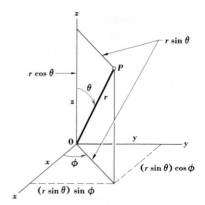

Fig. 8-2 *Diagram showing the spherical coordinates (r,θ,ϕ) of a point P and their relation to the rectangular (cartesian) coordinates (x,y,z). The transformations given by Eqs. (8-4) can be obtained from this diagram.*

potential-energy function of Eq. (8-3) is facilitated by transforming from rectangular coordinates (x,y,z) to spherical polar coordinates (r,θ,ϕ). The usual definition of the spherical coordinates is illustrated in Fig. 8-2, which shows that the spherical coordinates of a point are related to its cartesian coordinates by the transformation equations

$$x = r \sin \theta \cos \phi$$
$$y = r \sin \theta \sin \phi \tag{8-4}$$
$$z = r \cos \theta$$

The derivatives with respect to x, y, and z can be transformed into derivatives with respect to the spherical coordinates, by making use of the chain rule.   For example,

$$\frac{\partial \psi}{\partial \phi} = \frac{\partial \psi}{\partial x}\frac{\partial x}{\partial \phi} + \frac{\partial \psi}{\partial y}\frac{\partial y}{\partial \phi} + \frac{\partial \psi}{\partial z}\frac{\partial z}{\partial \phi}$$
$$= \frac{\partial \psi}{\partial x}(-r \sin \theta \sin \phi) + \frac{\partial \psi}{\partial y}(-r \sin \theta \cos \phi) + \frac{\partial \psi}{\partial z}(0) \tag{8-5}$$

This transformation, although straightforward, is somewhat tedious, and the details of the mathematical manipulations are of no particular physical interest.

In terms of spherical coordinates, the Schrödinger equation for the hydrogen atom is

$$-\frac{\hbar^2}{2m}\left[\frac{1}{r^2}\frac{\partial}{\partial r}\left(r^2\frac{\partial \psi}{\partial r}\right) + \frac{1}{r^2 \sin \theta}\frac{\partial}{\partial \theta}\left(\sin \theta \frac{\partial \psi}{\partial \theta}\right)\right.$$
$$\left. + \frac{1}{r^2 \sin^2 \theta}\frac{\partial^2 \psi}{\partial \phi^2}\right] - \frac{e^2}{4\pi\epsilon_0}\frac{1}{r}\psi = E\psi \tag{8-6}$$

in which ψ is now understood to be a function of r, θ, and ϕ. It may appear that the introduction of spherical coordinates has complicated rather than simplified the equation. The real advantage of using spherical coordinates, as we shall see shortly, is that they make it possible to represent the solutions as products of three functions, with each function containing only one of the three coordinates.

Lest the reader be intimidated by the apparent complexity of Eq. (8-6), we hasten to point out that at least some of its solutions are very simple in form and that the principal features of the general solutions can be appreciated without dwelling excessively on the details of how they are obtained. First, because of the *spherical symmetry* of the potential-energy function, which does not contain θ or ϕ, it would not be surprising if there were solutions of the equation that are also spherically symmetric, depending only on r and not θ or ϕ. We should not expect *all* the solutions to be spherically symmetric, since the form of the solution is not determined uniquely by the form of the potential; but at least it is worthwhile to look for spherically symmetric solutions.

If ψ depends only on r, then all the derivatives with respect to the angular coordinates in Eq. (8-6) are zero, and this equation reduces to

$$-\frac{\hbar^2}{2m}\frac{1}{r^2}\frac{d}{dr}\left(r^2\frac{d\psi}{dr}\right) - \frac{e^2}{4\pi\epsilon_0}\frac{1}{r}\psi = E\psi \tag{8-7}$$

which may also be written

$$-\frac{\hbar^2}{2m}\left(\frac{d^2\psi}{dr^2} + \frac{2}{r}\frac{d\psi}{dr}\right) - \frac{e^2}{4\pi\epsilon_0}\frac{1}{r}\psi = E\psi \tag{8-8}$$

Two terms in this equation contain the factor $1/r$; in one it is multiplied by $d\psi/dr$, and in the other by ψ itself. A little thought shows that the sum of these two terms can be made to equal zero for all values of r by choosing for ψ an exponential function of r. Furthermore, with an appropriate choice of E the term containing $d^2\psi/dr^2$ can be made to equal the term $E\psi$ for all values of r. Thus there is a solution in the form

$$\psi(r) = Ce^{-r/a} \tag{8-9}$$

where C and a are constants.

We note that for dimensional consistency the constant a must have units of length. The negative sign in the exponent reflects the fact that the wave function must approach zero at large values of r if it is to represent a bound state in which the electron is localized in the vicinity of the nucleus.

Substituting Eq. (8-9) into Eq. (8-8), rearranging, and dividing out the common factor $Ce^{-r/a}$, we find

$$\left[-\frac{\hbar^2}{2m}\left(\frac{1}{a^2} - \frac{2}{ar}\right) - \frac{e^2}{4\pi\epsilon_0}\frac{1}{r} \right]Ce^{-r/a} = ECe^{-r/a}$$

and

$$-\frac{\hbar^2}{2ma^2} + \left(\frac{\hbar^2}{ma} - \frac{e^2}{4\pi\epsilon_0}\right)\frac{1}{r} = E \tag{8-10}$$

This equation is satisfied for all values of r if, and only if, the coefficient of $1/r$ is zero and the two constant terms are equal. These requirements determine the values of a and E. We find

$$\frac{\hbar^2}{ma} - \frac{e^2}{4\pi\epsilon_0} = 0 \quad \Longrightarrow \quad a = \frac{4\pi\epsilon_0\hbar^2}{me^2} \tag{8-11}$$

and

$$E = -\frac{\hbar^2}{2ma^2} = -\left(\frac{e^2}{4\pi\epsilon_0}\right)^2\frac{m}{2\hbar^2} \tag{8-12}$$

With these values of E and a, Eq. (8-9) is a solution of the Schrödinger equation. The constant E is the energy of the state, and a characterizes the extension in space of the wave function; at a distance $r = a$ from the origin the function has dropped to $1/e$ of its value at $r = 0$. The most remarkable feature of these results, however, is that they are exactly equal to the orbit radius and energy of the $n = 1$ state in the Bohr model, as given by Eqs. (5-27) and (5-28). We therefore conclude that this wave function represents the *ground state* of the hydrogen atom. By replacing *one* of the factors of a in Eq. (8-12) by the expression of Eq. (8-11), we obtain

$$E = -\frac{1}{2}\frac{e^2}{4\pi\epsilon_0 a} \tag{8-13}$$

which shows directly that the energy is equal to the total energy of an electron in a Bohr orbit of radius a, as given by Eq. (5-25).

Equation (8-9) is a solution of the Schrödinger equation for any value of the constant C. Thus C may be chosen to *normalize* the wave function, in the manner discussed in Sec. 7-2. We recall that $\psi^*\psi\,dV$ represents the probability of finding the particle in the volume element dV, provided the wave function is normalized so that $\int\psi^*\psi\,dV = 1$. For the spherically symmetric situation it is natural to choose for dV a spherical shell with inner and outer radii r and $r + dr$, respectively.

The surface area of the shell is approximately $4\pi r^2$ and its thickness is dr, and so the volume element dV is given by $dV = 4\pi r^2\, dr$. Thus the normalization condition becomes

$$\int_0^\infty (Ce^{-r/a})^2\, 4\pi r^2\, dr = 1 \tag{8-14}$$

The integral can be evaluated by two successive integrations by parts or by one reference to a table of integrals. The result is

$$\pi C^2 a^3 = 1 \tag{8-15}$$

which shows that for the wave function to be normalized the constant C must have the value

$$C = \frac{1}{\sqrt{\pi a^3}} \tag{8-16}$$

Thus the normalized wave function for the ground state of the hydrogen atom is

$$\checkmark \quad \psi(r) = \frac{1}{\sqrt{\pi a^3}}\, e^{-r/a} \tag{8-17}$$

with a given by Eq. (8-11). Thus the Schrödinger equation yields a wave function representing a state with the same energy as the ground state in the Bohr model, which has already been shown to agree with experimental observations; furthermore the "size" of the wave function is of the same order of magnitude as the Bohr radius.

The angular-momentum properties of this state are worth noting. We recall from Sec. 7-7 that a state with definite angular momentum or component in a given direction is represented by a wave function that is an eigenfunction of the corresponding operator. The angular-momentum operators for L^2 and L_z, when expressed in terms of polar coordinates, contain derivatives only with respect to θ and ϕ. This result is given for L_z in Prob. 7-23, and can be shown similarly for L^2. The L^2 operator is given in Eq. (8-38). Since the present function contains only r, these derivatives are all zero. Thus we find

$$\begin{aligned} L^2\psi &= 0 \\ L_z\psi &= 0 \end{aligned} \tag{8-18}$$

That is, ψ is an eigenfunction of both L^2 and L_z, and in each case the eigenvalue is zero. Thus the state has zero total angular momentum and zero z component.

This result differs from the Bohr model, in which the angular momentum in the ground state is $\hbar$. Indeed, it may seem contrary to common sense that the electron can exist in a stable state with no dynamical quantity corresponding to rotational motion. Yet the function is a proper solution of the Schrödinger equation, and so we must accept the validity of this result, which is without a classical analog. Further consideration shows that the state *cannot* have a nonzero component of momentum in any direction; this would imply a directional nature of the wave function, and we have already seen that the function has *no* directional nature since it is spherically symmetric. From this point of view, therefore, the fact that $L_z = 0$ is to be expected.

Equation (8-17) is by no means the only spherically symmetric solution. Another is

$$\psi(r) = C\left(1 - \frac{r}{2a}\right)e^{-r/2a} \tag{8-19}$$

This function corresponds to the energy of the $n = 2$ level in the Bohr model, and the "size" of the wave function corresponds to the radius of the $n = 2$ orbit. Verification of these statements is left as a problem. More generally, it can be shown that corresponding to each value of n in the Bohr model there is a spherically symmetric wave function consisting of a polynomial of degree $n - 1$ in r, multiplied by $e^{-r/na}$, and representing a state with the same energy E_n as the corresponding state in the Bohr model. Thus the spherically symmetric solutions of the Schrödinger equation reproduce the energy-level scheme of the hydrogen atom completely and, in addition, provide a description of the electron distribution for each state.

8-3   General Wave Functions

The spherically symmetric solutions do not by any means exhaust all the possibilities for solutions of Eq. (8-6); the possibility of functions which depend on θ and ϕ as well as r has scarcely been mentioned. However, as soon as the requirement of spherical symmetry is dropped, the whole problem becomes considerably more complex, and a full treatment would be beyond the scope of this book. In the remainder of this section we sketch some of the most important ideas.

The key to finding the more general solutions is a technique known as *separation of variables*, which consists in representing the function $\psi(r,\theta,\phi)$ as a product of three functions, each containing only one of the three coordinates. Denoting these functions by $R(r)$, $\Theta(\theta)$, and $\Phi(\phi)$, respectively, we write

$$\psi(r,\theta,\phi) = R(r)\Theta(\theta)\Phi(\phi) \tag{8-20}$$

When this expression is substituted into Eq. (8-6) it is found to be a solution only if the individual functions satisfy the following ordinary differential equations:

$$-\frac{\hbar^2}{2m}\left(\frac{d^2R}{dr^2} + \frac{2}{r}\frac{dR}{dr}\right) + \left[\frac{\hbar^2}{2m}\frac{l(l+1)}{r^2} - \frac{e^2}{4\pi\epsilon_0 r}\right]R = ER \tag{8-21a}$$

$$\frac{1}{\sin\theta}\frac{d}{d\theta}\left(\sin\theta\frac{d\Theta}{d\theta}\right) + \left[l(l+1) - \frac{m_l^2}{\sin^2\theta}\right]\Theta = 0 \tag{8-21b}$$

$$\frac{d^2\Phi}{d\phi^2} + m_l^2\Phi = 0 \tag{8-21c}$$

where l, m_l, and E are constants.

The solutions of these equations are subject to certain boundary conditions. As already observed, the function $R(r)$ must approach zero at large r.   For $\Theta(\theta)$, there is the possibility of anomalous behavior of the solutions at $\theta = 0$, because of the factors $1/\sin\theta$ in Eq. (8-21b). Hence we must require that $\Theta(\theta)$ be a continuous function of θ, specifically that it may *not* have an infinite discontinuity at $\theta = 0$. The functions $\Phi(\phi)$ are restricted by the fact that the azimuthal coordinate ϕ has a *cyclic* nature, inasmuch as the points (r,θ,ϕ) and $(r, \theta, \phi + 2\pi)$ are the same point in space. Thus the functions $\Phi(\phi)$ must satisfy the condition

$$\Phi(\phi + 2\pi) \equiv \Phi(\phi) \tag{8-22}$$

These conditions are sufficient to restrict the possible values of the constants E, l, and m_l appearing in Eqs. (8-21).   We shall discuss the nature of these restrictions in detail only for the Φ equation.   It is easily verified that the solutions of Eq. (8-21c) can be written

$$\Phi(\phi) = (\text{const})e^{\pm im_l\phi} \tag{8-23}$$

For the condition of Eq. (8-22) to be satisfied, it must be true that

$$e^{\pm im_l(\phi+2\pi)} = e^{\pm im_l\phi}$$

or

$$e^{\pm i2\pi m_l} = 1 \tag{8-24}$$

But this equation is satisfied only when the quantity $2\pi m_l$ is an integral multiple of 2π, hence only when m_l is an *integer*. Thus we conclude that m_l must be a positive or negative integer or zero.

The boundary condition on Θ is less simple in nature, and we cannot discuss it in detail here. It can be shown that the continuity condition is satisfied only when l is zero or a positive integer. This result has in fact been anticipated by writing the factor $l(l + 1)$ in Eqs. (8-21a) and (8-21b) instead of some single letter. Furthermore, l must be at least as large as the absolute value of m_l.

Finally, solutions of Eq. (8-21a) which approach zero at large r are found to exist only when the energy E is given by

$$E_n = -\left(\frac{e^2}{4\pi\epsilon_0}\right)^2 \frac{m}{2n^2\hbar^2} \qquad n = 1, 2, 3, \ldots \qquad (8\text{-}25)$$

Further, such solutions exist only when n is at least as great as $l + 1$. We note that the spherically symmetric functions discussed above correspond to $l = 0$.

To summarize these results: Any function that satisfies the Schrödinger equation and the boundary conditions is identified by the values of three constants n, l, and m_l. Furthermore, as the roles of these constants in Eqs. (8-21) show, the function $R(r)$ depends on n and l, $\Theta(\theta)$ on l and m_l, and $\Phi(\phi)$ only on m_l. These integers are subject to the following requirements:

$$\begin{vmatrix} n \geq 1 \\ l \geq 0 \\ n \geq l + 1 \\ l \geq |m_l| \end{vmatrix}$$

For example, the following combinations of values are possible:

n	l	m_l
3	1	1
4	3	-2
1	0	0

but these are not possible:

n	l	m_l
2	2	2
2	1	2
2	3	-4

The quantity denoted above by m_l is usually denoted in the literature simply as m. This presents a slight danger of confusion, inasmuch

as *m* is also used universally to represent the electron mass. Nevertheless, we conform to convention and denote this quantity as *m* rather than
m_l from here on, at the same time cautioning the reader to be on the
lookout for this ambiguity.

The three integers are called *quantum numbers;* each state is identified uniquely by the values of these numbers. The value of *n* determines
the energy of the state, and *n* is called the *principal quantum number.*
Using the quantum numbers to identify the various component wave
functions, we write

$$\psi_{nlm}(r,\theta,\phi) = R_{nl}(r)\Theta_{lm}(\theta)\Phi_m(\phi) \tag{8-26}$$

The first few functions $R_{nl}(r)$ and $\Theta_{lm}(\theta)$ are shown in Tables 8-1 and
8-2. We note in Table 8-1, which expresses the functions $R_{nl}(r)$ in terms
of the dimensionless variable $\rho = r/a$, that each function contains a

Table 8-1   Radial Functions $R_{nl}(r)$ for Hydrogen Atom; $\rho = r/a$

$$R_{10}(r) = 2a^{-3/2}e^{-\rho}$$

$$R_{20}(r) = \frac{1}{\sqrt{2}a^{3/2}}\left(1 - \frac{\rho}{2}\right)e^{-\rho/2}$$

$$R_{21}(r) = \frac{1}{2\sqrt{6}a^{3/2}}\rho e^{-\rho/2}$$

$$R_{30}(r) = \frac{2}{3\sqrt{3}a^{3/2}}\left(1 - \frac{2\rho}{3} + \frac{2\rho^2}{27}\right)e^{-\rho/3}$$

$$R_{31}(r) = \frac{8}{27\sqrt{6}a^{3/2}}\rho\left(1 - \frac{\rho}{6}\right)e^{-\rho/3}$$

$$R_{32}(r) = \frac{4}{81\sqrt{30}a^{3/2}}\rho^2 e^{-\rho/3}$$

**Table 8-2   Angular Functions $\Theta_{lm}(\theta)$
for Hydrogen Atom***

$$\Theta_{00} = \frac{1}{\sqrt{2}} \qquad \Theta_{10} = \tfrac{1}{2}\sqrt{6}\cos\theta$$
$$\Theta_{11} = \tfrac{1}{2}\sqrt{3}\sin\theta$$
$$\Theta_{20} = \tfrac{1}{4}\sqrt{10}(3\cos^2\theta - 1)$$
$$\Theta_{21} = \sqrt{15}\sin\theta\cos\theta$$
$$\Theta_{22} = \tfrac{1}{4}\sqrt{15}\sin^2\theta$$

* For any Θ_{lm}, $\Theta_{l-m} = \Theta_{lm}$. This relation may
be used with Table 8-2 for negative values of *m*.

factor $e^{-\rho/n}$ multiplied by a polynomial of degree $n - 1$ in ρ; the coefficients in the polynomials are different for different values of l and the same n. Similarly, in Table 8-2, each function is a polynomial of degree l in $\sin \theta$ and $\cos \theta$.

We have now obtained a set of solutions of the Schrödinger equation for the hydrogen atom, each identified by a set of three quantum numbers n, l, m. The energy levels, determined by the principal quantum number n, are given by Eq. (8-26). Remarkably, this expression agrees exactly with the prediction of the Bohr model, Eq. (5-28), which in turn agrees with the energy levels deduced from the observed spectrum of hydrogen. This may not be very surprising; if the energy levels had proved to be different from those deduced from spectroscopic data, it would have been clear immediately that the theory cannot provide the correct description of the behavior of atoms, and it would have been forgotten or modified. But in 1925 the discovery that the solutions of the Schrödinger equation *do* predict the hydrogen energy levels correctly was a discovery of the first magnitude and provided very direct support for the basic correctness of the new concepts.

Next we examine the "size" of the wave functions we have just obtained. By size we mean simply the dimensions of the region of space in which the probability of finding the electron differs appreciably from zero. Clearly, this is determined by the radial function $R(r)$. Table 8-1 shows that the extension in space of the wave functions depends primarily on a factor of the form $e^{-\rho}$, $e^{-\rho/2}$, and in general $e^{-\rho/n}$. Thus the radius outside which the wave function is negligibly small increases with n. To examine the spatial extension of the wave function in more detail, we make use of the fact that the probability of finding the electron in the radius interval dr is given by $|\psi|^2 4\pi r^2 \, dr$, which is proportional to $r^2 |R(r)|^2$. This quantity is plotted for several radial functions in Fig. 8-3. Furthermore, it is possible to show that for the functions having the maximum l for a given n, that is, the functions $R_{n\,n-1}(r)$, the quantity $r^2 |R(r)|^2$ attains its *maximum* value at a value of r given by the quantity

$$r_{\max} = n^2 a = n^2 \frac{(4\pi\epsilon_0)\hbar^2}{me^2} \tag{8-27}$$

where a is, as usual, the radius of the first Bohr orbit, $a = 0.529 \times 10^{-10}$ m. This is just equal to the Bohr-orbit radius for the state n, as given by Eq. (5-27).

It is useful to visualize electron wave functions as clouds whose density is proportional to $|\psi|^2$ at various points. This picture should

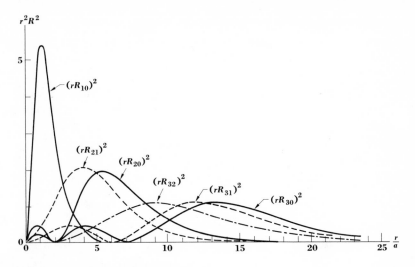

Fig. 8-3   *Graphs of the quantity $r^2|R(r)|^2$ for several radial functions.   Each graph represents the probability of finding the particle at various radii, for the corresponding state.*

not be taken too seriously; the size of the atom itself is smaller by 10^4 than wavelengths of visible light, so that there is no hope of actually *seeing* a hydrogen wave function.   Furthermore, the wave function itself is a complex quantity, while $|\psi|^2$ is always real.   Nevertheless, visualizing electron wave functions as clouds is useful in clarifying basic ideas. Pictorial representations of a few functions are shown in Fig. 8-4.

In regard to the *normalization* of the wave functions represented in Eq. (8-26), when the R and Θ functions in Table 8-1 and 8-2, respectively, are used with the numerical factors given there, the resulting wave functions are automatically normalized, provided that the functions Φ are

$$\Phi_m(\phi) = \frac{1}{\sqrt{2\pi}}\, e^{im\phi} \tag{8-28}$$

This choice of normalization constants has the consequence, however, that the radial functions are normalized to satisfy the condition

$$\int_0^\infty R^2 r^2 \, dr = 1 \tag{8-29}$$

rather than the condition

$$\int_0^\infty R^2 4\pi r^2 \, dr = 1 \tag{8-30}$$

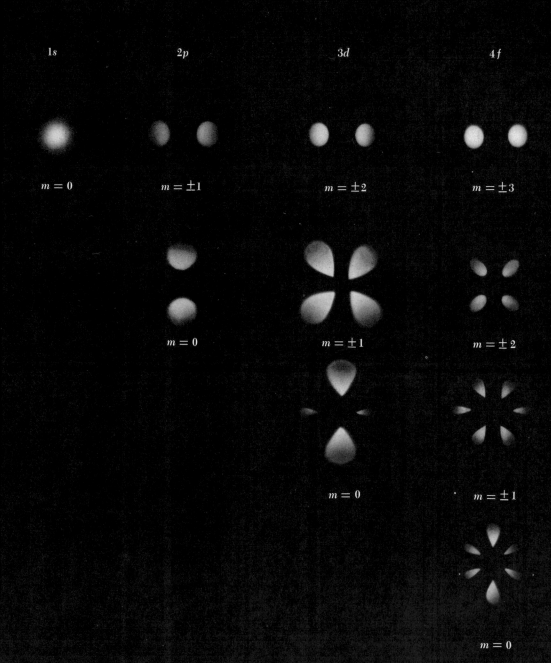

Fig. 8-4 *Pictorial representation of probability distribution $|\psi|^2$ for several hydrogen wave functions. Each figure is a cross section in a plane containing the polar axis (z axis), which is vertical and in the plane of the paper. The scale varies from figure to figure.*

2s

3p

4d

5f

$m = \pm 1$

$m = \pm 2$

$m = \pm 3$

$m = 0$

$m = 0$

$m = \pm 1$

$m = \pm 2$

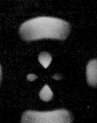

$m = 0$

$m = \pm 1$

$m = 0$

as for the spherically symmetric functions discussed in Sec. 8-2. Thus each function in Table 8-1 differs from the corresponding ones of Sec. 8-2 in having an additional factor $(4\pi)^{1/2}$.

An abbreviated scheme for labeling states, introduced by spectroscopists but now used quite generally, is to denote a state by a number equal to the principal quantum number n, followed by a lower case letter which corresponds to the angular-momentum number l according to the following scheme:

l	Spectroscopic notation
0	*s*
1	*p*
2	*d*
3	*f*
4	*g*
5	*h*

Thus a state with $n = 2$ and $l = 1$ is called a $2p$ state, and so on. In this notation the value of m is not specified.

In general, for a given n there are several values of l and m, corresponding to different states, which give the same total energy. An energy level that can correspond to any one of several distinct states is said to be *degenerate*. This is not to imply that the quantum numbers l and m are of no significance in describing the state. It is already clear that these quantum numbers are related to the angular distribution of the wave function about the nucleus; it will be shown in the next section that they are also directly related to the *angular momentum* and its z component.

In the above discussion we have considered only time-independent wave functions. Just as for the harmonic oscillator, discussed in Sec. 7-5, the complete time-dependent wave function Ψ is obtained by multiplying ψ by the factor $e^{-iEt/\hbar}$ which expresses the time dependence of a wave function with a definite total energy E. Thus we may write

$$\Psi_{nlm}(r,\theta,\phi,t) = \psi_{nlm}(r,\theta,\phi)e^{-iE_n t/\hbar} \tag{8-31}$$

with E_n given by Eq. (8-25). Correspondingly, the complex conjugate of the time-dependent wave function is given by

$$\Psi^*_{nlm}(r,\theta,\phi,t) = \psi^*_{nlm}(r,\theta,\phi)e^{+iE_n t/\hbar} \tag{8-32}$$

From this we see that the quantity $|\Psi|^2 = \Psi\Psi^*$, which represents the electron probability density in the sense discussed in Chaps. 6 and 7, is independent of time at any given point in space. In fact, as already remarked in Sec. 7-4, this is a property of *all* wave functions for states of definite total energy. Such states, it has been pointed out, are called *stationary states* for this reason. We define a stationary state in general as one having a definite total energy and having the property that $|\Psi|^2$ at any point in space is independent of time. On the other hand, the wave function itself varies with time according to the factor $e^{-iE_n t/\hbar}$. That is, the real and imaginary components of the wave function both vary sinusoidally with time with an angular frequency ω given by

$$\omega = \frac{E_n}{\hbar}$$

In summary, we have now seen how the solutions of the Schrödinger equation for the hydrogen atom can be used to predict the energy levels of the atom, as well as the general characteristics of the electron distribution. The analysis has been considerably more complex mathematically than in the Bohr theory, but the Schrödinger equation has the tremendous advantage that the energy levels and the permitted wave functions arise naturally from physically reasonable boundary conditions which the wave functions must satisfy, rather than having to be introduced artificially by *ad hoc* assumptions as in the Bohr theory. Considerable additional information can be obtained from the hydrogen-atom wave functions, as shown in the next section.

8-4   Angular Momentum

We now examine the angular-momentum characteristics of the wave functions developed in the preceding section. In the Bohr theory, the quantization of angular momentum was introduced as an explicit postulate, and the assumption that the angular momentum of the electron is an integral multiple of $\hbar$ led to the correct energy levels of the hydrogen atom. Thus it is of interest to examine the wave functions just developed to ascertain whether they too have definite angular momentum, and if so what correspondence exists between this angular momentum and that associated with the Bohr theory.

According to the discussion of Sec. 7-7, a state has a definite value of a component of angular momentum in a given direction only if the wave function representing this state is an eigenfunction of the corresponding angular-momentum operator. That is, when the operator is applied to the wave function, the result must be a constant times the original wave function, and the constant is equal to the definite value of the component of angular momentum. The operators corresponding to the three components of angular momentum in cartesian coordinates are given by Eqs. (7-57). Thus for a state to have a definite value of L_z, it must be true that

$$\frac{\hbar}{i}\left(x\frac{\partial}{\partial y} - y\frac{\partial}{\partial x}\right)\psi = (\text{const})\psi \tag{8-33}$$

and the constant is the value of L_z for the state.

Since the hydrogen wave functions have been represented in terms of spherical coordinates, it is most convenient to represent the angular-momentum operators also in terms of these coordinates, by means of the coordinate transformations given by Eqs. (8-4). The operator corresponding to L_z is given in spherical coordinates simply by

$$L_z \rightarrow \frac{\hbar}{i}\frac{\partial}{\partial\phi} \tag{8-34}$$

This result is obtained most easily by starting at the end and working backward. The chain rule for differentiation gives

$$\frac{\partial\psi}{\partial\phi} = \frac{\partial\psi}{\partial x}\frac{\partial x}{\partial\phi} + \frac{\partial\psi}{\partial y}\frac{\partial y}{\partial\phi} + \frac{\partial\psi}{\partial z}\frac{\partial z}{\partial\phi} \tag{8-35}$$

From Eqs. (8-4) we find

$$\frac{\partial x}{\partial\phi} = -r\sin\theta\sin\phi = -y$$

$$\frac{\partial y}{\partial\phi} = r\sin\theta\cos\phi = x$$

$$\frac{\partial z}{\partial\phi} = 0$$

Thus Eq. (8-35) becomes

$$\frac{\partial\psi}{\partial\phi} = -y\frac{\partial\psi}{\partial x} + x\frac{\partial\psi}{\partial y}$$

or, in operator notation,

$$\frac{\partial}{\partial\phi} = -y\frac{\partial}{\partial x} + x\frac{\partial}{\partial y} \tag{8-36}$$

which establishes the correctness of Eq. (8-34).

We now apply the operator for L_z to a hydrogen-atom wave function. The factor in each function that depends on ϕ is given by Eq. (8-28), and so we have

$$\frac{\hbar}{i}\frac{\partial}{\partial\phi}\psi_{nlm} = \frac{\hbar}{i}R_{nl}\Theta_{lm}\frac{\partial}{\partial\phi}\frac{e^{im\phi}}{\sqrt{2\pi}}$$

$$= \frac{\hbar}{i}(im)R_{nl}\Theta_{lm}\Phi_m$$

$$= m\hbar\psi_{nlm} \tag{8-37}$$

This result shows that applying the operator for L_z to the wave function ψ_{nlm} yields the same function multiplied by the constant $m\hbar$. That is, this function is an *eigenfunction* of the L_z operator, with the eigenvalue $m\hbar$. Thus ψ_{nlm} represents a state with a definite value of L_z equal to $m\hbar$; the quantum number m determines the value of L_z, just as n determines the energy of the state.

In exactly the same way, an operator can be derived which corresponds to the square of the total angular momentum, L^2. The structure of this operator is somewhat more complicated than that for L_z, and the details of its derivation need not be discussed here. The result is

$$L^2 \rightarrow -\hbar^2\left[\frac{1}{\sin\theta}\frac{\partial}{\partial\theta}\left(\sin\theta\frac{\partial}{\partial\theta}\right) + \frac{1}{\sin^2\theta}\frac{\partial^2}{\partial\phi^2}\right] \tag{8-38}$$

When the operator for L^2 is applied to ψ_{nlm}, the result is the quantity $l(l + 1)\hbar^2\psi_{nlm}$. That is, ψ_{nlm} is an eigenfunction of the L^2 operator, with eigenvalue $l(l + 1)\hbar^2$. Thus ψ_{nlm} represents a state with a definite value of L^2, given by

$$L^2 = l(l + 1)\hbar^2 \tag{8-39}$$

It is now clear that each of the three quantum numbers has a definite physical significance. The number n, usually called the *principal quantum number*, determines the energy of the state. The total angular momentum is determined by l, called the *orbital quantum number* or the *angular-momentum quantum number*. The component of angular momentum in the z direction is determined by m, called the *magnetic quantum number* for reasons which will become clear in Sec. 8-6.

The maximum value of L_z for any value of l is $l\hbar$. It might be thought that this corresponds to the case where the angular momentum is aligned precisely with the z axis, and therefore the square of the total angular momentum should be $L^2 = l^2\hbar^2$. Instead, as we have seen, it is $l(l + 1)\hbar^2$. That is, the magnitude of the total angular momentum is somewhat larger than its maximum component in any given direction. In classical mechanics this would make no sense, but quantum-mechanically it indicates that the *direction* of the angular-momentum vector is not a well-defined quantity. In fact, a state with a definite value of L_z *cannot* have definite values of L_x and L_y. This fundamental uncertainty in the direction of the angular-momentum vector is analogous to the uncertainty in position and momentum represented by the Heisenberg uncertainty principle.

It may seem strange that the hydrogen-atom wave functions have a definite value of the component of angular momentum in one particular direction. Does this imply that not all directions in space are equivalent? On the contrary; the fact that we have obtained states with definite L_z is a result of the particular coordinate system used. It is possible to construct states having, instead, a definite value of L_x or of L_y, but because of the fundamental uncertainty, it is *not* possible to construct states that have definite values of two or more components of **L**.

It is also possible to construct a mixture of states in which *no* component of angular momentum has a definite value. An example is a function in the form

$$a\Psi_{nlm_1} + b\Psi_{nlm_2}$$

where a and b are constants. The two functions correspond to the same total energy and angular momentum, but there are two different values of L_z. Therefore this state does not have a definite value of L_z. Correspondingly, adding wave functions with different values of l or n produces a state in which L^2 does not have a definite value, or in which E is indefinite. This should not be alarming; we have already seen that some wave functions represent states having a mixture of values of momentum, and correspondingly it is possible to make states having a mixture of energies, angular momentum, or the component of angular momentum in a given direction. The fact that several possible wave functions can be combined to obtain a new possible state of the system is an example of the superposition principle which we have already seen in action in various other contexts. Applied to the hydrogen atom, the superposition principle says that if any two wave functions Ψ_1 and Ψ_2 are individually possible states of the system, then any linear combination

$$a_1\Psi_1 + a_2\Psi_2 \tag{8-40}$$

is also a possible state of the system. This concept is of considerable importance in the analysis of *transitions* of a system from a state represented by one wave function to a state represented by another. Such transitions will be discussed in the next section.

8-5 *Transitions*

Thus far we have discussed mostly states of the hydrogen atom corresponding to a definite total energy. But in experimental observations what is always observed is not the energy of a particular state but the *change* in energy when a system makes a transition from one state to another. The wavelengths and frequencies of the various lines in the hydrogen spectrum are determined not by the positions of the energy levels but by the *differences* between various energy levels. Thus it is of interest to examine the mechanisms by which transitions from one energy state to another take place.

First, it is clear that an atom in a state with definite E, L^2, and L_z cannot make a transition to another state having different values of these dynamical quantities unless it interacts with its surroundings. Since the atom consists of charged particles, this interaction is electromagnetic in nature. In emission or absorption of radiation, the electron in the hydrogen atom is acted upon by the electric and magnetic fields of an electromagnetic wave. An atom can also change its energy state in a collision with another charged particle, such as an ion in a gas, in which case the interaction is simply the Coulomb force between the two charges.

Corresponding to the interaction of the atom with its surroundings, there is an interaction *energy*, which is represented by an additional term in the Schrödinger equation; in general, this term depends explicitly on time, since the interaction is time-dependent. As a result of the interaction, the state of the atom is not ordinarily a state with a definite total energy but rather a time-dependent mixture of states with various total energies. That is, the state of the atom is described by a function of the form

$$\Psi = \sum_i a_i \Psi_i \tag{8-41}$$

where Ψ_i is a state with energy E_i, and the coefficients a_i are functions of time. Suppose an atom in a state

$$\Psi_1 = \psi_1 e^{-iE_1 t/\hbar} \tag{8-42}$$

with energy E_1 makes a transition to another state

$$\Psi_2 = \psi_2 e^{-iE_2 t/\hbar} \tag{8-43}$$

with energy E_2 by emitting an electromagnetic photon of energy $E_1 - E_2$ and corresponding frequency

$$\omega = \frac{E_1 - E_2}{\hbar} \tag{8-44}$$

Then during the transition the state of the atom is represented by a function of the form

$$\Psi = a_1(t)\Psi_1 + a_2(t)\Psi_2 \tag{8-45}$$

in which we have explicitly shown that the coefficients a_1 and a_2 are functions of time. If the system starts in one state and ends in the other, the variation of the coefficients a_1 and a_2 might be as shown in Fig. 8-5.

Fig. 8-5 *Possible time variation of coefficients a_1 and a_2 in a superposition of two wave functions, corresponding to a transition from an initial state Ψ_1 to a final state Ψ_2. Graphs show the absolute values of a_1 and a_2, which in general may be complex. In order for the superposed function to remain normalized during the transition, the coefficients must satisfy the relation $|a_1|^2 + |a_2|^2 = 1$ at each instant.*

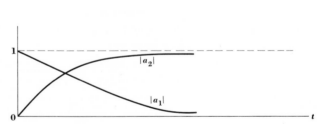

It is of interest to examine the probability density $|\Psi|^2 = \Psi^*\Psi$ for such a mixture of two states of different energies. Combining Eqs. (8-42), (8-43), and (8-45), we find

$$\Psi^*\Psi = (a_1^*\psi_1^* e^{iE_1 t/\hbar} + a_2^*\psi_2^* e^{iE_2 t/\hbar})(a_1\psi_1 e^{-iE_1 t/\hbar} + a_2\psi_2 e^{-iE_2 t/\hbar})$$

$$= |a_1\psi_1|^2 + |a_2\psi_2|^2 + a_1^* a_2\psi_1^*\psi_2 e^{i(E_1-E_2)t/\hbar}$$

$$+ a_1 a_2^*\psi_1\psi_2^* e^{-i(E_1-E_2)t/\hbar} \tag{8-46}$$

This is a significant result; it shows, as we might have expected, that such a state is *not* a stationary state; the quantity $|\Psi|^2$ at a given point in space is not independent of time. If the variation of the coefficients a_1 and a_2 is very slow compared with that of the wave functions themselves, then the first two terms in this expression also vary slowly. But the last two terms vary sinusoidally with a frequency given by

$$\omega = \frac{E_1 - E_2}{\hbar} \qquad (8\text{-}47)$$

which is the same as the frequency of the emitted radiation. Thus one can visualize the superposition of the two wave functions with different energies as resulting in a charge distribution in the atom which varies with just the right frequency to produce electromagnetic radiation of the observed frequency.

In atomic transitions the time during which the transition takes place is typically of the order of 10^{-8} sec. The frequency of the emitted radiation, on the other hand, is typically of the order of 10^{15} sec^{-1}. Thus usually a very large number of cycles occur during the emission of a photon. By considering the mechanism of the interaction of the atom and electromagnetic field in detail, it is possible actually to *calculate* the amount of time involved in a transition. This time, in turn, is closely related to the *intensity* of the resulting spectrum line; the most intense spectral lines are those corresponding to transitions with the greatest transition rates, and conversely. The prediction of intensities of spectral lines is one of the great successes of quantum mechanics in an area where the Bohr theory was completely powerless.

We have mentioned the oscillating charge density in an atom, resulting from the superposition of the two wave functions with different energies. The angular distribution of the resulting radiation depends on the spatial distribution of this oscillating charge. The transitions most likely to occur are those in which the charge distribution resembles an oscillating electric dipole. Much less likely are transitions for which the two superposed functions resemble a quadrupole, octopole, etc. The dipole-like charge distribution occurs when the two states involved in the transition have values of l that differ by unity and values of m that differ by zero or unity. Other transitions are not impossible, but they are much less likely.

Thus we obtain the following *selection rules* for transitions from one state to another:

$$\begin{cases} \Delta l = \pm 1 \\ \Delta m = 0, \pm 1 \end{cases} \tag{8-48}$$

Transitions that violate these rules are said to be *forbidden,* not because they cannot occur but because they are so much less likely than the others that they are not usually observed in optical spectra.

In the hydrogen spectrum, it is not obvious how one can determine whether or not the above selection rules are obeyed, since all the states for a given n have the same energy, independent of l and m. Thus one cannot determine from the spectrum which values of l and m are involved. However, when a magnetic field is applied to the atom, states having the same n but different m have slightly different energies as a result of the interaction of the electron with the external magnetic field. This energy shift results in a splitting of the spectrum lines, known as the *Zeeman effect;* it enables the experimenter to distinguish energy levels having different values of m and thus to investigate the selection rules just described. The Zeeman effect is the subject of the next section.

8-6 The Zeeman Effect

The Zeeman effect, mentioned briefly in Sec. 7-7, is the phenomenon of splitting of spectrum lines in atomic spectra when the atoms are placed in a magnetic field. Although this effect was first observed experimentally by the Dutch physicist Pieter Zeeman, the idea was not original with him. As early as 1862, Michael Faraday had speculated that, if vibrating electric charges in matter are responsible for the emission of line spectra, then imposing a magnetic field might produce changes in the frequency of the vibrations and corresponding changes in the frequency of the emitted light. The resolution of Faraday's spectroscope was not sufficient to detect any effect, but when Zeeman repeated some of Faraday's experiments at the University of Leyden in 1896, using improved spectroscopic equipment, he discovered that in the presence of a magnetic field individual spectrum lines are split into a number of closely spaced lines. Furthermore, following a suggestion by H. A. Lorentz (also at Leyden) in 1880, Zeeman discovered that the component lines have various definite states of polarization which can be measured. The Zeeman effect lends additional insight into the behavior and structure of atoms, and so we consider it here in some detail.

In order to understand the effect of a magnetic field on energy levels of the hydrogen atom, it is useful to make a brief regression to the language of the Bohr model. In that model, the electron moving in its circular orbit can be thought of as equivalent to a circular loop of current. Associated with a current loop there is always a magnetic-dipole moment μ. In the presence of a magnetic field **B**, a torque τ is exerted on this magnetic moment, given by

$$\tau = \mu \times \mathbf{B} \tag{8-49}$$

as discussed in Sec. 7-7. This torque tends to orient the dipole in the direction of the field. Corresponding to this interaction is a potential energy given by

$$V = -\mu \cdot \mathbf{B} = -\mu B \cos \theta \tag{8-50}$$

where θ is the angle between the directions of **B** and μ.

To evaluate μ in terms of the electron motion, we first recall that a conducting loop of area A, carrying a current I, has a magnetic moment given simply by $\mu = IA$. When the electron, with mass m and charge e, moves in a circular orbit of radius r with speed v, the circumference of the orbit is $2\pi r$, and the electron makes $v/2\pi r$ revolutions per second. The equivalent current, which is the amount of charge passing a given point per unit time, is

$$I = \frac{ev}{2\pi r} \tag{8-51}$$

The area A of the current loop is simply πr^2, and so the magnetic moment associated with the electron's motion is

$$\mu = \frac{ev}{2\pi r} \pi r^2 = \frac{evr}{2} \tag{8-52}$$

When this expression is multiplied and divided by m, the factor mvr appears in the numerator. This is simply the magnitude of the angular momentum L of a particle with momentum mv moving in a circle of radius r. Thus

$$\mu = \frac{e(mvr)}{2m} = \frac{e}{2m} L \tag{8-53}$$

Thus the magnitude of the magnetic moment is directly proportional to that of the angular momentum L, with the proportionality factor $e/2m$. This factor is called the *gyromagnetic ratio*. For a positive charge the vectors μ and **L** have the same direction. The electron charge is, of course, negative, and so the correct vector relationship for electrons is

$$\mu = -\frac{e}{2m}\mathbf{L}$$

(8-54)

The above discussion has been based on the Bohr model, which has already been shown to be inadequate. Nevertheless, it can be shown that the relationship given by Eq. (8-54) is valid for *any* rotating configuration of charge in which the charge-to-mass ratio is e/m, and so it is reasonable to postulate that this relationship is also valid in the quantum-mechanical description of electron motion. The final test of this hypothesis is whether or not it agrees with experimental observations of the Zeeman effect.

In computing the interaction energy of the magnetic moment μ in the magnetic field $\mathbf{B}$, it is convenient to choose the coordinate axes so that $\mathbf{B}$ lies along the direction of the $+z$ axis. In that case, combining Eqs. (8-50) and (8-54), we obtain

$$V = \frac{e}{2m}\mathbf{L} \cdot \mathbf{B} = \frac{e}{2m}L_z B$$

(8-55)

This expression is the magnetic interaction energy, which is added to the usual kinetic and potential energies, and so represents the amount by which each energy level is *shifted* by the magnetic interaction. Of course, L_z has different values for different levels; the possible values of L_z, as shown in Sec. 8-4, are given by $m_l \hbar$, where m_l is the magnetic quantum number for the state, an integer between $-l$ and l. We now see the reason for the name "magnetic quantum number."

Using the above expression for L_z together with Eq. (8-55), we find that a level with magnetic quantum number m_l is shifted by an amount ΔE given by

$$\Delta E = m_l \frac{e\hbar}{2m} B$$

(8-56)

In the presence of a magnetic field, then, the energy scheme of the hydrogen atom takes the form in Fig. 8-6. Levels with the same n and l but different m_l, which are *degenerate* in the absence of a $\mathbf{B}$ field, become *nondegenerate* in the presence of $\mathbf{B}$.

It is of interest to examine the numerical magnitude of the splitting of energy levels. A magnetic field of 1 weber/m² can readily be achieved in modern laboratories. For such a field, the numerical value

Fig. 8-6   Energy-level diagram showing the splitting of energy levels resulting from the interaction of the magnetic moment of the electron's orbital motion with an external magnetic field. Values of m_l are shown adjacent to the various levels; relative magnitudes of splittings are exaggerated for clarity. Some of the $n = 4$ levels are not shown; the reader should try to draw them in.

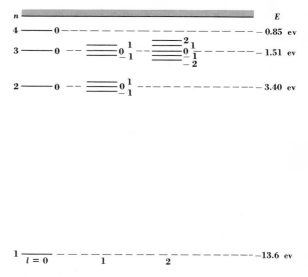

of the factor multiplying m_l in Eq. (8-56) is

$$\Delta E = \frac{e\hbar B}{2m}$$

$$= \frac{(1.60 \times 10^{-19}\ \text{coul})(1.054 \times 10^{-34}\ \text{joule sec})(1\ \text{weber/m}^2)}{2(9.10 \times 10^{-31}\ \text{kg})}$$

$$= 9.26 \times 10^{-24}\ \text{joule} = 5.80 \times 10^{-5}\ \text{ev}$$

For comparison, the energy of the $n = 3$ to $n = 2$ transition corresponding to the longest-wavelength line in the Balmer series, as Fig. 5-6 shows, is $3.40 - 1.51$ ev, or about 1.9 ev. The *fractional* change in transition energy is about 3×10^{-5}; the wavelength of the line in question is 6,562 Å, and so the corresponding shift in wavelength should be of the order of

$$\Delta\lambda = (6,562\ \text{Å})(3 \times 10^{-5}) \simeq 0.2\ \text{Å}$$

a shift which is well within the resolution of present-day grating spectrometers.

Referring again to the energy-level diagram of Fig. 8-6, we can now predict into how many component lines each spectrum line should be split. As an example, we consider again the $n = 3$ to $n = 2$ transition. The above calculation shows that the $n = 3$ level corresponding to $l = 2$ (3d in spectroscopic notation) is split into five equally spaced levels, with spacing given by Eq. (8-56). Correspondingly, the $n = 2$, $l = 1$ (2p) level is split into three levels. Let the splitting of adjacent levels be ΔE and the level spacing in the absence of a magnetic field E_0. If there were no selection rules, there would be 15 distinct transitions, ranging in energy from $E_0 - 3\Delta E$ for the $m_l = -2 \rightarrow +1$ transition to $E_0 + 3\Delta E$ for the $m_l = +2 \rightarrow -1$ transition, and differing by intervals of ΔE. The selection rule $\Delta m_l = 0, \pm 1$ eliminates several of these; the nine transitions consistent with this rule are shown in Fig. 8-7. As the figure shows, these all have energy E_0 or $E_0 \pm \Delta E$, and we therefore expect that the Zeeman effect should split this particular line into three lines.

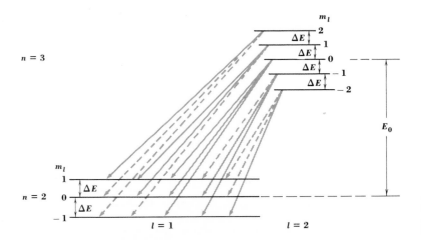

Fig. 8-7 *Detail of part of the hydrogen energy-level diagram, showing Zeeman-effect splitting of the 3d and 2p levels. Transitions forbidden by the selection rule* $\Delta m = 0, \pm 1$ *are shown as broken lines.*

The predictions of Lorentz regarding the *polarization* of the component spectrum lines are borne out experimentally. The state of polarization in each case depends in general on the direction in which the radiation is observed, relative to the direction of **B**. The radiation corresponding to the $m_l = 0$ transition is found always to be plane-polarized in a plane containing the **B** field and the direction from source to observer. This result can be understood qualitatively on the basis of the picture introduced in Sec. 8-5; during the transition from one state to another, the superposition of the two wave functions gives an electric

charge density which varies periodically with time.   In transitions for
which $\Delta m_l = 0$, each wave function contains the same factor $e^{im\phi}$; inspection of Eq. (8-46) shows that the charge distribution, which is proportional to $\Psi^*\Psi$, cannot have any dependence on ϕ but is axially
symmetric about the z axis.   Thus the periodically varying electric
charge resembles an electric dipole oriented along the z axis, and the
radiation pattern is therefore characteristic of such a dipole, as discussed
in Sec. 3-1.

The polarizations of the lines corresponding to transitions for which
$\Delta m_l = \pm 1$ are somewhat more subtle.   For these cases the periodically
varying charge density resulting from the superposition of the two wave
functions with different values of m_l is characteristic of two electric
dipoles in the xy plane, at right angles to each other and $90°$ out of
phase.   For these lines, the light emerging in a direction parallel to **B**
is circularly polarized; that perpendicular to the direction of **B** is plane-
polarized, and in general for all other directions the light is elliptically
polarized.   The states of polarization of the three component lines are
shown in Fig. 8-8 for the directions parallel and perpendicular to the
field.

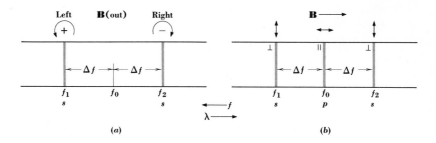

Fig. 8-8   *Polarization of the components of a line
split by the Zeeman effect.   (a) Magnetic field pointing
out of the plane; (b) magnetic field in the plane, as
shown.   Why is the central line absent when viewed
parallel to the magnetic field?*

Thus the Zeeman effect provides direct confirmation of a number
of predictions of the "new" quantum mechanics, as applied to the hydrogen atom.   Not only does the Schrödinger equation provide a correct
prediction of spectrum lines; it also provides a basis for computing intensities of lines, shifts resulting from the application of a magnetic field,
and the states of polarization of the component lines in the Zeeman effect.

The theory is not yet complete, however. Careful examination of the fine details of the hydrogen spectrum reveals some discrepancies in the Zeeman splittings. Even more interesting, some spectrum lines show splitting even in the absence of an external magnetic field. In some cases there are an *even* number of component lines, although the above discussion suggests that there should always be an odd number, corresponding to the fact that the number of values of m_l for a given level is always odd. These and numerous other features of atomic spectra point to the necessity for further refinements in the basic principles. One of the most important refinements, introduced in the next section, is the concept of *electron spin* with its associated magnetic moment and magnetic interaction energy.

8-7 Electron Spin

Although the Schrödinger equation is quite successful in accounting for many features of atomic spectra, some phenomena are not explained by the Schrödinger equation in the form we have discussed. In some cases, the spectrum of an element suggests the existence of a pair of closely spaced energy levels (a *doublet*) where the Schrödinger equation predicts only a single level. In the splitting of spectrum lines in the Zeeman effect, sometimes five or seven lines or even more are found instead of the three predicted by the above discussion, and in cases where there are only three, the splitting is sometimes greater than that predicted. Several examples of this "anomalous Zeeman effect" are shown in Fig. 8-9.

On the basis of these anomalies, Goudsmit and Uhlenbeck postulated in 1925 the existence of *electron spin,* in which the electron is assumed to have an intrinsic angular momentum and corresponding magnetic moment, in addition to the angular momentum and magnetic moment resulting from its orbital motion about the nucleus. In the conceptual framework of the Bohr theory this electron spin was represented by a model in which the electron is not a point but rather a small sphere which *spins* on its axis as it travels around the orbit, thereby making additional contributions to the angular momentum and magnetic moment. This picture may be compared with the angular momentum of the earth with respect to the sun, which has two components, one associated with the spin of the earth on its axis and the other with its orbital motion around the sun. The terms *spin* and *orbital angular momentum,* in fact, originated in celestial mechanics.

In the conceptual framework of wave mechanics, there is no simple

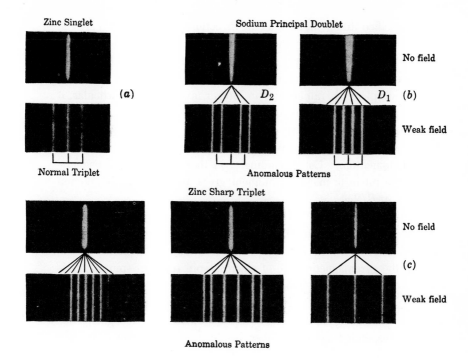

Fig. 8-9   *Photographs showing the normal and anomalous Zeeman effects for several elements.   The brackets under each photograph show the "normal" splitting predicted by neglecting the effect of electron spin.*

way to picture the phenomenon of electron spin.   Mathematically, one can describe an electron with spin by a wave function which, instead of being simply one complex number at each point in space, is a quantity with two components, each of which may be complex, corresponding to two possible orientations of electron spin relative to a specified direction. We cannot go into the details of this formulation here, but it can be developed into a complete description of the behavior of the electron, including its intrinsic angular momentum.

The anomalies in atomic energy levels mentioned above are consistent with the assumption that the electron possesses an intrinsic magnetic momentum which can have a component

$$\mu = \pm \frac{e\hbar}{2m}$$

(8-57)

in any specified direction, such as the direction of an external magnetic field. The spin magnetic moment, unlike the orbital magnetic moment, cannot have a zero component in the direction of the field; this fact suggests that the corresponding angular-momentum component is a *half-integer* multiple of $\hbar$, rather than an integer multiple. In particular, it appears that the intrinsic angular momentum must have a component $\pm\frac{1}{2}\hbar$ in the direction of a given reference axis. This component may then change by $\pm\hbar$ in a transition between states, just as with orbital angular momentum. Correspondingly, in the presence of a magnetic field B the intrinsic magnetic moment gives an additional interaction energy $\pm e\hbar B/2m$.

Direct measurement of the intrinsic angular momentum of the electron is less simple than that of the magnetic moment, which can be obtained directly from spectroscopic observations. The first measurement of the gyromagnetic ratio of electron spin (ratio of spin magnetic moment to spin angular momentum) was suggested by Einstein and actually performed by De Haas, using an experimental arrangement shown schematically in Fig. 8-10. A cylinder of ferromagnetic material is suspended by a fine fiber inside a solenoid, which magnetizes the sample axially. When the direction of the magnetic field is reversed, the electron magnetic moments (and thus their spins) change direction as the direction of magnetization reverses. But since the system is isolated (i.e., there is no external torque along the axis of rotation),

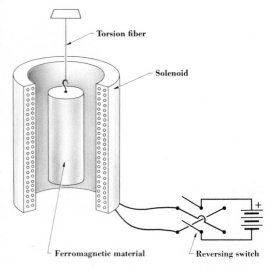

Fig. 8-10 *Apparatus for measuring electron-spin angular momentum. A cylinder of ferromagnetic material is suspended by a fine fiber in a solenoid (shown in cross section), which magnetizes the material by orienting the electron magnetic moments parallel to the field. When the field is reversed, the spins flip over; since the total angular momentum cannot change, the specimen begins to rotate. The angular velocity may be measured precisely by reflecting a beam of light from a mirror mounted on the cylinder, as with a reflecting galvanometer.*

its *total* angular momentum must be constant, and this can happen only if the sample as a whole begins to rotate. By measuring the angular velocity of rotation immediately after field reversal, one can calculate the total change in angular momentum of the electron spin. The total change in magnetic moment can also be measured from the magnetization of the sample, and so the ratio of angular momentum to magnetic moment can be measured.

The results of this measurement are consistent with the assumption that the component of angular momentum in the direction of the field is $\pm\frac{1}{2}\hbar$ and that the gyromagnetic ratio corresponding to the intrinsic angular momentum is not $e/2m$, as for orbital angular momentum and magnetic moment, but rather twice that value, e/m. This result is unique to quantum mechanics. Within the framework of classical electrodynamics, there is no possible configuration of charge that leads to a gyromagnetic ratio different from $e/2m$, and so this aspect of the behavior of the electron spin cannot be understood on the basis of classical theory.

It is clear how the intrinsic magnetic moment of the electron can produce anomalous results in the Zeeman effect, but it is perhaps not so obvious how it can affect energy levels when no external field is applied. The reason is that, in the moving frame of reference of the electron, the positively charged nucleus appears to be in motion, and so the electron "sees" not just a static electric field but also a magnetic field. This is intrinsically a relativistic effect, and relativistic electrodynamics must be used to calculate the interaction energy between the magnetic moment of the electron and the magnetic field which appears in its frame of reference. The apparent motion of the nucleus can be expressed in terms of the electron's orbital angular momentum $\mathbf{L}$, and so the interaction energy depends on the relative orientation of $\mathbf{L}$ and the electron spin. Denoting the spin angular momentum by $\mathbf{S}$, we can express the interaction energy in terms of the quantity $\mathbf{L} \cdot \mathbf{S}$ and the potential energy $V(r)$ corresponding to the electric field of the nucleus. Specifically, the interaction energy is given by

$$E = \frac{1}{2m^2c^2r}\frac{dV(r)}{dr}\mathbf{L} \cdot \mathbf{S}$$

(8-58)

Because of its dependence on the spin and orbital angular momenta of the electron, this interaction is called *spin-orbit coupling.*

In many atoms the energy-level splittings resulting from spin-orbit coupling are comparable in magnitude to those associated with the strong-field Zeeman effect. As an example of the magnitude of the energy given by Eq. (8-58), we evaluate this expression approximately with the assumption that $\mathbf{L} \cdot \mathbf{S}$ is of the order of $\hbar^2$ and with a typical value of r corresponding to the radius of the $n = 2$ Bohr orbit; that is,

$$r = 4\frac{4\pi\epsilon_0\hbar^2}{me^2} = 2.12 \times 10^{-10} \text{ m}$$

The order of magnitude of the spin-orbit energy is then

$$E \simeq \frac{1}{2m^2c^2}\frac{e^2}{4\pi\epsilon_0 r^2}\hbar^2$$

Inserting the appropriate numerical magnitudes, we find

$$E \simeq 2 \times 10^{-24} \text{ joule} \simeq 10^{-5} \text{ ev}$$

Comparing this figure with the numerical example of Zeeman-effect splitting, we see that the two are comparable. Furthermore, the spin-orbit coupling energy increases rapidly with the principal quantum number n, which governs the average value of r for the wave function. As an example, the splitting of the $3p$ level of the sodium atom leading to the famous yellow sodium doublet (5,890, 5,896 Å) in the $3p-3s$ transition is the result of spin-orbit coupling.

It may seem that the concept of electron spin is merely an *ad hoc* hypothesis, introduced to explain experimental facts but without any fundamental basis. This, it must be admitted, is a deficiency of the nonrelativistic Schrödinger equation with electron spin. It is, however, a deficiency that is avoided in relativistic formulations, when one develops a wave equation based on relativistic kinematics. In the relativistic wave equation for the electron, the Dirac equation, the spin and its associated interaction energy come out automatically rather than having to be added separately. Furthermore, the Schrödinger equation can be obtained from the Dirac equation as an approximation when the energies are sufficiently small compared with mc^2. Thus the concept of electron spin, although introduced as an *ad hoc* explanation of certain spectral anomalies, has now been justified thoroughly on theoretical grounds, through the methods of relativistic quantum mechanics.

The existence of electron spin necessitates the introduction of a fourth quantum number to describe the state of the electron in the hydrogen atom. As we have seen, the component of angular momentum in the direction of a given axis (for example, the z axis) can only be $\pm\frac{1}{2}\hbar$. This orientation is conveniently described by introducing a quantum number s which takes the values $\pm\frac{1}{2}$. Thus the *four* quantum numbers n, l, m, and s constitute a complete description of the state of an electron in the hydrogen atom. As we shall see in the next chapter, this description is especially useful in more complex atoms.

PROBLEMS

8-1   The radius of the gold nucleus is about 7×10^{-13} cm. In a Rutherford-scattering experiment, what minimum energy must the α particle have to measure this radius? That is, what energy is needed for it to approach within 7×10^{-13} cm of the center of the nucleus? Express your result in ev.

8-2   Verify by direct substitution that the wave function given by Eq. (8-19) is a solution of the spherically symmetric Schrödinger equation (8-8), and find the energy of the state described by this function.

8-3   Find the value of the constant C necessary to normalize the wave function given by Eq. (8-19). The calculation is simplified by making the change of variable $x = r/2a$ and by using a table of integrals.

8-4   Show that the solutions of Eq. (8-21c) can be written in the alternative forms $\sin m_l\phi$ and $\cos m_l\phi$. Show that the solutions given by Eq. (8-23) can be represented as combinations of these functions, and conversely.

8-5   Show by direct substitution that the functions Θ_{10}, Θ_{11}, and Θ_{20} in Table 8-2 are solutions of Eq. (8-21b) when appropriate values of l and m are used.

8-6   Show by direct substitution that the functions R_{10} and R_{20} in Table 8-1 are solutions of Eq. (8-21a) with the appropriate value of l.

8-7   By examining the solutions of Eqs. (8-21b) and (8-21c) for the particular case $l = 0$ and $m = 0$, show that all wave functions with $l = 0$ are spherically symmetric; i.e., that they do not depend on the angles θ and ϕ.

8-8   For the radial functions R_{21} and R_{32} in Table 8-1, show that the quantity $r^2|R(r)|^2$ has a maximum at $\rho = 2^2$ and $\rho = 3^2$, respectively. Compare these results with the predictions of Eq. (8-27).

8-9   For the radial functions in Table 8-1, show that $R(0) = 0$, except for the functions for which $l = 0$.

8-10   For the angular functions in Table 8-2, show that, for a given value of l, the function is most concentrated along the polar axis for $m = 0$ and that, for increasing values of m, it becomes more and more concentrated in the equatorial plane (the xy plane).

8-11   Consider the ion He$^+$, which has one electron. How are the wave functions for this ion related to those of the hydrogen atom?

8-12   For the hydrogen wave function ψ_{100}, what is the probability that the electron is in the region outside a sphere of radius equal to the radius of the first Bohr orbit, given by Eq. (8-11)?

8-13   Show that, if the functions $\sin m_l\phi$ and $\cos m_l\phi$ are used for Φ instead of Eq. (8-23), the resulting hydrogen wave functions are *not* eigenfunctions of the L_z operator but are mixtures of states having $L_z = m_l\hbar$ and $L_z = -m_l\hbar$.

8-14   A quantum-mechanical harmonic oscillator makes a transition from the state $n = 3$ to the state $n = 2$ by emitting an electromagnetic photon.
  a.   Find the frequency of the time variation of each of the functions Ψ_2 and Ψ_3.
  b.   Find the frequency of the time variation of the quantity $\Psi^*\Psi$ during the transition.
  c.   Find the frequency of the emitted radiation.

8-15   Consider the $4p-3d$ transitions in hydrogen, in the presence of a magnetic field of 2.0 webers/m^2, and assume that the electron has zero spin.
  a.   Draw an energy-level diagram showing the Zeeman-effect splitting, and calculate the magnitude of the splitting.
  b.   Indicate the permitted transitions, and calculate the shifts in their energies compared with the zero-field values.
  c.   Calculate the wavelength shifts of the resulting spectrum lines.

8-16   For the $2p-1s$ transition in hydrogen, consider the shape of the part of the quantity $\Psi^*\Psi$ that results from the superposition of the two wave functions. From this, predict the state of polarization of the radiation associated with each value of m_l in the initial state. Assume the electron has no spin.

8-17   Draw a diagram showing the polarization of each component of the $2p-1s$ transition line, split by the Zeeman effect, for the hydrogen atom, if electron spin can be ignored.

8-18   In the Bohr model of the hydrogen atom, how does the spin-orbit coupling energy depend on the quantum number n?

8-19   Draw an energy-level diagram showing the Zeeman-effect splitting of the $3d$ and $2p$ levels in hydrogen, including electron spin.   Analyze the splitting of the line resulting from $3d-2p$ transitions.

8-20   From Eq. (8-58), estimate the spin-orbit interaction energy for the $2p$ state of the hydrogen atom, by evaluating the quantities $1/r$ and dV/dr at $r = 4a$, where a is the first Bohr radius, given by Eq. (8-11).

8-21   A student asserts that any wave function for the hydrogen atom can be multiplied by a factor $e^{i\alpha}$, where α is a real constant, without changing any of the physical properties of the corresponding state.   Discuss this assertion.

IN THIS CHAPTER the principles of quantum mechanics are applied to atoms containing more than one electron. A new principle, the exclusion principle, is needed to understand the structure of many-electron atoms. This principle, which can be stated as a restriction on the permissible quantum numbers of electrons in an atom, or alternatively as a condition on the symmetry properties of the wave function, provides the basis for understanding the chemical properties of elements and the periodic table of the elements. Next we discuss x-ray spectra, associated with transitions of inner electrons in many-electron atoms. The relation of electronic structure of atoms to valence is discussed next, together with some important properties of molecules, including molecular spectra associated with transitions between vibration and rotation states.

9-1 Exclusion Principle

Thus far, in discussing the fundamental principles of quantum mechanics, we have considered only systems containing one electron. This is a natural way to begin, just as in studying classical mechanics one begins by trying to understand the dynamical laws governing the motion of a single point mass before trying to apply these laws to more complicated systems. Now, however, we shall consider applications of quantum mechanics to systems containing several electrons.

To illustrate the general nature of the problem, we consider first the helium atom, which has two electrons and a nucleus consisting of two protons and two neutrons. The stationary states for an electron in the hydrogen atom are described by time-independent wave functions of a single position vector $\mathbf{r}$ or a set of three coordinates such as (x,y,z) or (r,θ,ϕ); the stationary states of an atom containing two electrons are represented by a wave function containing the coordinates of both particles, such as $\psi(r_1,\theta_1,\phi_1,r_2,\theta_2,\phi_2)$, or $\psi(\mathbf{r}_1,\mathbf{r}_2)$. Just as the quantity

$$\psi^*(\mathbf{r})\psi(\mathbf{r})\ dV \tag{9-1}$$

for a one-electron wave function represents the probability that the particle will be found in a volume element dV in the vicinity of the point $\mathbf{r}$, the quantity

$$\psi^*(\mathbf{r}_1,\mathbf{r}_2)\psi(\mathbf{r}_1,\mathbf{r}_2)\ dV_1\ dV_2 \tag{9-2}$$

for a two-electron wave function represents the probability that the first particle will be found in a volume element dV_1 near point $\mathbf{r}_1$ and simultaneously the second particle will be found in a volume element dV_2 near $\mathbf{r}_2$. In general, the wave function is a function of as many position vectors or sets of three coordinates as there are particles in the system.

Correspondingly, the total-energy operator, introduced in Sec. 7-7, depends on the coordinates of both particles. There are terms for the kinetic energy of each particle, a potential energy associated with the interaction of each particle with the nucleus, and an additional term representing interaction of the two particles with each other. Thus the time-independent Schrödinger equation for two electrons in a helium atom, including all these energies, is

$$-\frac{\hbar^2}{2m}\left(\frac{\partial^2\psi}{\partial x_1{}^2}+\frac{\partial^2\psi}{\partial y_1{}^2}+\frac{\partial^2\psi}{\partial z_1{}^2}+\frac{\partial^2\psi}{\partial x_2{}^2}+\frac{\partial^2\psi}{\partial y_2{}^2}+\frac{\partial^2\psi}{\partial z_2{}^2}\right)$$

$$+\frac{e^2}{4\pi\epsilon_0}\left(-\frac{2}{r_1}-\frac{2}{r_2}+\frac{1}{|\mathbf{r}_1-\mathbf{r}_2|}\right)\psi = E\psi \tag{9-3}$$

The presence of the last term on the left side of Eq. (9-3), representing the interaction between the two electrons, makes the solution of this equation more complicated than the corresponding problem for the one-electron atom; in fact, it has never been solved exactly. The situation is comparable to that of the three-body problem in celestial mechanics, as, for example, the sun, the earth, and the moon. Although the fundamental principles underlying the motion of these bodies, Newton's laws of motion and the law of gravitation, are well known, the differential equations which result from applying these laws are so complicated that they have never been solved exactly. Instead, one resorts to approximations of various kinds in order to obtain approximate descriptions of the motion. So it is with the helium atom and with all more complicated atoms.

To any reader who feels disappointment at the necessity of having to make approximations at so early a stage in the applications of quantum mechanics, we remark that this procedure is practically always necessary in applying physical principles to new situations and, furthermore, that it is often an advantage rather than a disadvantage. Even in cases where exact solutions of complicated problems exist, they are often so complex mathematically that their physical meaning is not readily grasped. Frequently, by making sensible approximations, one can obtain results that are reasonably good representations of the real physical situation and are much simpler, thereby facilitating a grasp of their physical meaning. Equally important, there are many cases in which even approximate quantum-mechanical discussions bring understanding to areas where classical mechanics is powerless, with or without approximations.

The simplest possible approximation in the treatment of many-electron atoms is simply to disregard the interactions of the electrons with each other and include only the interaction of each electron with the nucleus. In this model, each electron moves as though the others were not present, and its possible wave functions are the same as those for the hydrogen atom, with the modification that the nuclear charge is not e but Ze, where Z is the atomic number, equal to the number of protons in the nucleus. In this approximation, the wave function for the two-electron system of the helium atom is simply a product of two one-electron wave functions of the hydrogen-atom type, and the total energy of the state is the sum of the energies of the two electrons.

Formally, if $\psi_1(x_1,y_1,z_1)$ is a solution of the equation

$$-\frac{\hbar^2}{2m}\left(\frac{\partial^2\psi_1}{\partial x_1{}^2} + \frac{\partial^2\psi_1}{\partial y_1{}^2} + \frac{\partial^2\psi_1}{\partial z_1{}^2}\right) - \frac{2e^2}{4\pi\epsilon_0 r}\psi_1 = E_1\psi_1 \tag{9-4}$$

with energy E_1, and if $\psi_2(x_2,y_2,z_2)$ is a solution of the corresponding equation for the second particle, with energy E_2, then it can readily be shown that the product function $\psi = \psi_1(\mathbf{r}_1)\psi_2(\mathbf{r}_2)$ is a solution of Eq.

(9-3) with the term in $|\mathbf{r}_1 - \mathbf{r}_2|$ omitted and that the energy of the state represented by this function is $E_1 + E_2$. Detailed proof of this statement is left as a problem. The state of each electron is described by a set of four quantum numbers, just as for the hydrogen atom, and so the state of the composite system is described by a set of eight quantum numbers.

This approximation is quite drastic; especially when there are many electrons present, the interactions of the electrons with each other are at least as important as the interaction of each with the nucleus. Fortunately, a considerably better approximation can be made without sacrificing the essential features of the simple one. Instead of ignoring the electron-electron interactions, we regard each electron as moving in an electric field which is the combined result of the nuclear charge and the charges of the other electrons and which, on an average, can be assumed to be spherically symmetric. Thus the wave function for each electron is a solution of a Schrödinger equation similar in form to that of the hydrogen atom but with the $1/r$ potential-energy term replaced by a different function $V(r)$. The state of each electron may then be described by a set of four quantum numbers, just as with the hydrogen atom, although since the potential-energy function is different the dependence of the energy levels on the quantum numbers is not the same as that for the hydrogen atom.

The scheme just described, representing each electron as moving in an *average* potential resulting from all the other electrons and the nucleus, includes the interactions between the electrons in an approximate way, while still preserving the simplifying features of the description in terms of quantum numbers for individual electrons. Much of the discussion of the behavior of complex atoms which follows is based on this approximate model.

Every atom, no matter what its structure, has a "ground state," or state of lowest energy; for the hydrogen atom the $1s$ state ($n = 1, l = 0$) is the ground state. In the picture we have just described, how does the ground state of a many-electron atom look? Offhand, one might expect that in the ground state all the electrons would fall into the lowest-energy states, so that every electron would be in a $1s$ state. In that case, looking at atoms with increasing numbers of electrons, we should expect gradual changes in the chemical and physical properties of the elements corresponding to these atoms.

There are several different kinds of evidence that this is *not* what happens. First, the chemical properties of elements change quite abruptly with atomic number. Consider, for example, the elements fluorine, neon, and sodium, with 9, 10, and 11 electrons, respectively. Fluorine tends strongly to form compounds in which it acquires an extra electron, sodium forms compounds in which it *loses* an electron, and neon forms no compounds at all.   If the explanation of the chemical behavior of elements is to be found in the electronic structure of their atoms, the simple picture of a ground state with all the electrons in the $1s$ states is clearly in need of modification.

Other evidence points with equal force to this deficiency. In the spectrum of lithium, which contains three electrons, there are lines that can be interpreted as transitions from the $3p$ state, split by spin-orbit coupling into a doublet, to the $2s$ state, but there are none that can be interpreted as transitions to the $1s$ state.   Why not?

The key to the unraveling of this mystery was discovered in 1925 by a German theoretical physicist, Wolfgang Pauli, in a principle now known as the *Pauli exclusion principle*.   This principle can be stated very simply, and yet it is of the utmost importance in the understanding of many-electron systems.   It is this: *In a system containing several electrons, no two electrons can be in states in which all four of their quantum numbers are the same.*

To illustrate this principle, we apply it to the mystery of the lithium spectrum.   For the $n = 1$ states, there can be only $l = 0$ and $m = 0$, and the spin quantum number can be $+\frac{1}{2}$ or $-\frac{1}{2}$.   Thus only two electrons can be accommodated in the $n = 1$ states.   The third electron must be in a state with $n = 2$ or higher.   This accounts for the absence of transitions of the third electron into $n = 1$ states; the $n = 1$ states are all "full," and the third electron must be content with the $n = 2$ states.

The exclusion principle immediately offers hope of understanding the periodic table of the elements.   We picture the electronic structure of complex atoms in terms of successive filling up of higher and higher energy levels, with the assumption that the chemical properties of elements are determined mostly by the outermost electrons.   For example, an atom with one electron considerably farther away from the nucleus than the others should have a tendency to lose this electron and thus behave chemically as an element with a valence of $+1$.   The periodic table will be discussed in detail in Sec. 9-2.

The Pauli exclusion principle can be stated in another way which, although equivalent to the statement just given, is in some respects more fundamental.   To introduce this alternative statement, we consider again a quantum-mechanical system containing two electrons, described by a time-independent wave function $\psi(\mathbf{r_1},\mathbf{r_2})$.   As already remarked, Eq.

(9-2) represents the probability that particles 1 and 2 are found in volume elements dV_1 and dV_2, respectively, in the vicinity of $\mathbf{r}_1$ and $\mathbf{r}_2$. Since all electrons are presumed to be identical, any experiment designed to observe the positions of both electrons cannot distinguish between them. Another way of saying this is that, if we were to interchange the two electrons, the result would be a state of the system that is physically indistinguishable from the first. Mathematically, this interchange corresponds to interchanging the coordinates of the two particles in the wave function, and so what we are saying is that

$$\psi^*(\mathbf{r}_1,\mathbf{r}_2)\psi(\mathbf{r}_1,\mathbf{r}_2) \equiv \psi^*(\mathbf{r}_2,\mathbf{r}_1)\psi(\mathbf{r}_2,\mathbf{r}_1) \tag{9-5}$$

That is, the product $\psi^*\psi$ must be *symmetric* with respect to the interchange of the coordinates of the two electrons.

This statement needs some additional explanation because the wave functions discussed so far in this section say nothing about the *spin* orientations of the particles. This information may be included symbolically by regarding each single-particle wave function as a function of the spin quantum number s in addition to the space coordinates. That is, we write $\psi_1(\mathbf{r}_1,s_1)$ for the state of the first electron, and a corresponding function for the second electron. As discussed in Sec. 8-7, the possible values of each s are $\pm\frac{1}{2}$.

Thus it is necessary to generalize the symmetry requirement given by Eq. (9-5) to include exchange of both space and spin coordinates, and in this generalized form the symmetry requirement is

$$\psi^*(\mathbf{r}_1,s_1;\mathbf{r}_2,s_2)\psi(\mathbf{r}_1,s_1;\mathbf{r}_2,s_2) \equiv \psi^*(\mathbf{r}_2,s_2;\mathbf{r}_1,s_1)\psi(\mathbf{r}_2,s_2;\mathbf{r}_1,s_1) \tag{9-6}$$

What does this symmetry imply about the wave function $\psi(\mathbf{r}_1,s_1;\mathbf{r}_2,s_2)$ itself? There are two simple cases which satisfy Eq. (9-6), namely,

$$\psi(\mathbf{r}_1,s_1;\mathbf{r}_2,s_2) \equiv \psi(\mathbf{r}_2,s_2;\mathbf{r}_1,s_1)$$

and

$$\psi(\mathbf{r}_1,s_1;\mathbf{r}_2,s_2) \equiv -\psi(\mathbf{r}_2,s_2;\mathbf{r}_1,s_1) \tag{9-7}$$

These two kinds of functions are said to be *symmetric* and *antisymmetric*, respectively, with respect to the interchange of the coordinates $\mathbf{r}_1$ and $\mathbf{r}_2$ of the two particles. An example of a function of the first type, in the case of motion in one dimension, is $\cos(x_1 - x_2)$, and of the second, $\sin(x_1 - x_2)$. Generalizing, for an n-electron system, the quantity $\psi^*\psi$ must be symmetric with respect to the interchange of the coordinates of any pair of electrons, and so the wave function ψ for the system can be either symmetric or antisymmetric with respect to interchange of pairs of coordinates.

It is easy to construct wave functions having either of these properties from single-electron wave functions. Consider two one-electron functions ψ_1 and ψ_2 whose quantum numbers are (n_1, l_1, m_1, s_1) and (n_2, l_2, m_2, s_2). The symmetric and antisymmetric two-electron functions are, respectively,

$$\psi_1(\mathbf{r}_1, s_1)\psi_2(\mathbf{r}_2, s_2) + \psi_2(\mathbf{r}_1, s_1)\psi_1(\mathbf{r}_2, s_2)$$

and

$$\psi_1(\mathbf{r}_1, s_1)\psi_2(\mathbf{r}_2, s_2) - \psi_2(\mathbf{r}_1, s_1)\psi_1(\mathbf{r}_2, s_2) \tag{9-8}$$

Now we consider the case where ψ_1 and ψ_2 are the same function, that is, $n_1 = n_2$, $l_1 = l_2$, etc. Nothing particularly extraordinary happens to the symmetric function, but the antisymmetric function automatically becomes zero. This coincidence of all four quantum numbers is forbidden by the original statement of the Pauli exclusion principle. Thus if we insist that the two-electron function should be *antisymmetric* with respect to interchange of all the coordinates of electrons 1 and 2, we are automatically protected from the error of having all four quantum numbers the same for both one-electron states. Generalizing to the case of n electrons, we state the Pauli exclusion principle in the following alternative form: *Every wave function describing a state of a many-electron system must be antisymmetric with respect to interchange of the coordinates (space and spin) of any pair of electrons.* This second statement of the Pauli principle is of considerable importance in the analysis of chemical bonds, to be discussed in Sec. 9-5.

9-2   Periodic Table

The variation of the chemical and physical properties of the elements with atomic number forms a pattern best exhibited by the well-known periodic table of the elements. This table is reproduced here, for convenient reference, as Table 9-1. One of the most important features of the table is that all elements in a particular column or *group* have very similar chemical and physical properties. We now consider the relation of these properties to the electron configurations of atoms. Most of this discussion will be based on the central-field model introduced in the previous section, in which each electron is represented as moving in a potential resulting from the nucleus and the average positions of all the other electrons. In this model each electron is described by a set

Table 9-1 *The Periodic Table of the Elements*

The number above the symbol of each element is its atomic mass, and that below is its atomic number. The elements whose atomic masses are given in parentheses do not occur in nature, but have been prepared artificially in nuclear reactions. The atomic mass in such a case is the mass number of the most long-lived radioactive isotope of the element.

Period	Group I	Group II											Group III	Group IV	Group V	Group VI	Group VII	Group VIII
1	1.00 H 1																	4.00 He 2
2	6.94 Li 3	9.01 Be 4											10.81 B 5	12.01 C 6	14.01 N 7	16.00 O 8	19.00 F 9	20.18 Ne 10
3	22.99 Na 11	24.31 Mg 12											26.98 Al 13	28.09 Si 14	30.98 P 15	32.07 S 16	35.46 Cl 17	39.94 Ar 18
4	39.10 K 19	40.08 Ca 20	44.96 Sc 21	47.90 Ti 22	50.94 V 23	52.00 Cr 24	54.94 Mn 25	55.85 Fe 26	58.93 Co 27	58.71 Ni 28	63.54 Cu 29	65.37 Zn 30	69.72 Ga 31	72.59 Ge 32	74.92 As 33	78.96 Se 34	79.91 Br 35	83.8 Kr 36
5	85.47 Rb 37	87.66 Sr 38	88.91 Y 39	91.22 Zr 40	92.91 Nb 41	95.94 Mo 42	(99) Tc 43	101.1 Ru 44	102.91 Rh 45	106.4 Pd 46	107.87 Ag 47	112.40 Cd 48	114.82 In 49	118.69 Sn 50	121.75 Sb 51	127.60 Te 52	126.90 I 53	131.30 Xe 54
6	132.91 Cs 55	137.34 Ba 56	* 57–71	178.49 Hf 72	180.95 Ta 73	183.85 W 74	186.2 Re 75	190.2 Os 76	192.2 Ir 77	195.09 Pt 78	197.0 Au 79	200.59 Hg 80	204.37 Tl 81	207.19 Pb 82	208.98 Bi 83	(210) Po 84	(210) At 85	222 Rn 86
7	(223) Fr 87	226.05 Ra 88	† 89–103															

* Rare earths

138.91 La 57	140.12 Ce 58	140.91 Pr 59	144.24 Nd 60	(145) Pm 61	150.35 Sm 62	152.0 Eu 63	157.25 Gd 64	158.92 Tb 65	162.50 Dy 66	164.92 Ho 67	167.26 Er 68	168.93 Tm 69	173.04 Yb 70	174.97 Lu 71

† Actinides

227 Ac 89	232.04 Th 90	231 Pa 91	238.03 U 92	(237) Np 93	(242) Pu 94	(243) Am 95	(247) Cm 96	(249) Bk 97	(251) Cf 98	(254) Es 99	(253) Fm 100	(256) Md 101	(254) No 102	(257) Lw 103

285

of four quantum numbers. The number of electrons in the atom, called the *atomic number,* is denoted by Z. This is also equal to the number of protons in the nucleus, and each proton has charge $+e$. Thus the total nuclear charge for an atom with atomic number Z is Ze.

In the Bohr theory the radius of the electron orbit is proportional to n^2, as shown by Eq. (5-27). Correspondingly, the sizes of the wave functions for the hydrogen atom increase proportionately to n^2. A similar dependence on n also occurs for complex atoms, and it is in fact enhanced, for the following reason. Electrons close to the nucleus are influenced by nearly the full nuclear charge Ze, while for electrons moving in the outer periphery of the atom the positive nuclear charge is partly canceled by the negative charge of the inner electrons. The basis for this statement is Gauss' law of electrostatics; from Gauss' law it is easy to show that for any spherically symmetric charge distribution the electric field at any point a distance r from the center is determined entirely by the charge contained in the sphere of radius r passing through the point; furthermore, the field at that point is exactly the same as it would be if all the charge inside the sphere of radius r were concentrated at the center. Thus the outer electrons experience a smaller electric field and hence are more loosely bound than would be the case if the inner electrons were not present. This partial cancellation of the nuclear field by inner electrons is called *shielding* or *screening,* and it is a very important concept in the understanding of the structure and properties of many-electron atoms.

Thus the average distance of an electron from the nucleus is strongly dependent on n, and it is customary to speak of *shells* of electrons for various values of n. The innermost shell of electrons consists of those in the $n = 1$ states, the next shell those in the $n = 2$ states, etc. These shells are sometimes identified by capital letters, starting with K, as follows:

$$n: \quad 1 \quad 2 \quad 3 \quad 4 \quad \cdots$$
$$\text{Shell:} \quad K \quad L \quad M \quad N \quad \cdots$$

Although in the hydrogen atom the energy of the state depends *only* on n, this is an accident resulting from the particularly simple form of the potential-energy function, $1/r$. For the screened potential-energy functions resulting from the combined effect of the nucleus and the other electrons, the electron energies, in general, depend on both n and l. In most cases the smallest values of l for a given n have the lowest energy levels, since for a given n the electron is, on the average, somewhat closer to the nucleus for small values of l than for large values. Thus, within each electron shell, electrons are subdivided into *subshells* according to the value of l.

These subshells are often labeled with the spectroscopic notation introduced in Sec. 8-3. Table 9-2 summarizes the various notations in common use as well as the number of levels in each shell and subshell, including the possibility of two electrons with opposite spins for each set of values of n, l, and m.

Table 9-2

Shell	n	l	m	Spectroscopic notation	Number of levels	
K	1	0	0	1s	2	
L	2	0	0	2s	2	} 8
	2	1	0, ±1	2p	6	
M	3	0	0	3s	2	
	3	1	0, ±1	3p	6	} 18
	3	2	0, ±1, ±2	3d	10	
N	4	0	0	4s	2	
	4	1	0, ±1	4p	6	} 32
	4	2	0, ±1, ±2	4d	10	
	4	3	0, ±1, ±2, ±3	4f	14	

General expressions can be derived for the number of levels in each shell or subshell. For a given l there are $2l + 1$ values of m, each corresponding to a distinct state, and for each of these there are two possible values of the spin quantum number s. Thus in the subshell identified by n and l there are $2(2l + 1)$ states, and this subshell can accommodate that number of electrons. Correspondingly, a shell with a given n can have values of l ranging from 0 to $n - 1$, and so the total number of electrons that can be accommodated in each shell is

$$\sum_{l=0}^{n-1} 2(2l + 1) = 4\sum_{l=0}^{n-1} l + 2n$$
$$= 2(n - 1)n + 2n$$
$$= 2n^2 \tag{9-9}$$

where we have used the fact that the sum of the first r integers is $\frac{1}{2}r(r + 1)$.

We can now describe simply the electron configuration of any atom. For hydrogen, the ground state is simply 1s. In the ground state of the helium atom, both electrons are in 1*s* levels, with opposite spins, a state denoted as 1*s*². In the ground state of helium the *K* shell is completely filled, and there are no electrons in any other shells.

Next in the list of elements is lithium, with three electrons. In the ground state two are in the *K* shell and one in the *L* shell; the ground state of lithium is denoted as 1*s*²2*s*. The 2*s* electron is, on the average, considerably farther from the nucleus than the 1*s* electrons, and so the *net* charge influencing its motion is approximately *e*, as shown schematically in Fig. 9-1, rather than the nuclear charge 3*e*. Thus we expect this electron to be rather loosely bound. The observed chemical behavior of lithium bears out this prediction; it forms ionic compounds in which each atom loses an electron, and thus in chemical language it is said to have a valence of +1. Salts of lithium in aqueous solution dissociate into positively charged lithium ions with the 2*s* electron removed, and negatively charged cations.

Fig. 9-1   *Schematic representation of the shell structure of the lithium atom. The nucleus has a charge +3e; the two 1s electrons are, on the average, much closer to the nucleus than the 2s electron. According to Gauss' law of electrostatics, a spherically symmetric charge distribution produces an electric field which at points outside the distribution is the same as that produced by a point charge with the same total charge. Hence the 2s electron moves in a field approximately equal to that of a point charge +3e − 2e, or simply e.*

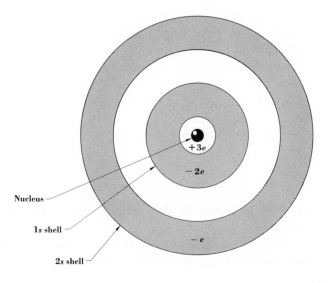

+3e

−2e

−e

Nucleus

1s shell

2s shell

Proceeding, we note that beryllium, with four electrons, has the ground-state configuration $1s^2 2s^2$, with two electrons in the L shell, and thus behaves chemically with a valence of $+2$.

The ground-state electron configurations of the next several elements are shown in Table 9-3. At $Z = 10$ the L shell, with a capacity for eight electrons, is completely filled, and there are no electrons in the

Table 9-3   Ground-state Electron Configurations†

Element	Symbol	Atomic number (Z)	Electron configuration
Hydrogen	H	1	$1s$
Helium	He	2	$1s^2$
Lithium	Li	3	$1s^2 2s$
Beryllium	Be	4	$1s^2 2s^2$
Boron	B	5	$1s^2 2s^2 2p$
Carbon	C	6	$1s^2 2s^2 2p^2$
Nitrogen	N	7	$1s^2 2s^2 2p^3$
Oxygen	O	8	$1s^2 2s^2 2p^4$
Fluorine	F	9	$1s^2 2s^2 2p^5$
Neon	Ne	10	$1s^2 2s^2 2p^6$
Sodium	Na	11	$1s^2 2s^2 2p^6 3s$
Magnesium	Mg	12	$1s^2 2s^2 2p^6 3s^2$
Aluminum	Al	13	$1s^2 2s^2 2p^6 3s^2 3p$
Silicon	Si	14	$1s^2 2s^2 2p^6 3s^2 3p^2$
Phosphorus	P	15	$1s^2 2s^2 2p^6 3s^2 3p^3$
Sulfur	S	16	$1s^2 2s^2 2p^6 3s^2 3p^4$
Chlorine	Cl	17	$1s^2 2s^2 2p^6 3s^2 3p^5$
Argon	Ar	18	$1s^2 2s^2 2p^6 3s^2 3p^6$
Potassium	K	19	$1s^2 2s^2 2p^6 3s^2 3p^6 4s$
Calcium	Ca	20	$1s^2 2s^2 2p^6 3s^2 3p^6 4s^2$

† A complete table of ground-state configurations for all the elements is given in Appendix F.

M shell. Thus we should expect this to be a particularly stable configuration, with no pronounced tendency either to gain or to lose electrons. The element is, in fact, neon, an inert gas with no known compounds. The preceding element, with $Z = 9$, lacks one electron for a filled shell and thus might be expected to have an affinity for electrons and a tendency to form electrovalent bonds in which it acquires an extra electron. This element is fluorine, and it is observed to have just these properties. The other element adjacent to neon, sodium, has completely filled K and L shells, and one electron in the M shell. Thus its electron configuration is similar to that of lithium, and, as expected, it tends to form compounds in which it has a valence of $+1$. Lithium and sodium are the first two of the *alkali metals,* and they both have the "filled-shell-plus-one *s*-electron" configuration.

One can proceed similarly through the entire periodic table. With the M and N shells a slight complication arises because of the dependence of energy levels on l. The $3d$ and $4s$ levels overlap in energy, so that some electrons go into the N shell before the M shell is completely filled. Potassium, with $Z = 19$, is the first element exhibiting this effect; its outermost electron is $4s$ rather than $3d$. This effect gives rise to a series of elements with fairly similar chemical properties, having one or two electrons in $4s$ levels and partially filled $3d$ subshells. These elements form the first *transition series,* starting with scandium ($Z = 21$) and terminating with zinc ($Z = 30$), at which point the $3d$ subshell is completely filled.

The partially filled $3d$ subshell in the transition elements is responsible for the ferromagnetic behavior of the transition elements iron, cobalt, and nickel. Because the $3d$ subshell is only partially full, the exclusion principle permits several electrons in these levels to have parallel spins; thus each atom can have a substantial magnetic moment. In a filled shell, conversely, the magnetic moments must add up to zero because of the opposite spins of pairs of electrons.

A complete list of the probable electron configurations of all the known elements is given in Appendix F. From this, it can be seen that the order of filling up of energy levels is

$$1s,\ 2s,\ 2p,\ 3s,\ 3p,\ 4s,\ 3d,\ 4p,\ 5s,\ 4d,\ 5p,\ 6s,\ 4f,\ 5d,\ 6p,\ 7s,\ 6d$$

Appendix F is worthy of careful study. It can be seen that all the inert gases (helium, neon, argon, krypton, xenon, and radon) have configurations consisting of completely filled shells or subshells. All the alkali metals (lithium, sodium, potassium, rubidium, cesium) have "filled-shell-plus-one-electron" configurations, and all the halogens (fluorine, chlorine, bromine, iodine, astatine) have "filled-shell-minus-one" configurations.

Thus a qualitative understanding of the principal features of the periodic table of the elements emerges from this table of electron configurations. In all cases, two atoms having similar configurations of their outermost electrons are found to have similar chemical properties, corroborating the view that the chemical properties of an element are determined mostly by the behavior of its outer electrons. This also accounts for the very close similarity of behavior of the lanthanide or rare-earth series, including elements 57 through 71. These elements differ only in the number of electrons in $4f$ and $5d$ levels, not in the $6s$ electrons which determine the chemical properties. A similar phenomenon occurs with the actinide series, starting with element 91. The reader is encouraged to check the electron structure of other groups in the periodic table, to see the basis for the similarities of chemical behavior of the various elements in a group.

Some physicists like to say that all of chemistry is contained in the Schrödinger equation. This may be a slight exaggeration, but it is true that the Schrödinger equation provides the theoretical foundation and the basic principles necessary for the understanding of the chemical behavior of matter, in terms of its microscopic structure.

As an introduction to the analysis of the origins of x-ray spectra in the following section, we now consider the configuration of the innermost electrons in a many-electron atom. First, in most complex atoms the energy required to remove one of the outer electrons, called the *ionization energy* or *ionization potential*, has the same order of magnitude as that for hydrogen, namely, about 1 to 20 ev. The reason, as already pointed out, is that, while the nucleus contains a positive charge of Ze, where Z is the atomic number, the effect of this charge is largely canceled or shielded by the negative charges of the inner electrons. Thus the total electric field at the position of an outer electron is not radically different from that in hydrogen.

For the inner electrons, the situation is quite different. According to Gauss' law of electrostatics, any spherically symmetric charge distribution which lies entirely outside a certain radius r produces no electric field at points inside that radius. Thus, for example, the electrons in the K shell are affected only slightly by those in the L, M, and outer shells, since the charge distributions corresponding to the latter shells are mostly outside the region of the K shell. Thus the K electrons experience the field of almost the entire nuclear charge Ze.

It is easy to see how the energy levels and sizes of wave functions are affected. The Coulomb interaction between two particles of charge e contains the factor e^2. The corresponding factor for an electron and a nucleus with Z protons is Ze^2. Thus the energy level for a K electron, which in the case of hydrogen would be given by Eq. (8-25) with $n = 1$, is given instead by a similar formula but with e^4 replaced by Z^2e^4. That is, the energy should be larger by a factor of the order of Z^2 than for hydrogen. Correspondingly, the size of the $1s$ wave function, as characterized by the Bohr-orbit radius given by Eq. (8-27) with $n = 1$, becomes smaller by a factor of Z. Thus in a complex atom the inner electrons are closer to the nucleus, and much more tightly bound, than in the ground state of hydrogen.

Conversely, the outer electrons in a complex atom are fairly completely shielded from the nucleus, so that they interact with a net charge of the order of only e, rather than Ze. Thus the energies associated with transitions between levels of the outer electrons are of the same order of magnitude (1 to 20 ev) as for hydrogen, a fact that is borne out by the optical spectra of various elements. Similarly, the sizes of the outer electron wave functions are not drastically different from those of hydrogen in similar states, and so the *sizes* of complex atoms are not in general significantly different from those of the hydrogen atom. This prediction is borne out by measurements of the spacing of atoms in crystals, using x-ray diffraction techniques. Various studies have shown that lattice spacings are not strongly dependent on the atomic number of the material and, in fact, are of the same order of magnitude, typically 1 to 5 Å, for all elements, with few exceptions. Correspondingly, the density of an element in the solid state is determined primarily by the mass of its nucleus, with the "volume" of an atom varying in a manner of only secondary importance. Thus the elements that are most dense in the solid state are those near the end of the periodic table, and the least dense ones are generally toward the beginning.

9-3   X-ray Spectra

In the discussion of x-ray production in Sec. 5-3, it was pointed out that the *maximum* energy of an x-ray photon produced in a collision between a high-energy electron and a stationary target is determined by the energy of the electron. This prediction is borne out by measurements of wavelengths by crystal diffraction techniques, as discussed in Sec. 3-4. Experiment also shows, however, that some x-ray photons produced in such collisions have energies considerably *smaller* than this maximum. In fact, one sometimes finds a discrete set of energies, analogous to line spectra in optical spectroscopy, which are independent of the energy of the original electron but which depend on the target material. The origin of these lines can be understood in terms of the atomic structure of the target atoms.

Just as optical spectra result from transitions between two energy states of the outer electrons of an atom, discrete x-ray spectra, with photon energies of the order of 10^3 to 10^4 times as great as those of optical spectra, result from transitions between energy states of inner electrons.

As a simple example, suppose we could remove one of the K electrons completely from an atom, leaving a vacancy in the K shell. Then an electron in the L, M, or other shell could drop into the K shell, in a transition accompanied by the emission of a photon of energy equal to the difference of the two levels.

In estimating the magnitudes of the inner-electron energy levels, it is useful to consider the shielding or screening effects mentioned at the end of Sec. 9-2. For an atom with atomic number Z and nuclear charge Ze, each inner electron is shielded by considerably *less* than the other $Z - 1$ electrons. On an average, a K electron is shielded only by the other K electron, and therefore it should see a net charge of approximately $(Z - 1)e$. Thus, according to the discussion at the end of Sec. 9-2, we expect the K energy level to be larger than for hydrogen by a factor of $(Z - 1)^2$. The $1s$ energy for hydrogen is about -13.6 ev, and so for an element of atomic number Z it should be about $-(Z - 1)^2(13.6$ ev). Correspondingly, the $2p$ subshell of the L shell is shielded by two K electrons, two L electrons in the $2s$ subshell, and perhaps, on the average, by three of the six L electrons in the $2p$ subshell, for an average total of about seven. Thus we might guess that a $2p$ electron in the L shell should have an energy of $-(Z - 7)^2(3.4$ ev), where 3.4 ev is the corresponding energy for hydrogen. A transition of an inner electron from such an L state to a previously vacant K level should be accompanied by the emission of a photon whose energy is the difference of these two energies. For example, if the atom is iron, with $Z = 26$, this energy difference should be

$$\Delta E = (26 - 1)^2(13.6 \text{ ev}) - (26 - 7)^2(3.4 \text{ ev})$$
$$= 7{,}240 \text{ ev} = 1.16 \times 10^{-15} \text{ joule} \tag{9-10}$$

and the corresponding wavelength should be

$$\lambda = \frac{hc}{E} = \frac{(6.62 \times 10^{-34} \text{ joule sec})(3.00 \times 10^8 \text{ m/sec})}{1.16 \times 10^{-15} \text{ joule}}$$

$$= 1.98 \times 10^{-10} \text{ m} = 1.98 \text{ Å} \tag{9-11}$$

As a matter of fact, a prominent x-ray line for iron is observed at a wavelength of 1.93 Å, which agrees reasonably well with the prediction of Eq. (9-11). The difference results from the fact that in the above calculation shielding effects have been included only in a very approximate way.

Any state of an atom in which an electron has been completely removed from an inner shell, leaving a vacancy, is called an x-ray energy level. Although these levels have been introduced with reference to the energies of individual electrons, it should be emphasized that they are actually energies of the entire atom viewed as a system. For example, the K energy state is the state in which one of the K electrons has been removed from the atom and is at rest; this state of the system has higher energy than the state in which the electron occupies the K level. For the example mentioned above, the K energy level for iron is *higher* than that of the ground state by about $(26 - 1)^2 \times 13.6$ ev = 8,500 ev. Similarly, the L level of the system is at about $(26 - 7)^2 \times 3.4$ ev = 1,200 ev above the ground state.

Clearly, various transitions between such levels lead to a series of x-ray spectrum lines for each element. When the vacancy is originally in the K shell, an electron can go from the M shell to the K shell, rather than from L to K, provided, of course, that it *has* an electron in the M shell originally. Furthermore, if an electron goes from the L shell to the K shell, this leaves a vacancy in the L shell which may be filled from the M shell, and so on. In the notation usually employed by x-ray spectroscopists, the line resulting from a transition in which an electron *ends* in the K shell is called a K line, etc. To identify the shell in which the electron started, a Greek letter is added to the final shell designation, starting with α for the lowest-energy transition, proceeding with β, γ, and so on. This scheme is illustrated by Table 9-4. Furthermore, all the levels except the K levels are usually multiple rather than single levels, as a result of the dependence of energy on the angular-momentum quantum number and spin-orbit coupling.

We have not yet discussed the mechanism by which atoms are raised to x-ray energy levels in the first place, but the nature of the process of x-ray production makes it fairly clear that the mechanism is simply

Table 9-4 X-ray Spectrum Notation

Transition	Notation
$L \to K$	$K\alpha$
$M \to K$	$K\beta$
$N \to K$	$K\gamma$
$O \to K$	$K\delta$
$M \to L$	$L\alpha$
$N \to L$	$L\beta$
$O \to L$	$L\gamma$
$\dots$	$\dots$

one of collision of high-energy electrons (or other charged particles) with the inner electrons of an atom by means of their electrostatic repulsion, resulting sometimes in the transfer of enough energy to one of these electrons to remove it from the atom completely.   Thus K x-ray lines are observed only when the energy of the initial bombarding electron is sufficiently great to remove an electron from the K shell.   This energy is determined by the accelerating voltage in the x-ray tube, and so measurement of the voltage at which the K lines begin to appear provides a direct measurement of the energy required to remove a K electron, i.e., of the K energy level.   This procedure is analogous to the use of the Franck-Hertz experiment (Sec. 5-4) for investigation of energy levels associated with optical spectra.

Just as with optical spectra, one can observe absorption spectra as well as emission spectra for x-ray transitions.   Unlike optical spectra, the absorption wavelengths are not the same as those for emission.   For example, the $K\alpha$ line results from the transition from a K level to an L level.   The corresponding transition from an L level to a K level cannot be observed ordinarily because there is no vacancy in the L shell in the target atom.   Thus the incident radiation must have enough energy to remove an electron completely from the shell, not just boost it to the L shell.   As a result, as the energy of the incident x-rays is gradually increased, sudden increases in absorption are observed, called absorption edges, corresponding to energies just sufficient to remove electrons from a certain shell.

Thus the existence of characteristic x-ray spectra for elements can be understood in terms of precisely the same basic concepts used to understand optical spectra and several other phenomena associated with atomic structure.   In fact, the extension of these concepts to the understanding of x-ray spectra seems almost obvious.   Still, it must be recalled that in the years when x-ray spectra were first investigated in detail, that is, in the decade from 1910 to 1920, the origin of atomic spectra in transitions between discrete energy levels in an atom was just beginning to be understood.   Thus the analysis of x-ray spectra provided in those days additional strong support of the explanation of optical spectra in terms of atomic-energy-level transitions.

9-4   *Ionic Bond*

The principles of quantum mechanics provide important insight into the phenomenon of chemical binding, that is, the association of two or more atoms in a stable structure called a molecule.   In some respects, the simplest kind of chemical bond to understand is the *ionic bond,* in which one or more electrons from one atom are transferred completely or nearly so to another atom. A common example is the molecule of sodium chloride, NaCl, in which the sodium atom gives its outermost electron completely to the chlorine atom and becomes positively charged. We preface the discussion of the ionic bond with a brief consideration of the interaction energies of the outermost or *valence* electrons of atoms.

As mentioned in Sec. 9-2, sodium and the other alkali metals have an electronic structure characterized by filled shells with one additional *s* electron. The filled shell, corresponding to a spherically symmetric charge distribution, shields the outermost electron almost completely from the nuclear charge, and it moves in a field corresponding to a charge *e* rather than the total nuclear charge *Ze*. Relatively little energy is needed to detach the *s* electron, and the alkali metals form positive ions readily.

The minimum energy needed to detach one of the outermost electrons in an atom is called the *ionization potential;* successive energies needed to detach the second, third, and fourth outer electrons are called the second, third, and fourth ionization potentials, and so on. Atoms with more than one electron in the outermost shell would be expected to form positive ions less readily than the alkali metals, that is, to have higher ionization potentials, since the shielding of the nuclear charge is less complete than for the filled-shell configuration of the alkali metals. Thus across any period in the periodic table a more or less steady increase in ionization potential could be expected. This prediction is substantiated by the experimental values of ionization potentials in Table 9-5.

As the table shows, the last element in the second period, neon, has a large ionization potential, with a correspondingly small tendency to form positive ions. Furthermore, neon, as we have seen, has a filled-shell configuration and therefore has little tendency to acquire additional electrons, thereby accounting for its chemical inertness. But the element adjacent to neon, fluorine, has a "filled-shell-minus-one" structure. Because of this incomplete outer shell, the electrons, even in a neutral fluorine atom, do not completely shield the nuclear charge except at rather large distances. An additional electron can be added to the outermost $(2p)$ shell, where it is only partially shielded by the other $2p$ electrons and hence is bound by the nuclear attraction. Thus a fluorine atom tends to acquire an additional electron to become a negative ion with a filled-shell electron configuration. This ion has a *lower energy*

Table 9-5 *Ionization Potentials (in Electron Volts)*

Period	Group							
	I	II	III	IV	V	VI	VII	VIII
1	H							He
	13.6							24.5
2	Li	Be	B	C	N	O	F	Ne
	5.4	9.3	8.3	11.3	14.5	13.6	17.4	21.6
3	Na	Mg					Cl	A
	5.1	7.6					13.0	15.7
4	K	Ca					Br	Kr
	4.3	6.3					11.8	13.9
5	Rb	Sr					I	Xe
	4.2	5.7					10.6	12.1
6	Cs	Ba						
	3.9	5.2						

than a neutral atom with an electron at a great distance; correspondingly, energy must be added in order to remove the extra electron. This energy, called the *electron affinity*, is a measure of how tightly the extra electron is bound. Electron affinities for the halogens are shown in Table 9-6.

Table 9-6 *Electron Affinities*

Fluorine	3.6 ev
Chlorine	3.8
Bromine	3.5
Iodine	3.2

Now we return to the problem of the sodium chloride molecule. To remove an electron from a sodium atom requires 5.1 ev. When this electron is attached to a chlorine atom, 3.8 ev is returned, for a net loss of 1.3 ev. But now there are two ions, one positive and one negative, a great distance apart. When they approach each other, there is an attractive electrostatic force and thus a negative potential energy. When the distance between the ions is of the same order as their size, 3 or 4 Å, the potential energy is of the order of −5 ev, as shown by the magnitudes of the corresponding energies in the hydrogen atom. This is more than enough to repay the 1.3-ev investment in creating the ions initially, and so the bound state is energetically favorable, by a balance of the order of 4 ev. Experiment shows that the amount of energy necessary to dissociate a sodium chloride molecule into the separate atoms is 4.2 ev. This close agreement is partly fortuitous, inasmuch as we have ignored the distortion of the filled-shell electron configuration of each ion resulting from the electric field of the other, but the calculation illustrates why the ionic bond is energetically favorable.

In view of the electrostatic attraction between the two ions, we might well ask why the two atoms do not continue to approach each other until the electron structures overlap completely. In that case the electrons would no longer shield the nuclei so effectively, and so there would be a strong electrostatic repulsion of the nuclei. In addition, when the electron clouds of the two atoms begin to overlap, they must be considered not as independent systems but rather as parts of a single system. Hence the Pauli exclusion principle must be applied to the whole system rather than to the individual atoms. Roughly speaking, the exclusion principle is the quantum-mechanical analog of the classical statement that two objects cannot occupy the same space at the same time. When the overlap becomes significant, some of the electrons have to go into higher energy states in order to avoid violating the exclusion principle. At sufficiently close distances, the energy required to produce these configurations is greater than the corresponding decrease in potential energy, and this limits the minimum separation of the atoms.

The equilibrium spacing of the two atoms in a sodium chloride molecule is about 2.4 Å. Thus the interaction between the two atoms is attractive up to a certain point but becomes repulsive when they are closer than a certain critical distance. At the critical distance, there is a state of equilibrium in which the two ions are neither attracted nor repelled from each other. For separations close to the equilibrium value, the interaction can be represented as a force approximately proportional to the displacement from equilibrium, which can be visualized in terms of a fictitious spring with a spring constant determined by the strength of the interionic force. Such a molecule can undergo a vibrational motion in which each atom undergoes approximately simple harmonic motion with respect to its equilibrium position. This fact is important in the analysis of molecular spectra, to be discussed in Sec. 9-6.

In some cases a metallic element can become doubly ionized by losing two electrons and form ionic bonds with two halogen or other atoms. This does not occur for sodium; the first ionization potential is

5 ev, but the *second* ionization potential (the energy necessary to remove a second electron from a singly ionized atom) is over 47 ev, and there is no case where the removal of the second electron is energetically favorable.   But for magnesium, the element following sodium in the periodic table, the first ionization potential is 7.6 ev, the second only 15 ev, and the third about 80 ev.   Thus magnesium forms ionic compounds, such as $MgCl_2$, in which it loses one electron to each of two chlorine atoms to become doubly ionized.   An analysis of the energy balance of such a process can be made precisely in the same way as that made above for the sodium chloride molecule.   All the other elements in group II, the so-called alkaline-earth metals, have the same filled-shell-plus-two-electrons structure, and all behave chemically in a similar manner.

In all cases, the number of ionic bonds a given atom can form is determined by the successive ionization potentials, which in turn depend on the shell structure of the electrons.   Thus all ionic bonds exhibit the phenomenon called *saturation,* which means that an atom tending to form ionic bonds does not attract other atoms without limit, but rather only to the extent of the number of bonds its electronic configuration permits.   In chemical language, elements that tend to take the role of positive ions in ionic bonds are called *metals.*   Elements having a strong tendency to become negatively ionized in ionic bonds are called nonmetals; the strongest nonmetals, as we have seen, are the halogens.

An important feature of ionic bonds is the absence of *directional* character of the interatomic force.   Each ion has a filled-shell electron configuration and is therefore spherically symmetric, and there is no reason for the interaction to be stronger in any direction than any other. This behavior is in sharp contrast to that of the covalent bond, discussed in the next section, which is often highly directional.   This distinction is important in connection with the structure of crystalline solids, to be discussed in Sec. 11-1.

9-5   *Covalent Bond*

The ionic bond provides insight into the structure of molecules involving strong metals and nonmetals, such as the alkali halides (compounds containing an alkali metal and a halogen).   But there are many chemical bonds which clearly cannot be of this type; the most obvious examples are diatomic molecules of gases, such as hydrogen, nitrogen, oxygen, and chlorine.   Specific-heat measurements, infrared spectroscopy, and molecular-mass determination all clearly indicate that in the gaseous state these gases are composed of diatomic molecules, in which two atoms of the same element are bound in a symmetric molecule. The corresponding valence bond, in which the two atoms of the molecule participate equally, is called a *covalent* or *homopolar* bond.

Just as in the analysis of atomic structure, the simplest example of the homopolar bond is that of hydrogen, which therefore is selected as a prototype problem. To understand why a bound state of two hydrogen atoms should be energetically favorable, we consider first a very crude pictorial model. Figure 9-2 shows two electric dipoles, which can be thought of as two separated hydrogen atoms. In Fig. 9-2a the two dipoles are far apart. In Fig. 9-2b they are brought together with opposite orientations. Each charge in one dipole exerts a force on each charge in the other. Because pairs of unlike charges are closer together than pairs of like charge, there is a net *attractive* force between the dipoles

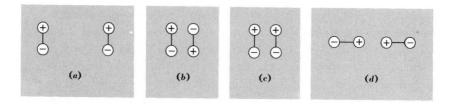

Fig. 9-2 *Interaction of two electric dipoles. In* (b) *the net force between the dipoles is attractive; in* (c) *and* (d) *it is repulsive.*

in this configuration, and correspondingly a potential energy which is less than that when they are separated. In Fig. 9-2c and d the repulsion between the two positive charges is greater than the attraction of the unlike charges, and so there is a net *repulsive* force. Thus in this simple model, the configuration in which the two electrons lie between the two nuclei and are shared by them is energetically more favorable than that of two separated atoms.

A slightly less crude picture can be built, using the Bohr model. We imagine the two electrons in an orbit lying in a plane perpendicular to the line joining the nuclei, as shown in Fig. 9-3. A calculation based on this model shows that the total energy of the system in the state shown is lower than that corresponding to the lowest energies of the two separated atoms. It is not surprising that this model does not yield correct quantitative results for the energy levels of the hydrogen molecule, but

Fig. 9-3 *Bohr model of the hydrogen molecule.   The two protons are stationary, held in equilibrium by a balance of their mutual repulsion and the attraction of the electrons, which move in a circular orbit in the mid-plane between the protons.   This state has lower total energy than one in which the two atoms are separated.   This model does not yield quantitatively correct predictions of the energy levels of the molecule.*

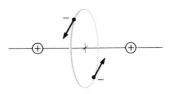

at least it makes the existence of a bound state plausible.   The point of both these simple models is that the state in which the two electrons lie between the protons and are shared by them is energetically more favorable than the state in which each proton has its own electron, and the two atoms are separated by a considerable distance.   Figure 9-3 is readily translated into wave-mechanical language, in which we visualize the charge clouds corresponding to the electron wave functions as concentrated in the region between the nuclei, as in Fig. 9-4*b*, or in the outer regions, as in Fig. 9-4*c*.

Thus we are led to the notion of a *shared-electron bond,* in which two atoms each contribute an electron to the region of space between them, with a resultant decrease in the total energy of the state.   Correspondingly, in the correct quantum-mechanical description of the hydrogen molecule the wave function describing the electrons is more concentrated in the region between the two nuclei, and less concentrated outside, than for individual atoms.

If the two electrons are to occupy more or less the same region of space between the two nuclei, they must have more or less the same wave function and therefore the same quantum-mechanical state.   According to the exclusion principle, this is possible only if the two electrons have opposite spins.   When the spins are parallel, the state that is energetically most favorable is forbidden by the exclusion principle, and the lowest energy state permitted is one in which the electrons are concentrated in the region outside the pair of nuclei.   In this case, the nuclei are not shielded, they repel each other, and no molecular binding occurs.

Thus antiparallel spins are an essential characteristic of the co-

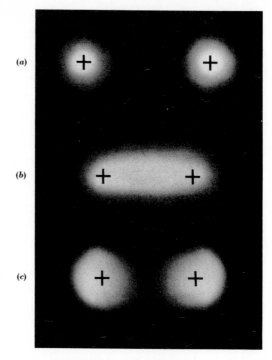

(a)

(b)

(c)

Fig. 9-4 *Pictorial representation of electron clouds in the hydrogen molecule. (a) Two separated atoms. (b) Charge cloud concentrated in the region between the nuclei, resulting in an attractive interaction. In this state the electron spins must be antiparallel. (c) Charge cloud depleted in the region between the nuclei, resulting in a repulsive interaction. In this state the electron spins are parallel.*

valent bond; we also see immediately that no more than two electrons can participate in such a bond, since the exclusion principle would not permit this.   On the other hand, an element can have several electrons in its outermost shell, and *each* of them can form an electron-pair or covalent bond with another atom.   This occurs frequently in hydrocarbon molecules.   An isolated carbon atom has two 2s electrons and two 2p electrons in its L shell.   In the presence of other atoms, with their associated noncentral electrical forces, the state of each L electron becomes a mixture of angular-momentum states, and the wave functions correspondingly take on a lopsided appearance.   In the molecule of methane (CH₄), the simplest hydrocarbon, the nucleus of the carbon atom is at the center of a regular tetrahedron, with the nuclei of four hydrogen atoms at the four corners.   In the vicinity of the line joining the center to each corner, the wave functions for the corresponding electrons have a large amplitude, corresponding to the existence of a pair of electrons with opposite spins.   Because of the symmetry of the situation, the angles between the various bonds are all equal; this is the state having the lowest total energy consistent with the Pauli principle.   The structure of the methane molecule is shown pictorially in Fig. 9-5.   A

Fig. 9-5 *Pictorial representation of the methane (CH$_4$) molecule, showing the four covalent bonds. The electron cloud between the central carbon atom and each of the four hydrogen nuclei represents the two electrons of a covalent (shared-electron) bond. The four bonds are arranged symmetrically, with the hydrogen nuclei at the corners of a regular tetrahedron.*

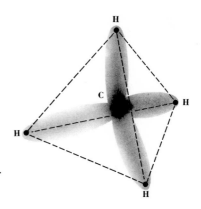

similar pattern occurs often in more complex organic molecules; a carbon atom forms four covalent bonds with other atoms. Each of these bonds consists of a pair of electrons, one contributed by each of the atoms, and always the two electrons have opposite spins.

In any molecule containing several covalent bonds, the relative directions of these bonds are always determined by energy considerations and by the Pauli principle. The angular-momentum states of the associated electrons are also important empirically. As we have seen, electrons in *s* states have spherically symmetric wave functions, while those with angular momentum different from zero have "lumps" in certain directions. For example, for a given *n*, three *p* wave functions ($l = 1$) can be constructed with lumps in three mutually perpendicular directions, and so in a state which involves the sharing of two *p* electrons one might expect the two bonds to be perpendicular. In the molecules H$_2$O and H$_2$S, the actual bond angles are 105° and 92°, respectively. Similarly, in the NH$_3$ molecule we should expect the three hydrogen bonds to be formed in three mutually perpendicular directions. The actual angle between the bond directions is 109°. These deviations from the perpendicular directions predicted by our overly simple picture are a result of the mutual repulsion of the hydrogen atoms for each other.

In all cases, the *directions* of the bonds are determined by the particular electron configurations of the individual atoms. This directionality is also one of the predominant factors in determining the crystal structure of solids. A crystal of a solid element is essentially a very large molecule held together by ionic or covalent bonds. When the bonding is covalent, the particular structure in which an element crystallizes is determined by the number and directions of the covalent bonds that are energetically most favorable. Sometimes one form is favored under certain conditions of temperature and pressure, and another form under other conditions; hence the existence of various *allotropic* modifications of crystalline solids. A third type of bond, neither ionic nor covalent, also occurs in some solids. This bond, called the *metallic bond,* has no counterpart in molecular binding. We shall return to the study of the crystal structure of solids in Sec. 11-1.

9-6 Molecular Spectra

Thus far in the discussion of atomic spectra, we have not considered the possibility of motion of the nucleus. For a single atom, this neglect can be justified either by making the approximation that the nucleus is so much more massive than the electrons that it can be considered as stationary or by assuming that the *center of mass* is stationary, in which case the motion of the nucleus is completely determined by the motion of the electrons, and the appropriate (very small) corrections to the energy levels can be calculated. One could, of course, consider the additional energy that would result from motion of the center of mass of the entire atom, corresponding to a free particle moving in some kind of container. As shown in Sec. 7-2, the energy levels associated with this motion are so very closely spaced for a container of any reasonable size that transitions between such levels can occur with extremely small energy changes, and for all practical purposes this set of energy levels can be regarded as a continuum rather than a discrete set.

In diatomic or polyatomic molecules, new features appear. Even when the center of mass of the molecule is stationary, several varieties of motion of the individual nuclei are still possible. The simplest is *rotation* of the molecule as a whole about an axis through the center of mass. The classical kinetic theory of gases suggests that such rotational motion does occur, and the observed specific heats of polyatomic gases indicate that kinetic energy is associated with rotational degrees of freedom, in accordance with the theorem of equipartition of energy, which states that an amount of kinetic energy $\frac{1}{2}kT$ is associated with each degree of freedom.[1]

In a quantum-mechanical description of rotation of a polyatomic molecule, we anticipate that the energy may be *quantized.* That is, there may be discrete energy levels, just as the electron rotating about the nucleus in the hydrogen atom has discrete energy levels. This possibility is suggested even more strongly by the fact that in classical mechanics

[1] H. D. Young, "Fundamentals of Mechanics and Heat," sec. 16-4, McGraw-Hill Book Company, New York, 1964.

the *energy* of rotational motion and the *angular momentum* of the system are closely related, since each can be expressed in terms of the moments of inertia and the components of angular velocity. In all the systems examined thus far, angular momentum is quantized, and so we expect the rotational kinetic energy of a molecule also to have discrete levels.

In order to exhibit principles as simply as possible, the following discussion will be confined entirely to diatomic molecules. We consider first a model in which the molecule is represented as a rigid dumbbell, with two point masses m_1 and m_2 separated by a constant distance r, as shown in Fig. 9-6. This model is consistent with the fact that practically all the mass of an atom is concentrated in the nucleus, whose

Fig. 9-6 *Model of a diatomic molecule, regarded as a rigid dumbbell consisting of two point masses m_1 and m_2 (the two nuclei) separated by a constant distance r. The distances r_1 and r_2 given by Eqs. (9-12) are determined by the definition of the center of mass (labeled CM), which requires that $m_1r_1 = m_2r_2$, and by the requirement that $r_1 + r_2 = r$. The rotational motion of the molecule can be described as a combination of rotations about two mutually perpendicular axes through the center of mass, as shown.*

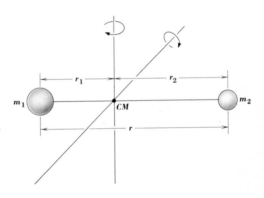

dimensions are smaller by a factor of the order of 10^5 than the separation between nuclei in a molecule or crystal. The angular position of such a dumbbell is described completely by two angular coordinates, and any rotational motion can be represented as a combination of rotations about two mutually perpendicular axes through the center of mass, perpendicular to the axis of the dumbbell. Rotations about the axis of the dumbbell are not considered, since in this model there is no moment of inertia about the dumbbell axis.

The distances r_1 and r_2 in Fig. 9-6 are given by

$$r_1 = \frac{m_2 r}{m_1 + m_2} \qquad r_2 = \frac{m_1 r}{m_1 + m_2} \tag{9-12}$$

and the moment of inertia I about an axis through the center of mass, perpendicular to the dumbbell axis, is

$$
\begin{aligned}
I &= m_1 r_1{}^2 + m_2 r_2{}^2 \\
&= \frac{m_1 m_2{}^2 r^2}{(m_1 + m_2)^2} + \frac{m_1{}^2 m_2 r^2}{(m_1 + m_2)^2} \\
&= \frac{m_1 m_2}{m_1 + m_2} r^2
\end{aligned}
\tag{9-13}
$$

In the last form we recognize the reduced mass[1] μ of the system, defined as

$$
\mu = \frac{m_1 m_2}{m_1 + m_2}
\tag{9-14}
$$

in terms of which the moment of inertia becomes simply

$$
I = \mu r^2
\tag{9-15}
$$

In a complete quantum-mechanical analysis of the rotational motion, the next step is to express the kinetic energy of the system in terms of the components of momentum of each particle and then to construct the corresponding energy operator H for use in the Schrödinger equation, as discussed in Sec. 7-7. Solutions of the time-independent Schrödinger equation then give the possible energy levels corresponding to rotational motion of the molecule.

Instead of giving this complete analysis, we shall take a shortcut which makes use of the classical relationship between rotational kinetic energy and angular momentum. In classical mechanics, the rotational kinetic energy of a rigid body rotating with angular velocity ω about a fixed axis is

$$
E = \tfrac{1}{2} I \omega^2
\tag{9-16}
$$

where I is the moment of inertia of the body about the axis of rotation. Similarly, the angular momentum **L** has a magnitude L given by

$$
L = I \omega
\tag{9-17}
$$

Strictly speaking, this last relationship is true only if the axis of rotation is a *principal axis of inertia*. However, for any body having axial symmetry, as in the case of the diatomic molecule, any axis perpendicular to the molecular axis is a principal axis of inertia.

---

[1] *Ibid.*, sec. 10-5.

Combining Eqs. (9-16) and (9-17) to eliminate the kinematic quantity ω in favor of the two dynamical quantities E and L, we obtain

$$E = \frac{L^2}{2I} \tag{9-18}$$

With angular momentum of electrons in atoms, the component of **L** in any given direction must be an integer multiple of $\hbar$, and the square of the magnitude of the total angular momentum is given by

$$L^2 = l(l + 1)\hbar^2 \qquad l = 0, 1, 2, \ldots \tag{9-19}$$

In the present case the angular momentum is associated with the motion of nuclei rather than electrons, but since it is the same dynamical quantity it seems reasonable that Eq. (9-19) should be valid also for the rotational angular momentum of a diatomic molecule. Hence, substituting the above expression for the permitted values of L^2, we find that the permissible energies associated with rotation of a diatomic molecule are

$$E_l = l(l + 1)\frac{\hbar^2}{2I} \qquad l = 0, 1, 2, \ldots \tag{9-20}$$

Although this derivation is somewhat intuitive, a complete and rigorous calculation based on solution of the Schrödinger equation yields the same result. As we shall see, the rotational energy levels given by Eq. (9-20) also agree with experimental observations. This energy-level scheme is illustrated in Fig. 9-7.

As an indication of the magnitudes of the quantities involved, we estimate roughly the numerical value of $\hbar^2/2I$ for a typical diatomic molecule, say oxygen. The mass of an oxygen atom is determined from the fact that the atomic mass of oxygen is 16, which means that a mole of oxygen (6.02×10^{23} molecules) has a mass of 16 g. Thus the mass of one oxygen atom is approximately

$$m = \frac{16 \times 10^{-3} \text{ kg}}{6.02 \times 10^{23}} = 2.7 \times 10^{-26} \text{ kg} \tag{9-21}$$

To obtain an estimate of the distance r between nuclei, we note that molecular binding of two atoms is the same phenomenon in principle as that of the binding of atoms in a crystalline solid, in which x-ray diffraction experiments have shown that the spacing of atoms is typically of the order of 2×10^{-10} m. This approximate magnitude also agrees with estimates of the size of the oxygen molecule obtained from measurements of the mean free path of molecules in the gaseous state, observa-

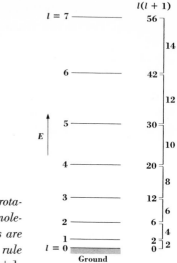

Fig. 9-7 *Energy levels for rotational motion of a diatomic molecule. The possible transitions are governed by the selection rule $\Delta l = \pm 1$.*

tions of van der Waals corrections to the ideal-gas equation, and other data.

Using these numbers, we find for the moment of inertia of an oxygen molecule

$$I = \tfrac{1}{2}(2.7 \times 10^{-26}\ \text{kg})(2 \times 10^{-10}\ \text{m})^2 = 5.4 \times 10^{-46}\ \text{kg m}^2 \qquad (9\text{-}22)$$

Finally, the constant $\hbar^2/2I$ has the numerical value

$$\frac{\hbar^2}{2I} = \frac{(1.06 \times 10^{-34}\ \text{joule sec})^2}{2(5.4 \times 10^{-46}\ \text{kg m}^2)} = 1.0 \times 10^{-23}\ \text{joule}$$
$$= 0.6 \times 10^{-4}\ \text{ev} \qquad (9\text{-}23)$$

This energy may be compared with energies corresponding to optical spectra, which in the visible region are typically 2 to 3 ev. The spacing of these rotational energy levels is smaller by a factor of the order of 10^4, and transitions from one level to another correspond to photons in the far-infrared region of the electromagnetic spectrum. According to the classical equipartition theorem, the *average* rotational kinetic energy for a diatomic molecule with two rotational degrees of freedom is kT, which at ordinary temperatures, say $T = 300°K$, is

$$kT = (1.38 \times 10^{-23}\ \text{joule/K}°)(300°K) = 4.14 \times 10^{-21}\ \text{joule}$$
$$= 0.0258\ \text{ev} \simeq \tfrac{1}{40}\ \text{ev} \qquad (9\text{-}24)$$

Comparing this number with Eq. (9-20) and the numerical value given in Eq. (9-23) we see that a diatomic molecule with this much rotational energy is in a state with a quantum number of the order of $l = 20$. Thus, in a transition between two adjacent quantum states, the gain or loss of energy is relatively small compared with the average total energy at ordinary temperatures.

The infrared spectrum associated with transitions between rotational states may be obtained from the energy-level diagram shown in Fig. 9-7. Just as for atomic spectra, there are selection rules based on the transitions corresponding to electric-dipole radiation patterns, which are ordinarily the only transitions with significant probabilities. The selection rules, as before, are that the angular momentum must change by one unit, and its component in a given direction by one unit or zero. That is,

$$\Delta l = \begin{cases} +1 & \text{absorption} \\ -1 & \text{emission} \end{cases} \tag{9-25}$$

$$\Delta m_l = 0, \pm 1$$

As Fig. 9-7 shows, the level spacing increases uniformly with l, and so the frequencies in the rotation spectrum of a diatomic molecule are all integral multiples of a fundamental frequency given by $\omega = \hbar/I$. Detailed proof of this statement is left as a problem.

Pure rotation spectra of diatomic molecules are observable only when all other kinds of energy transitions can be neglected; this occurs for some diatomic molecules at sufficiently low temperatures. At higher temperatures, other forms of motion, to be discussed next, introduce additional energy levels and corresponding complications in the molecular spectrum.

The next generalization in the model of a diatomic molecule is to regard it not as a rigid structure but rather as one in which the two nuclei are elastically bound so that a vibrational motion along the axis of the molecule is possible. In a classical description of this vibrational motion,[1] there is a certain equilibrium spacing of the two nuclei, and for small displacements from this equilibrium position the interatomic force can be represented as approximately proportional to this displacement. As a result, each nucleus undergoes simple harmonic motion with an angular frequency ω given by

$$\omega = \sqrt{\frac{k}{\mu}} \tag{9-26}$$

---

[1] *Ibid.*, sec. 10-5.

where μ is the reduced mass defined by Eq. (9-14) and k is the effective spring constant for the interatomic force. The magnitude of the force constant k can be estimated from the macroscopic elastic properties of solids, by using a simple model of the structure of the solid.[1] Such calculations suggest that typical molecular force constants are of the order of 50 nt/m. Thus, in a classical calculation, the frequency of oscillation of the atoms in the diatomic oxygen molecule discussed above is

$$\omega = \sqrt{\frac{k}{\mu}} = \sqrt{\frac{50 \text{ nt/m}}{1.4 \times 10^{-26} \text{ kg}}} = 6 \times 10^{13} \text{ sec}^{-1} \qquad (9\text{-}27)$$

These results suggest a way to proceed in a quantum-mechanical analysis of vibrational motion of a diatomic molecule. In classical mechanics the behavior of a two-body oscillator is equivalent in all respects to the motion of a harmonic oscillator whose mass is the reduced mass of the two-body system, and there is no reason not to expect the same to be true in the quantum-mechanical formulation. The simple harmonic oscillator has already been discussed in detail, in Sec. 7-5, using Schrödinger's equation. To apply the results of this calculation to the present problem, we need only note that the total separation r between nuclei at any instant may be represented as the sum of the equilibrium separation r_0 and the displacement x from this equilibrium separation. Thus the wave functions of Sec. 7-5, applied to the diatomic molecule, represent the probability of finding the molecule in a position where the nuclei are displaced a distance x from their equilibrium separation. The corresponding energy levels are

$$E = \left(n + \frac{1}{2}\right)\hbar\omega = \left(n + \frac{1}{2}\right)\hbar\sqrt{\frac{k}{\mu}} \qquad n = 0, 1, 2, 3, \ldots \qquad (9\text{-}28)$$

As with the harmonic oscillator of Sec. 7-5, this expression represents a series of equally spaced levels. The spacing of adjacent levels, given by $\hbar\omega$, may be estimated for the oxygen atom we have used as an example. We find

$$\hbar\omega = (1.06 \times 10^{-34} \text{ joule sec})(6 \times 10^{13} \text{ sec}^{-1}) = 6 \times 10^{-21} \text{ joule}$$
$$= 0.014 \text{ ev}$$

Thus the energy associated with a transition between vibrational states of a diatomic molecule is typically of the order of 10^{-2} of optical-

---

[1] *Ibid.*, sec. 17-4.

spectrum energies, and the corresponding radiation is in the near-infrared region of the spectrum.

For the oxygen molecule, this level spacing is of the order of 100 times as great as that of the rotational states and is also of the same order of magnitude as the quantity kT at ordinary temperatures, indicating that, according to the equipartition theorem, at room temperature most of the oxygen atoms are in the lowest few quantum states, with a fairly large number in the $n = 0$ state. This observation has important implications in the quantum theory of specific heats, to which we shall return in Sec. 10-4.

In general, at sufficiently high temperatures, a molecule can be expected to possess both vibrational and rotational energy, and so the composite energy-level scheme can be represented as shown in Fig. 9-8, which shows several relatively widely spaced vibrational levels, each

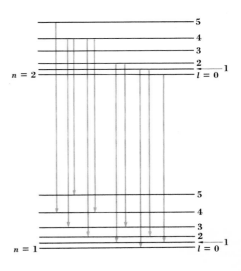

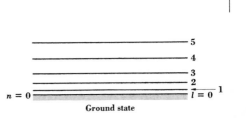

Fig. 9-8 *Vibration-rotation energy-level scheme. For each vibrational level there is a series of more closely spaced rotational levels. Several transitions consistent with the selection rule* $\Delta l = \pm 1$ *are shown.*

with a set of rotational levels much more closely spaced. Correspondingly, in transitions between these states, there are several transitions for a given initial value of n, corresponding to different initial values of l. The result is a series of spectrum lines that are closely spaced. Originally, the resolution of infrared spectroscopic equipment was not sufficient to resolve these as separate lines, and they were called *band spectra*. It is now understood that each band corresponds to a definite pair of initial and final values of n with various values of l, according to the selection rules

$$\Delta l = \pm 1$$
$$\Delta m_l = 0, \pm 1$$

(9-29)

For a molecule containing more than two atoms, additional interesting features appear. A triatomic molecule whose atoms do not lie along a single line has nonzero moments of inertia along all three principal axes, and thus there are three degrees of freedom associated with rotational motion. For such a triatomic molecule, such as water or CO_2, there are also various ways in which the molecule can vibrate. Each of them is called a normal mode and is a state of motion in which each atom, classically speaking, undergoes simple harmonic motion about its equilibrium position. Three normal modes of oscillation for a linear triatomic molecule are shown in Fig. 9-9. In general, each of these normal modes has a different frequency and correspondingly different spacing of energy levels of quantum states. Analysis of the infrared spectrum resulting from transitions among various vibrational

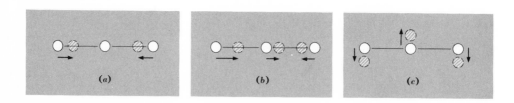

(a)   (b)   (c)

Fig. 9-9 *Normal modes of vibrational motion for a linear triatomic molecule. Modes (a) and (b) correspond to stretching and compressing the bonds, and mode (c) to bending. Thus the energy levels of these modes, determined from infrared spectra, provide information about the strength and rigidity, respectively, of the bonds.*

and rotational states provides information concerning the vibrational states, force constants, and structure of the molecules. Infrared spectroscopy has been of enormous importance as a tool for the investigation of molecular structure.

PROBLEMS

9-1 Prove the statement following Eq. (9-4).

9-2 The ion He^+ has only one electron and therefore has hydrogenlike wave functions and energy levels.

   a. What is the relationship between the energy-level scheme for He^+ and that for H?

   b. In what regions of the spectrum do the Lyman, Balmer, and Paschen series (transitions terminating at $n = 1$, 2, 3, respectively) lie?

9-3 Show that in any "filled-shell" electron configuration the total z component of angular momentum is zero.

9-4 If for some reason atoms could contain only electrons with principal quantum numbers up to and including $n = 5$, how many elements would there be? Use the energy-level sequence given in Sec. 9-2.

9-5 Long before the details of atomic structure were understood, it was observed that the atomic numbers (Z) of the inert gases are given by the following scheme:

   He: $Z = 2(1^2) = 2$
   Ne: $Z = 2(1^2 + 2^2) = 10$
   Ar: $Z = 2(1^2 + 2^2 + 2^2) = 18$
   Kr: $Z = 2(1^2 + 2^2 + 2^2 + 3^2) = 36$
   Xe: $Z = 2(1^2 + 2^2 + 2^2 + 3^2 + 3^2) = 54$
   Rn: $Z = 2(1^2 + 2^2 + 2^2 + 3^2 + 3^2 + 4^2) = 86$

   How can this sequence be understood in terms of the electron configurations of the atoms?

9-6 The ionization potentials of the transition metals (atomic numbers 21 to 30) are very nearly equal. How can this observation be understood on the basis of their electron configurations?

9-7 Considering the difference in ionization potentials of the various alkali metals, as shown in Table 9-5, which would you expect to be most active chemically, in terms of propensity to form compounds rather than exist as an element? Explain. Why are the ionization potentials different?

9-8   Considering the difference in electron affinity of the halogens, as shown in Table 9-6, which would you expect to be most active chemically, in terms of propensity to form compounds? Explain. Why are the electron affinities different?

9-9   Which of the "inert gases" is most likely to be capable of forming compounds? Explain.

9-10   Although the $2s$ and $2p$ states for hydrogen have exactly the same energy, the $2s$ state for the valence electron of lithium has lower energy than the $2p$ state. How can this difference be understood qualitatively on the basis of difference in wave-function shapes?

9-11   Estimate the K and L x-ray energy levels for molybdenum, and compute the wavelength corresponding to the $K\alpha$ transition.

9-12   What minimum voltage is necessary in an x-ray tube to excite the K x-ray energy level in an aluminum target?

9-13   Calculate the position of the K absorption edge for nickel.

9-14   Consider the molecule KBr. Using a consideration similar to that given in Sec. 9-4, calculate the maximum separation of the ions that still permits the existence of a stable molecule.

9-15   Consider the molecule $MgCl_2$. Using the ionization potentials and electron affinities given in Sec. 9-4, calculate the values of ion spacing for which this molecule should be stable.

9-16   Using the considerations of Sec. 9-4, analyze the energy balance for formation of the molecule HF, assuming that the bond is ionic. From the results, can you draw any conclusions about the probable actual nature of this bond?

9-17   An approximate wave function for the hydrogen molecule can be constructed from products of one-electron wave functions centered on the two nuclei, or from sums of such products. For example, if ψ_1 is a $1s$ wave function centered on nucleus 1, with ψ_2 a corresponding function centered on nucleus 2, then an approximate wave function is some combination of the products

$$\psi_1(\mathbf{r}_1)\psi_2(\mathbf{r}_2) \qquad \text{and} \qquad \psi_1(\mathbf{r}_2)\psi_2(\mathbf{r}_1)$$

where $\mathbf{r}_1$ and $\mathbf{r}_2$ are the coordinates of the two electrons. Show that, if the two electrons have parallel spins, the wave function must be antisymmetric with respect to interchange of electron coordinates and therefore that the wave function is zero at a point halfway between the two nuclei.

9-18   Discuss the valence-bond structure of the ethylene molecule, C_2H_4.

9-19   Compute the energy levels in the Bohr model of the hydrogen molecule, shown in Fig. 9-3, using the condition that the total angular momentum must be an integer multiple of $\hbar$. For a stable molecule, the repulsion of the two protons must just cancel the attractive forces of the electrons, and the vector sum of all forces on each electron must be equal to mv^2/r for that electron. These conditions, together with the quantization of angular momentum, are sufficient to determine the spacing of the protons and the orbit radii, from which the energy levels can be obtained.

9-20   The rotation spectrum of HCl contains the following wavelengths:

120.4 μ
 96.4 μ
 80.4 μ $1 \mu = 10^{-6}$ m
 69.0 μ
 60.4 μ

Find the distance between nuclei in the HCl molecule.

9-21   In the vibration-rotation spectrum of HCl, there appear two lines at 3.43 μ and 3.48 μ, which correspond to the transitions $\Delta n = -1$, $\Delta l = \pm 1$.
a.   For which wavelength is $\Delta l = +1$?
b.   From these data, find the effective spring constant for the interatomic force in the HCl molecule.

9-22   How is the vibration-rotation energy-level scheme of the oxygen molecule for the common isotope O^{16} related to that for the rare isotope O^{18}?

9-23   Show that the frequencies in a pure rotation spectrum are all integer multiples of the quantity $\hbar/I$. [Cf. statement following Eq. (9-25).]

9-24   When a molecule undergoes both vibrational and rotational motion, the moment of inertia of the molecule is not constant because of the varying distance between atoms. How should this fact affect the rotational energy levels?

9-25   Find the separation of the first two rotational energy levels for the H_2 molecule and the corresponding wavelength. How does the wavelength for the corresponding transition in the deuterium molecule D_2 differ?

IN A PHYSICAL system containing a very large number of particles, atoms, molecules, or other constituents, it is usually impossible, for practical reasons, to apply the basic physical laws directly to each particle.   Instead, it is often advantageous to take a statistical approach, in which one describes the distribution of particles in various states in a statistical manner; the existence of a very large number of parts of a system can often be used to advantage in this statistical description.   The basic ideas of a statistical description of a state of a many-particle system are introduced, and then the Maxwell-Boltzmann distribution function is derived.   A simple application of this function to the calculation of specific heats of gases is discussed in detail.   Finally we show that the quantum-mechanical notion of indistinguishability of identical particles necessitates changes in the development of the distribution function, and the appropriate modifications are developed.

10-1   Statistical Descriptions of States

The principal objective of this section is to introduce methods for describing the state of a complicated system in statistical terms.   An elementary example of the statistical point of view is found in the classical kinetic theory of gases. In the kinetic-molecular model of an ideal gas, the gas molecules are regarded as a collection of particles in random motion, colliding with each other and with the walls of their container. Although the motion of these particles is governed by Newton's laws of motion, the large number of particles makes direct application of these laws impractical. Instead, we concentrate on a *statistical* description of the state of the system. For example, the pressure on a wall of the container is directly related to the *average* kinetic energy of the molecules, which in turn is directly related to the *temperature* of the gas.

When a more detailed description of the motion of the gas molecules is needed, we do not try to specify the velocity or energy of each individual molecule but instead we describe how many molecules have velocities in each of various intervals by means of a *distribution function*. For example, the distribution of molecular speeds can be characterized by a function $f(v)$ having the property that $f(v)\ dv$ is the fraction of all the molecules having speeds in the interval dv. If there are N molecules, the total number dN having speeds in the interval dv is

$$dN = Nf(v)\ dv \tag{10-1}$$

Since every molecule must have some speed, the integral of Eq. (10-1) over all possible speeds must be equal to N. That is,

$$N = \int dN = \int_0^\infty Nf(v)\ dv \tag{10-2}$$

Thus $f(v)$ must satisfy the condition

$$\int_0^\infty f(v)\ dv = 1 \tag{10-3}$$

Any distribution function satisfying this requirement is said to be *normalized*. It is also possible to work with distribution functions that do not satisfy Eq. (10-3), in which case Eq. (10-1) must be generalized to

$$dN = \frac{Nf(v)\ dv}{\displaystyle\int_0^\infty f(v)\ dv} \tag{10-4}$$

In the following discussion normalized functions will always be used, and this generalization is unnecessary.

The distribution function can also be interpreted in terms of *probability*. If a molecule is selected from the gas at random, the probability that its speed will fall in the interval dv is given by $f(v)\ dv$. This reflects the fact that the probability of finding an object with specified characteristics among a large group is proportional to the *number* of objects in the group having these characteristics.

If the distribution function $f(v)$ is known, various quantities of interest can be calculated. They include the *average* speed, denoted by $\bar{v}$, which is given by

$$\bar{v} = \int_0^\infty v f(v) \, dv \tag{10-5}$$

and the average of v^2, denoted as $\overline{v^2}$, given by

$$\overline{v^2} = \int_0^\infty v^2 f(v) \, dv \tag{10-6}$$

The latter quantity is of special significance because of its relation to the average *kinetic energy* of the molecules, which is given by

$$(\tfrac{1}{2}mv^2)_{\text{av}} = \tfrac{1}{2}m\overline{v^2}$$

where m is the mass of a molecule.

The function which describes the distribution of molecular speeds in an ideal gas in thermodynamic equilibrium at absolute temperature T is the *Maxwell-Boltzmann* distribution; its expression is

$$f(v) = 4\pi \left(\frac{m}{2\pi kT}\right)^{3/2} v^2 e^{-mv^2/2kT} \tag{10-7}$$

where k is a fundamental physical constant called the Boltzmann constant. This expression is derived in detail in Sec. 10-3 after some preliminary developments.

From the statistical description of the speeds of the various molecules given by the function $f(v)$, or from a corresponding function for the distribution of molecular energies or other dynamical quantities, observable properties of the system such as temperature, pressure, specific heat, and magnetization can be calculated. Thus, although such distributions do not give detailed information about individual molecules, they are nevertheless very useful.

There are analogous problems in quantum-mechanical systems. Let us consider a large number of identical atoms or molecules, each of which has a series of energy levels. Under a given set of conditions, how many molecules are in the lowest state (the ground state), how many are in the next state, and so on? As a specific example, suppose we want to know the temperature to which a container filled with sodium vapor must be heated in order to obtain a certain intensity of emitted light resulting from radiative transitions between energy states of the atoms. In order to answer this question, we must know what fraction of all the atoms can acquire enough energy to exist temporarily in states above the ground state, so that they can later make transitions to the ground state with emission of the characteristic radiation of the sodium spectrum. It is to this general kind of situation that the discussion of this chapter is addressed.

Our procedure will be to derive, from very general considerations, distribution functions which give the numbers of molecules that are in various energy states or, alternatively, the *probability* for each molecule to be in a given state. The distribution functions can then be used to compute the total energy of the system, its specific heat, and other physical quantities of interest.

10-2   Maxwell-Boltzmann Distribution

Let us consider a physical system consisting of a very large number N of identical parts, each of which has a series of energy levels. For the sake of definiteness, we shall usually refer to these parts as molecules, although they might also be atoms, electrons, or other entities. We denote the energy levels by ϵ_i. For example, if the individual parts are hydrogen atoms, the energy levels are given by

$$\epsilon_i = -\left(\frac{e^2}{4\pi\epsilon_0}\right)^2 \frac{m}{2\hbar^2 i^2} \tag{10-8}$$

where i corresponds to the principal quantum number, previously denoted as n.

The most general statement of the Maxwell-Boltzmann distribution law is as follows: In a system of N identical molecules in thermodynamic equilibrium, each having a set of possible states with energies ϵ_i, the number of molecules in a specified state with energy ϵ_i is proportional to the quantity

$$e^{-\epsilon_i/kT}$$

where T is the absolute temperature and k is Boltzmann's constant, which in mks units has the value

$$k = 1.381 \times 10^{-23} \text{ joule/K}° \tag{10-9}$$

This section is devoted to deriving this law from fundamental probability considerations.

First, we assume that the molecules move nearly independently but that there are interactions of sufficient strength so that a state of thermal equilibrium can be established. That is, each molecule has at any instant a definite energy, but it can interact with other molecules from time to time to gain or lose energy as required by thermal equilibrium.

Second, we recognize that, in general, each molecule may have a number of different possible states with the same energy. For example, if the "molecule" is a hydrogen atom, there are various angular-momentum states, identified by the quantum numbers l and m, for each value of the principal quantum number, which determines the energy of the state. It was shown in Sec. 9-2 that the total number of states corresponding to the principal quantum number n is $2n^2$. The existence of several physically distinct states with the same energy is called *degeneracy*; the energy level is said to be *degenerate*, and the number of distinct states having a given energy ϵ_i is called the *degree of degeneracy*, denoted by g_i. Thus the degree of degeneracy of the hydrogen-atom energy levels is $g_i = 2i^2$, where again we have used i rather than n for the principal quantum number, in order to conform to later usage.

How shall we describe the possible states of the entire system? Two possibilities come to mind. The most detailed description of a state would be a specification of the state of each of the N molecules. We could make a chart showing which molecules are in each of the various states having energy ϵ_1, which ones in the states of energy ϵ_2, and so on. This description specifies a state of the system which we shall call a *microscopic* state or simply a *micro* state. It is easy to find the total number of possible micro states. Since there are g_i different states associated with energy ϵ_i for an individual molecule, the total number of distinct states in which a given molecule can exist is

$$\sum_i g_i \tag{10-10}$$

Each molecule has its choice of any one of these states, and so the total number of ways the N molecules can be arranged among the various states is

$$\left(\sum_i g_i\right)^N = M \tag{10-11}$$

where M denotes the *total* number of micro states.

Usually the micro states themselves are not very useful. Since the molecules are identical, it is of no concern precisely which molecules are in which energy states. Instead, we want to know *how many* are in each energy state, without regard to *which* molecules they are. Thus a different and more directly useful kind of state description consists in specifying only the total number of molecules having each of the possible energies, n_1 molecules in all the states having energy ϵ_1, n_2 in the states with energy ϵ_2, and in general n_i in the states having energy ϵ_i. This description of a state constitutes what we shall call a *macroscopic* state of the system, or *macro* state. This name is appropriate inasmuch as this description is most directly related to the macroscopic properties of the system. The principal objective of this section is to derive a *distribution* function $n = f(\epsilon)$ which gives the number of atoms n_i in each energy level ϵ_i and thus describes the macro state for a system in thermodynamic equilibrium.

Since the macro state is a less detailed specification than the micro state, there are, in general, several micro states for each macro state. As a simple example, suppose there are four molecules numbered from 1 to 4, with two energy states. If these states are not degenerate, then $g_1 = 1$ and $g_2 = 1$, $N = 4$, and the total number of micro states is

$$M = (1 + 1)^4 = 16$$

These states are shown schematically in Table 10-1. The number of macro states, on the other hand, is only five. As the table shows, one macro state has six corresponding micro states, two have four micro states each, and the other two have one each.

The heart of the derivation of the Maxwell-Boltzmann distribution, as will be seen shortly, is the assumption that the most probable macro state, that is, the macro state in which the system is most likely to exist, is the one with the largest number of corresponding micro states. Thus it is useful to work out a general formula for the number of micro states corresponding to any given macro state. Suppose we want to put n_i molecules in the states with energy ϵ_i. Since the corresponding degeneracy is g_i, *each* of the n_i molecules can be put in any one of the g_i states with energy ϵ_i, and the *total* number of ways the states can be chosen for any particular set of n_i molecules is $(g_i)^{n_i}$. There is a corresponding number of choices for each energy level, and so for a macro state described by the set of numbers n_1, n_2, . . . the *total* number of choices is

$$g_1{}^{n_1}g_2{}^{n_2}g_3{}^{n_3} \cdots \tag{10-12}$$

where the product ranges over all the energy states.

This is by no means the end of the possible choices, however. This would be the number of choices if we specified that a specific group of n_1 molecules had to be placed in energy ϵ_1, and so on, but clearly there

Table 10-1   States of Four Particles with Two Energy Levels

Micro states		Macro states	
ϵ_1	ϵ_2		
Molecule numbers		n_1	n_2
1234	— }	4	0
123	4		
124	3		
134	2	3	1
234	1		
12	34		
13	24		
14	23		
23	14	2	2
24	13		
34	12		
1	234		
2	134		
3	124	1	3
4	123		
—	1234 }	0	4

are still different combinations if we permute the various particles. Instead of taking the *first* n_1 molecules and putting them in the first states, we may select n_1 molecules from anywhere in the collection, and similarly for the other states. The number of distinct ways N molecules can be rearranged, which is called the *number of permutations of N molecules,* is simply $N!$ To see this, we observe that any of the N molecules may be placed first in the sequence; for each of these N choices we have $N - 1$ choices for the second in the sequence, for each of these $N - 2$ for the third, and so on, so that the total number of ways of arranging N molecules is

$$N(N - 1)(N - 2) \cdots (3)(2)(1) = N! \tag{10-13}$$

where $N!$ is read "N factorial" and is simply an abbreviation for the left side of Eq. (10-13).

It might appear that the number of distinct micro states corresponding to any macro state is the product of Eqs. (10-12) and (10-13). However, if we include *all* the possible permutations of N molecules, of which there are $N!$, we are *overcounting* the number of possibilities, for the following reason: A permutation in which the molecules are simply rearranged within a given energy state should not be counted, since we need to know *which* molecules are in the n_i in energy level ϵ_i, not *in what sequence* they appear. Thus we should divide the total number of permutations $N!$ by a factor $n_i!$ for each energy level.

Putting all the pieces together, we find that the total number of micro states corresponding to a macro state specified by the numbers $n_1, n_2, \ldots$ is given by

$$\frac{N!}{n_1!n_2!n_3! \cdots} g_1{}^{n_1}g_2{}^{n_2}g_3{}^{n_3} \cdots \tag{10-14}$$

We now make a fundamental postulate concerning the relative likelihood of occurrence of the various states. The postulate is this: *In a state of thermal equilibrium with a certain total energy, all the various micro states with that energy are equally likely to occur.* This postulate seems reasonable, but perhaps somewhat arbitrary; its final justification is that we are able to derive from it results that agree with observations of the macroscopic properties of matter.

Given the postulate that all the micro states are equally probable, we see that the macro states are *not* all equally probable, since the different macro states correspond to different numbers of micro states. Thus the *probability* of occurrence of a given macro state is equal to the number of micro states corresponding to it, divided by the *total* number M of micro states. That is, denoting the probability of a certain macro state $(n_1, n_2, \ldots)$ by $P(n_1, n_2, \ldots)$ we have

$$P(n_1, n_2, \ldots) = \frac{1}{M} \frac{N!}{n_1!n_2! \cdots} g_1{}^{n_1}g_2{}^{n_2} \cdots \tag{10-15}$$

Because ordinarily a large number of molecules are involved, it is clear that some macro states are much more likely to occur than others. The *most probable* macro states are clearly of greatest significance in characterizing the actual observed behavior of a system. It can be shown, in fact, that a relatively small number of closely related macro states are so overwhelmingly more probable than all the others that it can be said, to a very good approximation, that only *one* macro state has an appreciable probability of occurrence, and this macro state is therefore a suitable description of the state of the real physical system.

Thus the next task is to find the distribution of particles $(n_1, n_2, \ldots)$ which *maximizes* the value of Eq. (10-15). Rather than maximize this quantity itself, it is more convenient to deal with the logarithm of it, for reasons which will become apparent soon. Clearly, since $\ln P$ is a monotonic increasing function of P, maximizing the logarithm is equivalent to maximizing the function itself. Using the familiar properties of logarithms, we find

$$\ln P = -\ln M + \ln N! - \sum_i \ln n_i! + \sum_i n_i \ln g_i \qquad (10\text{-}16)$$

In varying the numbers n_1, n_2, . . . to maximize $\ln P$, we observe that n_i cannot all be varied independently, for two reasons. First, their sum must be equal to the total number N of molecules, which is constant. That is,

$$N = \sum_i n_i \qquad (10\text{-}17)$$

Second, the sum of the energies of all the molecules must equal the total energy of the system, which is also constant. Since there are n_i molecules in the states with energy ϵ_i, the total energy of these molecules is $n_i \epsilon_i$, and the total energy E of the entire system is

$$E = \sum_i n_i \epsilon_i \qquad (10\text{-}18)$$

Any set of numbers n_i appearing in Eq. (10-16) must be consistent with these two constraints.

Now, because N is very large, the n_i are also large, and so an insignificant error is introduced if we regard them as *continuous* variables rather than as integers. This has the great advantage that in maximizing Eq. (10-16) we can take derivatives with respect to the n_i. Another useful approximation, also based on the assumption that the n_i are very large, is to represent $n!$ by a continuous function of n, as follows:

$$\ln n! \cong n \ln n - n \qquad (10\text{-}19)$$

This formula, known as *Stirling's approximation*, is derived in Appendix G. As an example, for $n = 50$, we have

$$\ln 50! = 148.5$$

$$50 \ln 50 - 50 = 145.6$$

Even for this small value of n, the error in the approximation is only 2 percent. In practical problems, where the number of molecules typically ranges from 10^{10} to 10^{25}, the error is completely negligible. With the help of Eq. (10-19), Eq. (10-16) can be written

$$\ln P = -\ln M + \ln N! + \sum_i n_i \ln g_i - \sum_i (n_i \ln n_i - n_i) \qquad (10\text{-}20)$$

We shall now find the values of n_i that maximize this function. The function attains an extreme (or at least stationary) value when all quantities $\partial \ln P / \partial n_i$ are simultaneously zero. But, as already pointed out, the n_i cannot all be varied independently; they are subject to the two constraints given by Eqs. (10-17) and (10-18). To take this fact into consideration, we could use these two equations to eliminate two of the n's, take the derivatives with respect to the remaining ones, and solve the resulting set of simultaneous equations for the values of n_i that make the function a maximum. Instead, it is easier to preserve the symmetry of the expressions with respect to all the n_i by making use of a trick developed by Lagrange and known as the method of undetermined multipliers. We shall not prove the validity of this method in detail, but it is plausible and, in fact, almost obvious even without formal proof. The procedure is as follows: Instead of taking the derivatives of $\ln P$ as indicated, we consider the following function:

$$f(n_i) = \ln P - \alpha \left(\sum_i n_i - N \right) - \beta \left(\sum_i n_i \epsilon_i - E \right) \qquad (10\text{-}21)$$

where α and β are arbitrary constants. Because of Eqs. (10-17) and (10-18), the two terms on the right are zero no matter what values α and β have, and so this function is equal to $\ln P$. Now we take the derivative of Eq. (10-21) with respect to each n_i and set it equal to zero. The resulting set of equations can then be solved for the n_i that maximize the function.

This procedure can be justified roughly as follows: For any set of n_i satisfying the constraints of Eqs. (10-17) and (10-18), Eq. (10-21) is identical with $\ln P$. But because of the constraints, not all the n_i can be varied independently; if all but two are specified, the last two are determined by the constraints. Suppose, specifically, that n_1 and n_2 are the two that are not independent. Then for each of the others, all of which can be varied independently, we are at liberty to require that $\partial f / \partial n_i = 0$. But by appropriate choices of α and β the derivatives with respect to n_1 and n_2 can *also* be made to vanish. Thus the solutions of the set of equations $\partial f / \partial n_i = 0$ are the set of n_i that maximizes $\ln P$, subject to the constraints. Carrying out this program, we have

$$\frac{\partial f}{\partial n_i} = \frac{\partial}{\partial n_i} \ln P - \alpha - \beta \epsilon_i = 0 \qquad (10\text{-}22)$$

with $\ln P$ given by Eq. (10-20). Carrying out the derivative and recalling that N and M are constants, we find

$$\frac{\partial}{\partial n_i} \ln P = \ln g_i - \left(\ln n_i + n_i \frac{1}{n_i} - 1 \right)$$

$$= \ln g_i - \ln n_i \tag{10-23}$$

Combining this result with Eq. (10-22), we find

$$\frac{\partial f}{\partial n_i} = \ln g_i - \ln n_i - \alpha - \beta\epsilon_i = 0 \tag{10-24}$$

Solving for n_i,

$$n_i = g_i e^{-\alpha} e^{-\beta\epsilon_i} \tag{10-25}$$

Equation (10-25) shows the general functional dependence of the n_i on the energy levels ϵ_i; the number n_i of molecules in states with energy ϵ_i is proportional to an exponential function of ϵ_i.

The meaning of the parameters α and β is not yet clear. The constant α simply contributes a multiplicative factor $e^{-\alpha}$; since Eq. (10-25) must always satisfy Eq. (10-17), we have

$$N = \sum_i n_i = e^{-\alpha} \sum_i g_i e^{-\beta\epsilon_i} \tag{10-26}$$

Since N, g_i, and ϵ_i are presumably known properties of the system, this determines α if the other parameter β is known. Thus α is associated with the *normalization* of the distribution function.

The significance of the other constant β is less obvious but more fundamental than that of α and is best appreciated by examining the form of Eq. (10-25). We consider for simplicity a system having non-degenerate energy levels, so that all the g_i are unity. Then Eq. (10-25) is represented graphically by a histogram, as in Fig. 10-1, which shows that, because of the exponential function, n_i is a decreasing function of ϵ_i. Furthermore, the *rate* at which the function drops off with increasing ϵ_i depends directly on β. When β is very small, it drops off relatively slowly, whereas for a large value of β it drops off very rapidly with increasing ϵ_i, as shown in the figure. This suggests a relationship between β and the *temperature* of the system; we expect that at very low temperatures nearly all the molecules should be in the lowest energy states, whereas for very high temperatures there should be a wide range of energy states that are nearly equally populated. Thus it appears that β is inversely proportional to the *temperature* of the system.

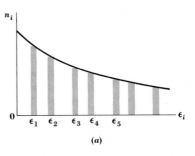

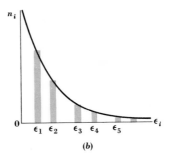

Fig. 10-1 *Maxwell-Boltzmann distributions for different values of β. (a) When β is small, corresponding to high temperature, the populations of the levels decrease only slowly with increasing energy, showing that states with rather high energy have substantial populations. (b) When β is large, corresponding to low temperature, the population drops off rapidly with increasing energy, showing that most molecules are in the lowest energy states.*

This interpretation of β is further supported by other results which will be obtained later in this chapter. For example, on the basis of Eq. (10-25) it will be shown that for the molecules of an ideal gas the average kinetic energy associated with translational motion of the molecules is given by $\bar{\epsilon} = 3/2\beta$. But according to the classical theorem of equipartition of energy[1] this average energy is equal to $\frac{3}{2}kT$, where k is again Boltzmann's constant and T the absolute temperature. Thus, at least in this case, β must be related to T by the equation

$$\beta = \frac{1}{kT} \tag{10-27}$$

Further support of this interpretation of β will appear later. Thus Eq. (10-26) may be rewritten

$$n_i = g_i e^{-\alpha} e^{-\epsilon_i/kT} \tag{10-28}$$

although for some calculations it is more convenient to express the distribution function in terms of β rather than kT.

As a simple application of the Maxwell-Boltzmann distribution, we

[1] H. D. Young, "Fundamentals of Mechanics and Heat," sec. 16-4, McGraw-Hill Book Company, New York, 1964.

consider a fictitious gas of diatomic molecules which have only rotational kinetic energy, with energy levels as discussed in Sec. 9-6, given by

$$\epsilon_l = \frac{l(l+1)\hbar^2}{2I} \qquad l = 0, 1, 2, \ldots \tag{10-29}$$

At a given temperature, what is the ratio of the number of molecules in the $l = 1$ states to the number in the $l = 0$?

First we note that, for any energy ϵ_l, the angular momentum is $[l(l+1)]^{1/2}\hbar$, and its z component can have any of the $2l + 1$ values between $-l\hbar$ and $+l\hbar$. Thus the degree of degeneracy of this state is $g_l = 2l + 1$. Specifically, $g_0 = 1$, $g_1 = 3$, $g_2 = 5$, and so on. The Maxwell-Boltzmann distribution, giving the number of molecules in each rotational energy state, then gives

$$n_l = e^{-\alpha}(2l+1)e^{-l(l+1)\hbar^2/2IkT} \tag{10-30}$$

The constant α is not known, but since only the ratio n_1/n_0 is required, we find immediately

$$\frac{n_1}{n_0} = \frac{e^{-\alpha}(3)e^{-\hbar^2/IkT}}{e^{-\alpha}(1)e^{-0}}$$
$$= 3e^{-\hbar^2/IkT} \tag{10-31}$$

At sufficiently low temperatures, the exponent becomes very large and negative, $n_1/n_0 \ll 1$, and practically *no* molecules are in the $l = 1$ states. As T increases, n_1/n_0 increases; at extremely *high* temperatures the exponent approaches zero, $n_1/n_0 \rightarrow 3$, and there are three times as many molecules in the $l = 1$ states as in the $l = 0$ states. That is, in the low-temperature limit *all* the molecules are in the lowest energy state, while in the high-temperature limit the distribution is determined entirely by the degree of degeneracy.

10-3 *Molecular Speeds*

The distribution function given by Eq. (10-25) is the general form of the *Maxwell-Boltzmann distribution*. Although derived in terms of a discrete set of energy levels, it may also be applied to a system in which the energy levels form a continuum. The most familiar example of such a system is an ideal gas, represented as a collection of N noninteracting molecules in a container, for which ϵ represents simply the translational kinetic energy of a molecule. For any container of reasonable size the possible energy levels are so closely spaced that they may be regarded as a continuum.   We now show how the Maxwell-Boltzmann distribution can be used to derive an expression for the distribution of molecular speeds in such a gas.

The energy levels are degenerate, since the energy of a state determines the magnitude of momentum of the molecule (through the relation $\epsilon = p^2/2m$) but not the direction of the momentum.   To determine the degree of degeneracy it is convenient to introduce a fictitious three-dimensional space whose coordinates p_x, p_y, and p_z represent the components of momentum of a molecule.   Each point in this space represents a possible momentum and therefore a possible state of motion of a molecule.   The magnitude of momentum p corresponding to a given point is given as usual by $p = (p_x^2 + p_y^2 + p_z^2)^{1/2}$ and is the distance from the origin to the point.

Any volume element in this space, which we may call the *momentum space* for the molecules, represents a certain range of momentum, and clearly the number of states in this range is proportional to the volume of the element.   In calculating the degree of degeneracy, however, we are interested in the number of states in an *energy* interval, say ϵ to $\epsilon + d\epsilon$.   We observe that all points corresponding to a given energy ϵ lie on a sphere in momentum space, whose radius is $p = (2m\epsilon)^{1/2}$. Likewise, points corresponding to the energy range ϵ to $\epsilon + d\epsilon$ lie within a spherical shell whose thickness dp is determined from the interval $d\epsilon$ by taking the derivative of the energy-momentum relation:

$$\epsilon = \frac{p^2}{2m}$$

$$d\epsilon = \frac{p\, dp}{m}$$

(10-32)

The *volume* of this spherical shell, assuming it is very thin, is approximately its surface area multiplied by its thickness; that is,

$$dV = 4\pi p^2\, dp$$

which may be written in terms of energy with the help of Eqs. (10-32):

$$dV = 4\pi mp\frac{p\, dp}{m} = 4\pi m(2m\epsilon)^{1/2}\, d\epsilon$$

(10-33)

Thus the number of states in the interval $d\epsilon$ is proportional to $\epsilon^{1/2}\, d\epsilon$, and the degeneracy factor simply to $\epsilon^{1/2}$.

The Maxwell-Boltzmann distribution function for this system can therefore be written

$$n(\epsilon)\ d\epsilon = A\epsilon^{1/2}e^{-\beta\epsilon}\ d\epsilon \tag{10-34}$$

The quantity $n(\epsilon)\ d\epsilon$ is the number of particles with energies in the interval $d\epsilon$, and A is a normalization constant which must be determined by requiring that the *total* number of particles be N. That is, A is chosen to satisfy the equation

$$\int_0^\infty n(\epsilon)\ d\epsilon = A \int_0^\infty \epsilon^{1/2}e^{-\beta\epsilon}\ d\epsilon = N \tag{10-35}$$

Evaluation of this integral requires some mathematical trickery, the details of which need not concern us. Its value, which can be found in integral tables, is

$$\int_0^\infty \epsilon^{1/2}e^{-\beta\epsilon}\ d\epsilon = \frac{\sqrt{\pi}}{2\beta^{3/2}} \tag{10-36}$$

A similar integral which is useful is

$$\int_0^\infty \epsilon^{3/2}e^{-\beta\epsilon}\ d\epsilon = \frac{3\sqrt{\pi}}{4\beta^{5/2}} \tag{10-37}$$

Using Eq. (10-36) to evaluate Eq. (10-35), we find

$$A = 2\pi N\left(\frac{\beta}{\pi}\right)^{3/2} \tag{10-38}$$

and the Maxwell-Boltzmann energy distribution function for an ideal gas becomes

$$n(\epsilon)\ d\epsilon = 2\pi N\left(\frac{\beta}{\pi}\right)^{3/2} \epsilon^{1/2}e^{-\beta\epsilon}\ d\epsilon \tag{10-39}$$

This function can be used to calculate the *average* kinetic energy $\bar{\epsilon}$ of a gas molecule. There are $n(\epsilon)\ d\epsilon$ molecules with energies ϵ in the interval $d\epsilon$, and the total energy of these molecules is $\epsilon n(\epsilon)\ d\epsilon$; the total energy of *all* the molecules is the integral of this expression; to obtain the average, we divide by the total number of molecules:

$$\bar{\epsilon} = \frac{1}{N}\int_0^\infty \epsilon n(\epsilon)\ d\epsilon = \frac{A}{N}\int_0^\infty \epsilon^{3/2}e^{-\beta\epsilon}\ d\epsilon \tag{10-40}$$

The value of the integral is given by Eq. (10-37); using this, we find

$$\bar{\epsilon} = \frac{2\pi N(\beta/\pi)^{3/2}}{N}\ \frac{3\sqrt{\pi}}{4\beta^{5/2}} = \frac{3}{2\beta} \tag{10-41}$$

We recall the simple kinetic-molecular theory of the ideal gas[1] in which the ideal-gas equation $PV = nRT$ can be derived from kinetic theory if it is assumed that the average molecular kinetic energy is $\frac{3}{2}kT$. It is seen that this agrees with the result of our more sophisticated calculation [Eq. (10-41)], provided we identify β with $1/kT$. This result thus supports this interpretation of β.

The Maxwell-Boltzmann distribution for an ideal gas can also be expressed in terms of the distribution of speed of gas molecules, using the relation $\epsilon = \frac{1}{2}mv^2$. Deriving the expression in terms of v is left as a problem; the result is

$$n(v) \, dv = 4\pi N \left(\frac{m}{2\pi kT} \right)^{3/2} v^2 e^{-mv^2/2kT} \, dv \qquad (10\text{-}42)$$

which agrees with Eq. (10-7).

This prediction can be compared with experimentally measured speed distributions. It is possible to measure speeds of *individual molecules* in a gas. A simple scheme for making such measurements is shown in Fig. 10-2. In this experiment a substance is vaporized in an oven, and molecules of vapor are permitted to escape, through a hole

Fig. 10-2 *Apparatus for producing a molecular beam and observing the distribution of molecular speeds in the beam.*

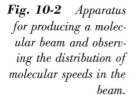
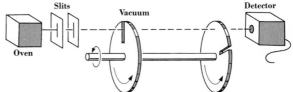

in the oven wall, into an evacuated region. A series of slits is constructed to block all molecules except those in one direction, so as to form a well-defined *beam;* this beam is aimed at a series of rotating disks as shown. The entire apparatus is enclosed in a container, which is evacuated so that the molecules may move freely without colliding with air molecules. When the disks are rotating, a molecule passing through the slit in the first disk will arrive at the second at just the right time to pass through its slit only if it has a certain speed. Other molecules with different speeds will strike the second disk. This apparatus may therefore be used as a speed selector which blocks all molecules except those in a narrow range of speeds. One may then measure *how many* molecules have speeds in various ranges.

[1] *Ibid.*, sec. 16-3.

Results of such experiments are consistent with the prediction of Eq. (10-42). This experiment provides a more detailed comparison of theory and experiment than the ideal-gas equation, which shows that the parameter β is to be identified with $1/kT$. The success of the theory in this example may therefore be regarded as an *a posteriori* justification of the initial assumption of equal probabilities of micro states.

In the following sections the Maxwell-Boltzmann distribution will be applied to systems quite different in nature from the classical ideal gas, and then we shall discuss modifications in the distribution function which are necessary in quantum-mechanical systems.

10-4   *Specific Heats of Gases*

The theory of specific heats of gases provides a simple illustration of some of the principles of statistical mechanics. Combined with some quantum-mechanical results derived in previous chapters, these principles lead to understanding of some phenomena in the behavior of specific heats which cannot be understood on the basis of classical theory alone.

We first review briefly the classical (non-quantum-mechanical) theory of specific heats.[1] Each molecule in a gas has a certain number of *degrees of freedom*, which is simply the number of different coordinates required to describe the position of the molecule completely or, alternatively, the number of velocities required to describe its motion completely. A monatomic molecule, considered as a point, has three degrees of freedom, corresponding to its three space coordinates or its three components of velocity. A diatomic molecule, considered as a dumbbell, has, in addition, two degrees of freedom associated with rotational motion. Further, such a molecule may have a vibrational motion with an additional degree of freedom. Molecules containing more than two atoms can, in general, have three degrees of freedom associated with rotational motion and several associated with vibrational motion.

According to the classical theorem of equipartition of energy, there is, on the average, kinetic energy $\frac{1}{2}kT$ per molecule associated with each degree of freedom; thus the average total energy per molecule is proportional to T. For an ideal monatomic gas, with three degrees of freedom, it is $\frac{3}{2}kT$. For a diatomic molecule there is an additional contribution $\frac{1}{2}kT$ for each of the two rotational degrees of freedom, $\frac{1}{2}kT$ for the vibrational kinetic energy, and $\frac{1}{2}kT$ for the vibrational

[1] *Ibid.*, sec. 16-4.

potential energy, for a total average energy per molecule of $\frac{7}{2}kT$. The specific heat, which is the energy that must be added for unit temperature change, is predicted to be $\frac{3}{2}k$ for a monatomic gas and $\frac{7}{2}k$ for a diatomic gas, independent of temperature. In these expressions it is assumed that *all* the energy added to the system to raise its temperature is used to increase the internal energy and none leaves the system as work done against a moving container wall or through any other mechanism. Thus we are considering the specific heats at constant volume, not at constant pressure.

The above expressions are readily converted into the more customary *molar* specific heat, which is the energy *per mole* required for unit temperature change. The number of molecules in a mole, called Avogadro's number, is given by

$$N_0 = 6.022 \times 10^{23} \text{ molecules/mole} \tag{10-43}$$

and the familiar ideal-gas constant R is related to Boltzmann's constant by

$$R = N_0 k \tag{10-44}$$

reflecting the fact that k may be interpreted as a gas constant in which the unit of matter is one molecule rather than one mole. In commonly used units R has the values

$$R = 8.314 \text{ joules/mole K}° = 1.99 \text{ cal/mole K}° \tag{10-45}$$

Thus the classical theorem of equipartition of energy predicts that the molar specific heat of an ideal monatomic gas should be $\frac{3}{2}R$ and that of an ideal diatomic gas $\frac{7}{2}R$. From the above discussion it should be clear that, in each case, the predicted specific heat is a constant, independent of temperature.

Although some gases are observed to have specific heats which are more or less independent of temperature over a wide range, others show a marked dependence on temperature. Figure 10-3 shows the specific

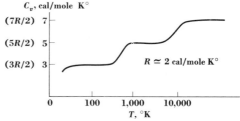

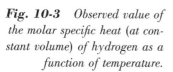

Fig. 10-3 *Observed value of the molar specific heat (at constant volume) of hydrogen as a function of temperature.*

heat of hydrogen as a function of temperature. We see that at low temperatures the molar specific heat is about $\frac{3}{2}R$, characteristic of a monatomic gas, despite the fact that other evidence indicates that hydrogen is diatomic at these temperatures. At successively higher temperatures it increases to $\frac{5}{2}R$ and becomes relatively constant; then at still higher temperatures it increases to a final value of $\frac{7}{2}R$. This clearly suggests that at sufficiently low temperatures the energies which we had thought would be associated with rotational and vibrational motion are absent.

The reason is not far to seek. We have already observed in connection with the discussion of molecular spectra in Sec. 9-6 that energies associated with both rotational and vibrational motion of a diatomic molecule are quantized. The vibrational energy levels, for example, are given by $E_n = (n + \frac{1}{2})\hbar\omega$. But now suppose that the temperature is sufficiently low that kT is much smaller than $\hbar\omega$. In this case most molecules should be in the $n = 0$ vibrational state, and there is little chance for a molecule to acquire enough energy from a collision to reach any higher energy state, since very few molecules *have* this much energy. Thus only a small fraction of the molecules change their vibrational state at all when the temperature changes slightly, and as a result the vibrational motion contributes much *less* to the specific heat than would be expected on the basis of the equipartition theorem. Under these circumstances, the vibrational degree of freedom is said to be "frozen out." The same argument is valid for the rotational energy levels.

The temperature dependence of the specific heat of hydrogen suggests that at very low temperatures both the vibrational and rotational degrees of freedom are "frozen out." Molecular spectroscopy shows that the rotational energy levels are much more closely spaced than the vibrational, and so we expect that as the temperature increases the rotational levels will begin to contribute to the specific heat before the vibrational levels. Thus at intermediate temperatures the specific heat becomes $\frac{5}{2}R$, corresponding to the contributions of the translational and rotational degrees of freedom but not of vibrational energy, which is still frozen out. At still higher temperatures the vibrational energy begins to contribute, and the specific heat attains a final value of $\frac{7}{2}R$. At still higher temperatures we might expect to obtain further contributions to the specific heat arising from the possibility of electron-energy-level excitation. As we have seen, the electron energy levels are spaced far apart compared with vibrational or rotational levels, and so any such contributions to the specific heat will occur only at extremely high temperatures. At such temperatures, enough of the hydrogen molecules are dissociated into single atoms to make the situation even more complicated.

To clarify and illustrate some of the above discussion and to show how more detailed calculations of specific heats can be made, we consider the vibrational specific heat of a gas of diatomic molecules. We assume that the temperature is such that the translational and rotational degrees of freedom contribute the classical $\frac{5}{2}R$ to the molar specific heat but that the vibrational motion is just beginning to contribute. That is, we assume that most of the molecules are in the $n = 0$ vibrational state, and only a few in higher states.

We now apply the Maxwell-Boltzmann distribution derived in Sec. 10-1 to this problem. To make the notation consistent with that of Sec. 10-1, we use i for the vibrational quantum number. That is, the possible vibrational energies of a molecule are given by

$$\epsilon_i = (i + \tfrac{1}{2})\hbar\omega = (i + \tfrac{1}{2})\epsilon_0 \tag{10-46}$$

where ϵ_0 is an abbreviation for the quantity $\hbar\omega$. If there are N molecules, the number n_i in the energy state ϵ_i is given by Eq. (10-25). Since for each molecule there is only one vibrational state corresponding to the given quantum number i, the degeneracy factors g_i are all equal to unity and may be omitted. Thus the number of molecules in state i is given by

$$n_i = Ae^{-\beta(i+1/2)\epsilon_0} \tag{10-47}$$

The normalization constant A is chosen to satisfy the condition

$$\sum_{i=0}^{\infty} n_i = A \sum_{i=0}^{\infty} e^{-\beta(i+1/2)\epsilon_0} = N \tag{10-48}$$

To determine A, we note that the sum in Eq. (10-48) can be written

$$\sum_{i=0}^{\infty} e^{-\beta(i+1/2)\epsilon_0} = e^{-(1/2)\beta\epsilon_0}(1 + e^{-\beta\epsilon_0} + e^{-2\beta\epsilon_0} + e^{-3\beta\epsilon_0} + \cdots) \tag{10-49}$$

The sum in parentheses is simply the sum of terms of a geometric progression and may be evaluated by using the relation

$$1 + a + a^2 + a^3 + \cdots = \frac{1}{1 - a} \tag{10-50}$$

which is valid when $a < 1$. This formula can be verified directly by long division. Using it, we find

$$\sum_{i=0}^{\infty} e^{-\beta(i+1/2)\epsilon_0} = \frac{e^{-(1/2)\epsilon_0}}{1 - e^{-\beta\epsilon_0}} = \frac{1}{e^{(1/2)\beta\epsilon_0} - e^{-(1/2)\beta\epsilon_0}}$$

$$= \frac{1}{2 \sinh \tfrac{1}{2}\beta\epsilon_0} \tag{10-51}$$

Using this result in Eq. (10-48), we find

$$A = 2N \sinh \tfrac{1}{2}\beta\epsilon_0 \tag{10-52}$$

and the complete distribution function is

$$n_i = 2N \sinh \tfrac{1}{2}\beta\epsilon_0 \, e^{-\beta(i+1/2)\epsilon_0} \tag{10-53}$$

The quantity β is given, as always, by $\beta = 1/kT$. We see that at very low temperatures, when β is very large, the distribution falls off very rapidly with increasing i, and most molecules are in the $i = 0$ state. On the other hand, when $kT = 1/\beta$ is equal to ϵ_0, a sizable fraction of the molecules are in higher vibrational states, and we expect the vibrational energy to contribute considerably to the specific heat of the gas.

To calculate the vibrational contribution to the specific heat in detail, we first observe that the total vibrational energy of the whole gas is given by

$$E = \sum_i n_i \epsilon_i \tag{10-54}$$

with n_i and ϵ_i given by Eqs. (10-53) and (10-46), respectively. Dividing this quantity by N gives the average energy *per molecule,* and taking the derivative of that quantity with respect to T gives the rate of change of energy with temperature per molecule, which is the specific heat per molecule. That is, the specific heat per molecule is

$$C = \frac{1}{N}\frac{\partial}{\partial T}\sum_i n_i \epsilon_i \tag{10-55}$$

The sum occurring in this expression and Eq. (10-54) is most readily calculated by means of a trick. Since the usefulness of this trick is by no means limited to this particular example, we shall first state the problem in somewhat more general terms. For a collection of N identical molecules, each with a set of energy levels ϵ_i, with degeneracies g_i, the Maxwell-Boltzmann distribution function is

$$n_i = A(\beta)g_i e^{-\beta\epsilon_i} \tag{10-56}$$

where A, a function of β, is chosen to satisfy the equation

$$\sum_i A(\beta)g_i e^{-\beta\epsilon_i} = N \tag{10-57}$$

For such a system, we now define a function as follows:

$$Z(\beta) \equiv \sum_i g_i e^{-\beta\epsilon_i} \tag{10-58}$$

in which the sum extends over all the molecular energy states. This is usually called the *partition function* for the system. In terms of $Z(\beta)$, Eq. (10-57) becomes simply

$$N = A(\beta)Z(\beta) \tag{10-59}$$

The total energy E of the system is given by

$$E = \sum_i n_i \epsilon_i = \sum_i A g_i e^{-\beta \epsilon_i} \epsilon_i = \frac{N}{Z} \sum_i g_i \epsilon_i e^{-\beta \epsilon_i} \tag{10-60}$$

The sum in the last form of this equation can be expressed in terms of the *derivative* of Z with respect to β. We have

$$\frac{\partial Z}{\partial \beta} = -\sum_i g_i \epsilon_i e^{-\beta \epsilon_i} \tag{10-61}$$

Thus Eq. (10-60) becomes

$$E = -\frac{N}{Z} \frac{\partial Z}{\partial \beta} \tag{10-62}$$

and the average energy per molecule, $\bar{\epsilon}$, is

$$\bar{\epsilon} = \frac{E}{N} = -\frac{1}{Z} \frac{\partial Z}{\partial \beta} = -\frac{\partial}{\partial \beta} \ln Z \tag{10-63}$$

Thus if we can evaluate the sum that defines the function $Z(\beta)$, we can immediately find $\bar{\epsilon}$ by performing the operation indicated by Eq. (10-63). Similarly, the specific heat (per molecule), which is $\partial \bar{\epsilon}/\partial T$, can be found from Eq. (10-63).

For the particular case of the vibrational states of a diatomic molecule, where the energy levels are $\epsilon_i = (i + \frac{1}{2})\epsilon_0$, with $\epsilon_0 = \hbar \omega$, and the degeneracies are all unity, $g_i = 1$, we have already essentially calculated the partition function $Z(\beta)$, which is just Eq. (10-51). Thus for this system

$$Z(\beta) = \frac{1}{2 \sinh \frac{1}{2} \beta \epsilon_0} \tag{10-64}$$

and

$$\ln Z = -\ln (2 \sinh \tfrac{1}{2} \beta \epsilon_0) \tag{10-65}$$

The average vibrational energy, according to Eq. (10-63), is given by

$$\bar{\epsilon} = \frac{\partial}{\partial \beta} \ln (2 \sinh \tfrac{1}{2} \beta \epsilon_0) = \tfrac{1}{2} \epsilon_0 \coth \tfrac{1}{2} \beta \epsilon_0 = \tfrac{1}{2} \epsilon_0 \coth \frac{\epsilon_0}{2kT} \tag{10-66}$$

It is instructive to examine this last expression in the limit of very high temperatures (small β), when $kT \gg \epsilon_0$. For very small values of x, sinh x is approximately equal to x, and cosh x to unity, as can be seen by expanding the exponentials used to define these functions in power series. Thus at small x the function coth x approaches $1/x$; in the high-temperature limit as $\beta \to 0$, Eq. (10-66) becomes

$$\bar{\epsilon} = \tfrac{1}{2}\epsilon_0 \frac{2}{\beta\epsilon_0} = \frac{1}{\beta} = kT \tag{10-67}$$

which is just the result predicted by the classical equipartition theorem. Conversely, at very *low* temperatures, $\beta \to \infty$, coth $\tfrac{1}{2}\beta\epsilon_0 \to 1$, and Eq. (10-66) approaches the value $\tfrac{1}{2}\epsilon_0$, corresponding to every molecule being in the ground state $i = 0$.

The vibrational specific heat C is simply the derivative of Eq. (10-66) with respect to T. The details of this calculation are left as a problem; the result is

$$\begin{aligned} C &= k\left[\frac{\epsilon_0/2kT}{\sinh\,(\epsilon_0/2kT)}\right]^2 \\ &= k\left(\frac{\tfrac{1}{2}\beta\epsilon_0}{\sinh \tfrac{1}{2}\beta\epsilon_0}\right)^2 \end{aligned} \tag{10-68}$$

We see that in the high-temperature limit ($\beta \to 0$) the vibrational specific heat approaches the classical value k per molecule (or R per mole), but at low temperatures it approaches zero, as expected. Equations (10-66) and (10-68) are plotted as functions of T in Fig. 10-4. For comparison, the values of these quantities predicted by the equipartition theorem are also shown. We see that the temperature dependence of the specific heat agrees qualitatively with the observed behavior of hydrogen at temperatures of several thousand degrees. A more quantitative comparison can be made by using the value of ϵ_0 obtained from the infrared spectrum of the hydrogen molecule. This value is found to be approximately 0.5 ev, which is equal to kT at a temperature of about $6000°$ K, characteristic of the temperature of the outer layers of the sun. This calculation thus shows in detail why at ordinary temperatures the vibrational motion of the hydrogen molecule makes no contribution to its specific heat.

In principle, this entire calculation can be repeated for the rotational energy levels. Because the degeneracy is different for different levels and because the energy states are expressed in terms of the square of a quantum number, the calculation is more complicated, and it is necessary to resort to approximation methods to compute the partition func-

Fig. 10-4 (a) *Average vibrational energy of a molecule as a function of temperature. For comparison, the prediction of the classical equipartition theorem is shown as a broken line. The temperature at which $\epsilon_0 = 4kT$ is shown for reference.*
(b) *Specific heat (per molecule) as a function of temperature. For comparison, the prediction of the classical equipartition theorem is shown as a broken line. The temperatures at which $\epsilon_0 = kT$ and $4kT$ are shown. The value of this function for a given value of T is proportional to the slope of the $\bar{\epsilon}$ versus T graph at the same T.*

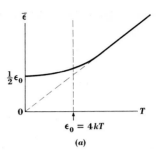

(a)

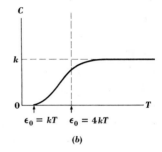

(b)

tion and its derivatives. Similar calculations may be carried out for polyatomic molecules having several different modes of vibration. The *total* specific heat, which ordinarily is the only quantity which can be measured directly, is always the sum of the translational, vibrational, and rotational contributions. In general these involve several different functions of temperature, and the various vibrational and rotational degrees of freedom begin to make significant contributions to the specific heat each at a different temperature. In all cases, it is possible to establish the relationship between molecular energy levels determined from molecular spectroscopy and the resulting temperature dependence of specific heats.

Similar considerations can be applied to calculating the specific heats of solids. For a solid, there is usually no energy corresponding to the rotational kinetic energy of a molecule but, instead, a large number of vibrational modes corresponding to various vibrations of the crystal lattice. For metals, there is an additional contribution to the specific heat resulting from closely spaced electron energy levels, and so electrons as well as nuclear motion contribute to the specific heat. For this reason, we postpone a detailed discussion of the quantum theory of specific heats of solids until Sec. 11-2. Meanwhile, we shall develop in the next section some statistical considerations which are fundamental to the understanding of the behavior of materials in the solid state.

10-5   *Quantum Statistics*

In this section we shall consider the modifications that must be made in the statistical description of states of a system when the constituents are electrons. The motivation of this development is its usefulness in understanding the properties of solids, which, as will be shown in Chap. 11, are intimately connected with the distribution of electrons in the various energy levels in a solid. Thermal and electrical conductivity, magnetic properties, specific heats, and a number of other properties of solid materials are directly related to the electron energy states, and so it is essential to be able to describe quantitatively the distribution of electrons in these states.

The correct statistical description of the energy distribution of electrons differs from the Maxwell-Boltzmann distribution in two important and closely related respects, one rather obvious and the other somewhat more subtle. First, electrons are governed by the exclusion principle, which states that no state may be occupied by more than one electron. In the Maxwell-Boltzmann case, conversely, the molecules are treated as independent entities, and there are no restrictions as to how many particles can occupy a given state.

Second, in the Maxwell-Boltzmann case we have assumed implicitly that the various molecules, although identical, can be *distinguished* from each other; that is, that in principle it is possible to *label* the molecules number 1, number 2, and so on. Thus a micro state in which molecule number 1 is in one energy state and number 2 in another is counted as distinct from the micro state in which they are reversed, even though the two molecules are identical. But, as we have seen in the discussion of the exclusion principle in terms of the symmetry of wave functions (Sec. 9-1), a quantum-mechanical description of a state containing several electrons does *not* distinguish among the particles in this way. The exclusion principle requires, to be sure, that the wave function be antisymmetric with respect to interchange of any two electrons, but quantum mechanics provides no basis on which to identify individual electrons in a given state, since they are not in principle distinguishable.

The distribution function that results from these two considerations differs in some important respects from the Maxwell-Boltzmann distribution. In honor of its discoverers, it is called the *Fermi-Dirac* distribution function. We shall now develop this distribution.

Again we consider a set of energy levels ϵ_i, with degeneracies g_i. That is, the energy level ϵ_i can accommodate g_i electrons without violating the exclusion principle. We proceed as in the development of the Maxwell-Boltzmann distribution, assuming equal probability of micro states, counting the number of micro states corresponding to a given macro state, and finding the most probable macro state.   Because of the fundamental indistinguishability of electrons, however, the definition of a micro state and the procedure for counting micro states have to be revised carefully.   It is no longer meaningful to state that a certain specific particle is a particular state with energy ϵ_i; the most detailed description that is possible *in principle* is to specify the number of electrons (always zero or one) in each of the g_i states of energy ϵ_i, but not *which* electrons they are, since that question now has no meaning.

A micro state is now specified by specifying which of the g_i states corresponding to each energy ϵ_i are occupied by electrons; this is the most detailed possible description of the state of the system.   A macro state is specified by the number n_i of electrons in each energy ϵ_i, without regard for *which* of the degenerate states with this energy are occupied. Thus the distinction between micro and macro states lies in the selection of the various levels with a given energy ϵ_i, and the number of micro states in a given macro state is determined by counting for each energy level the number of different ways n_i particles can be placed in the g_i states with energy ϵ_i.

If the electrons were distinguishable, this would be easy.   The first particle could be placed in any one of the g_i states.   For each of these choices there would be a choice of $g_i - 1$ for the second particle; for each of these, $g_i - 2$ for the third, and so on, to $g_i - (n_i - 1)$ for the last.   The total number of possible ways of placing these n_i particles in the g_i states would be the product of all these factors, which is

$$g_i(g_i - 1)(g_i - 2) \cdots (g_i - n_i + 2)(g_i - n_i + 1) = \frac{g_i!}{(g_i - n_i)!} \tag{10-69}$$

But now, since the particles are, in principle, indistinguishable, permuting the n_i particles among the various states does not produce a physically different state of the system.   We have *overcounted* the number of possibilities by a factor of the number of permutations of n_i particles, which is $n_i!$, and the number of physically different ways of putting n_i particles into g_i states of energy ϵ_i is not Eq. (10-69) but rather

$$\frac{g_i!}{(g_i - n_i)!n_i!} \tag{10-70}$$

For those familiar with combinatorial analysis, we point out that what we have done is to compute the number of *combinations* of g_i things taken n_i at a time, in this case, the number of different ways a group of

n_i energy levels can be selected from a larger group g_i. In general, the number of combinations of r objects taken s at a time is $r!/s!(r-s)!$.

Each macro state is characterized by a set of numbers $(n_1, n_2, \ldots)$, and the number of micro states corresponding to a given macro state is obtained by multiplying the factors given by (10-70) for all the energy states. That is, the number P of micro states corresponding to the macro state specified by the set of numbers n_i is

$$P = \frac{g_1! g_2! \cdots}{(g_1 - n_1)!(g_2 - n_2)! \cdots n_1! n_2! \cdots}$$

$$= \prod_i \frac{g_i!}{(g_i - n_i)! n_i!} \tag{10-71}$$

In the last form the symbol Π stands for *product* and indicates that we take the product of the factors following this symbol, one for each value of i. This notation is exactly analogous to using Σ for summation, except that we are talking about a product instead of a sum.

To derive the details of the actual electron distribution, we proceed just as in the derivation of the Maxwell-Boltzmann distribution. We assume that for a given total energy of the system all the micro states corresponding to this energy are equally likely. Again, because of Eq. (10-71), the macro states are *not* all equally likely, and the most probable macro state, which is also the most probable state of the actual system, is found by maximizing Eq. (10-71). The resulting macro state is the best estimate we can make of the actual state of the system. Just as before, it turns out that a group of closely related macro states are so very much more likely than all the others that we are justified in asserting that these represent *the* state of the system.

Proceeding exactly as in the derivation of the Maxwell-Boltzmann distribution, we next note that maximizing P is equivalent to maximizing $\ln P$, which is

$$\ln P = \sum_i \ln g_i! - \sum_i \ln (g_i - n_i)! - \sum_i n_i!$$

$$= \sum_i [g_i \ln g_i - g_i - (g_i - n_i) \ln (g_i - n_i) + (g_i - n_i)$$

$$- n_i \ln n_i + n_i] \tag{10-72}$$

where we have again used Stirling's approximation. To maximize this quantity, subject to the two subsidiary conditions given by Eq. (10-17) and (10-18), that the total number of particles be N and the total energy

E, we again take the derivative with respect to each n_i of the quantity

$$\ln P - \alpha\left(\sum_i n_i - N\right) - \beta\left(\sum_i n_i\epsilon_i - E\right) \tag{10-73}$$

and set each derivative equal to zero.   Carrying out this operation,

$$\ln (g_i - n_i) - \ln n_i - \alpha - \beta\epsilon_i = 0 \tag{10-74}$$

or

$$\ln \frac{g_i - n_i}{n_i} = \alpha + \beta\epsilon_i \tag{10-75}$$

Rearranging this and solving for n_i,

$$n_i = \frac{g_i}{e^{\alpha+\beta\epsilon_i} + 1} \tag{10-76}$$

which is the general form of the Fermi-Dirac distribution.

An argument similar to that used with the Maxwell-Boltzmann distribution can be used to show that the constant β is again related to the temperature of the system by $\beta = 1/kT$.   The value of the constant α must again be chosen to satisfy the condition $\Sigma n_i = N$.   It is customary to express α in terms of another constant ϵ_f, as follows:

$$\alpha = -\frac{\epsilon_f}{kT} \tag{10-77}$$

Since α is a dimensionless quantity, ϵ_f has units of energy; it is called the *Fermi energy* for the distribution.   With this notation, the distribution function becomes

$$n_i = \frac{g_i}{e^{\beta(\epsilon_i - \epsilon_f)} + 1} \tag{10-78}$$

It is instructive to compare the general behavior of this function with that of the Maxwell-Boltzmann distribution.   For simplicity, we consider only a system in which the energy levels are nondegenerate, so that all the g_i are unity.   In this case, the n_i are always numbers between zero and unity, and each n_i represents the probability that the nondegenerate state ϵ_i is occupied, sometimes called the *occupation index* for the state.   The general behavior of the function can be seen from Eq. (10-78).   For very low temperature (large β), the exponent is a large positive quantity when ϵ_i is even slightly greater than ϵ_f; the denominator of the fraction is then very large, resulting in a value of n_i close to zero.   When ϵ_i is slightly *less* than ϵ_f, the exponent is a large

Fig. 10-5 *Fermi-Dirac distribution function. At very low temperatures, all states below ϵ_f are occupied, and all those above ϵ_f are unoccupied. At higher temperatures the break becomes less sharp as more of the states above ϵ_f become occupied.*

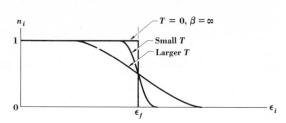

negative number, the exponential is near zero, and n_i is close to unity. The general shape of the function n_i is shown in Fig. 10-5. At successively higher temperatures, the function drops less rapidly from values near unity to values near zero, as ϵ_i passes the Fermi energy ϵ_f. Conversely, in the limit of extremely low temperatures, the function has nearly square corners.

This behavior is in sharp contrast to that of the Maxwell-Boltzmann distribution and is a direct result of the operation of the exclusion principle. Without the exclusion principle, at very low temperatures nearly all the electrons would be in the lowest energy states, but the exclusion principle prevents this. Instead, the lowest energy states are filled up successively, to whatever energy level is necessary to accommodate all the electrons, and from there on all energy states are empty. We also see that, at *any* temperature, ϵ_f represents the energy for which $n_i = \frac{1}{2}$.

It should be pointed out that ϵ_f is not a universal constant for any system but is a function of temperature. At very low temperatures, as we have seen, it is the highest energy state that is occupied; at extremely high temperatures, ϵ_f usually becomes large and negative. In this case, the exponent is always a fairly large positive number, and the exponential function in the denominator is much larger than unity. Thus in the high-temperature limit Eq. (10-78) becomes approximately

$$n_i = \frac{g_i}{e^{\beta(\epsilon_i - \epsilon_f)}} = e^{\beta \epsilon_f} g_i e^{-\beta \epsilon_i} \tag{10-79}$$

which has the form of the Maxwell-Boltzmann distribution. In this case, we note further that all the n_i are numbers much smaller than unity. That is, in the high-temperature limit, electrons occupy energy levels sufficiently high so that the probability of occupation of even the lowest levels is considerably less than unity. Correspondingly, in this limit the exclusion principle and the indistinguishability of particles become irrelevant and the function becomes identical with the Maxwell-Boltzmann form.

Although the discussion of this section has been confined entirely to a statistical description of indistinguishable particles which obey the exclusion principle, such as electrons, this is not the only possible distribution function. There are other particles which, although indistinguishable in a quantum-mechanical sense, do *not* obey the exclusion principle. It has been found, in fact, that all particles with a spin angular momentum that is a half-integer multiple of $\hbar$ obey the exclusion principle and hence are governed by the Fermi-Dirac distribution function. Conversely, all particles with spin angular momentum zero or an integer multiple of $\hbar$ are immune to the exclusion principle. The distribution function appropriate for these particles, which takes into account their indistinguishability, is called the *Bose-Einstein distribution function*. Rather surprisingly, it has exactly the same functional form as the Fermi-Dirac distribution except that the term $+1$ in the denominator becomes -1. Examples of particles obeying this distribution are photons and the various mesons. These particles are often collectively called *bosons*, with reference to this statistical behavior. Conversely, particles with half-integer intrinsic angular momentum, obeying the exclusion principle and the Fermi-Dirac distribution function, are called *fermions*. We shall return to this important distinction between classes of particles in Chap. 13.

PROBLEMS

10-1   For a gas obeying the Maxwell-Boltzmann distribution, find the *most probable* molecular speed, and show that a molecule having this speed has a kinetic energy equal to kT.

10-2   For a gas governed by the Maxwell-Boltzmann distribution, find the average translational kinetic energy of molecules by integrating Eq. (10-6), using the function given by Eq. (10-7). The following integral will be useful:

$$\int_0^\infty v^4 e^{-v^2/b^2}\, dv = \frac{3\sqrt{\pi}}{8} b^5$$

Compare your result with the prediction of the equipartition theorem.

10-3   Are relativistic corrections to the masses of gas molecules significant at ordinary temperatures? At approximately what temperature do they become significant? Does this temperature depend on the molecular mass?

10-4 Approximately what fraction of the molecules in an ideal gas have translational kinetic energy less than $0.1kT$? (Hint: In the Maxwell-Boltzmann distribution, when mv^2 is much less than kT the exponential factor is very close to unity and may be omitted.)

10-5 List all the possible micro states for six particles in two energy states. Also list all the macro states, and count the number of micro states for each macro state. If all micro states are equally likely, find the probability for each macro state.

10-6 For molecules obeying the Maxwell-Boltzmann distribution, show that the number n_1 of molecules in a nondegenerate energy state ϵ_1 is related to the number n_2 in another state ϵ_2 by

$$\frac{n_1}{n_2} = e^{-(\epsilon_1-\epsilon_2)/kT}$$

10-7 Using the result of Prob. 10-6, calculate the approximate temperature at which 1 percent of a gas of hydrogen atoms are in the $n = 2$ state, assuming most are in the $n = 1$ state.

10-8 At what temperature does kT equal 1 ev?

10-9 Derive Eq. (10-42) from Eq. (10-39).

10-10 For the HCl molecule, a transition in vibrational energy level corresponding to $\Delta n = -1$ results in the emission of a photon with a wavelength of 3.5×10^{-6} m. From this information, calculate the approximate fraction of HCl molecules that are in the $n = 1$ state at $T = 300°$K.

10-11 Suppose that the two nuclei in an oxygen molecule are separated by 2×10^{-10} m.
   a. Compute the moment of inertia of the molecule about an axis through the midpoint of the line joining the two nuclei, and perpendicular to it.
   b. At $T = 300°$K, if an oxygen molecule has a rotational kinetic energy equal to kT, what is its quantum state; i.e., what is the value of the rotational quantum number l?

10-12 Use the form of the Maxwell-Boltzmann distribution given by Eq. (10-42) to find the *average* speed of molecules in an ideal gas, as a function of temperature and molecular mass.

10-13 From Eq. (10-41) for the average translational energy of molecules of an ideal gas, show that the root-mean-square speed (the square root of the average value of v^2) is given by $(3kT/m)^{1/2}$. Compare this result with that of Prob. 10-12.

10-14 Estimate the temperature at which rotational kinetic energy begins to make a significant contribution to the specific heat of diatomic oxygen, assuming it is in the gaseous state at this temperature. Is this latter assumption realistic?

10-15 The rotational energy levels of a diatomic molecule are given by $E = E_0\, l(l + 1)$, where E_0 is a constant characteristic of the molecule and $l = 0, 1, 2, \ldots$. In transitions between rotational levels in which a photon is absorbed, the selection rule $\Delta l = \pm 1$ is obeyed. If $E_0 = 0.1$ ev, estimate the relative intensities of the $2 \to 1$ and $1 \to 0$ spectrum lines for a gas at $T = 300°$ by calculating the relative populations of the various states.

10-16 For a gas of diatomic molecules, the rotational energy begins to contribute significantly to the specific heat at a certain temperature T. How does T depend on the molecular mass, assuming all diatomic molecules have more or less the same dimensions?

10-17 Show that the specific heat of a system (per molecule) can be expressed in terms of the partition function Z as follows:

$$C = T\frac{d^2(kT \ln Z)}{dT^2}$$

10-18 Derive Eq. (10-68) from Eq. (10-66). Verify that in the limit as $T \to \infty$ it approaches k and that, as $T \to 0$, it approaches zero.

10-19 Write an expression for the *total* molar specific heat of a diatomic gas if all contributions except that of the vibrational energy are given by the equipartition theorem.

THE THREE PRECEDING chapters have been concerned with applications of the basic principles of quantum mechanics to various systems, the analysis of which is fundamental to an understanding of the microscopic structure of matter. It was shown that the Schrödinger equation can be solved exactly for the hydrogen atom to yield the energy levels and wave functions for the single electron in this atom. Next it was shown how the same principles can be used for an approximate analysis of systems containing several electrons in an atom and for those containing several atoms in a molecule, bound by the interaction associated with the electron configurations of the atoms. Then we discussed the statistical methods that can be used for the analysis of a system consisting of a large number of identical subsystems, which may be electrons, atoms, or molecules.

In the final three chapters we turn first to a discussion of matter in the solid state. In a solid there are strong interactions between the constituent atoms, and it is reasonable to think of a solid as essentially a molecule containing a very large number of atoms. In discussing solids, the central theme is the relation of macroscopic properties, including mechanical, thermal, electrical, and optical properties, to the microscopic structure of the material in terms of atomic and electronic configurations.

Because a solid ordinarily contains a very large number of atoms, a detailed analysis of such a system is much more difficult than for a simple system such as a hydrogen atom. Nevertheless, simple applications of the principles of quantum mechanics still lead to considerable insight into the behavior of solids. In all cases, it is found that the electron configurations in solids provide the key to the understanding and analysis of their macroscopic behavior.

Next we look inside the atomic nucleus, which up until now has been regarded as a fixed, unchanging structure within each atom. It is found that atomic nuclei are not unchangeable, as was once thought, but that there are reactions in which the internal structure of a nucleus is rearranged in a manner analogous to the rearrangement of atoms in molecules during chemical reactions. These so-called *nuclear reactions* were discovered much later than chemical reactions because of the much higher energies involved.

It is found that the interactions responsible for holding together the constituent parts of nuclei cannot be understood on the basis of known electromagnetic and gravitational interactions but that an interaction of a new and different character must be involved. As a result, there are some important differences between the internal structure of nuclei and the overall structure of atoms themselves, although it is believed that the same basic principles are applicable to both.

Finally, we bring this volume to a close with a brief discussion of what are believed to be the most basic building blocks of matter, the *fundamental particles*. Beginning with the few particles which constitute matter in its familiar forms, we then discuss the characteristics of the various unstable particles, many of which have been discovered only in the past fifteen years. We examine various schemes for classifying these particles and their interactions and then conclude with some indication that there are many remaining unanswered questions in the area of fundamental particles.

THE CONCEPTS OF quantum mechanics, particularly those of molecular binding and the associated electron distributions, are applied to a study of the behavior of systems consisting of a very large number of atoms or molecules bound in a solid structure. The structure of crystals is analyzed in terms of the kinds of bonds they contain, and the specific heats of these systems are discussed. Next the relation of thermal and electrical conductivity to electron motion is introduced, followed by a discussion of the electronic basis of paramagnetism. Finally, the band theory of solids is presented, along with applications to the properties of semiconductors and their uses in practical circuit devices.

11-1   *Structure of Solids*

The discussion of the structure and behavior of atoms and molecules presented in the three preceding chapters has dealt only with situations in which an individual atom or molecule can be considered as an isolated system. This assumption is characteristic of the *gaseous* state of matter, in which ordinarily the average distance between molecules is very much greater than the dimensions of the molecules themselves. Then interactions between molecules can be neglected or at least are small enough to permit approximate treatment, such as the van der Waals corrections to the ideal-gas equation of state.

At ordinary temperature and pressure, however, the great majority of chemical elements and compounds are in the solid state. This is a condensed state of matter in which the separation between atoms is of the same order of magnitude as the dimensions of the electron cloud surrounding each nucleus. Thus atoms of a solid are not independent entities; interactions between atoms are of fundamental importance in determining the structure and properties of the material.

As observed in Sec. 3-4, solids frequently have an orderly arrangement of atoms comprising a repeated pattern which extends over many atoms. Any solid having such a recurring pattern is said to be *crystalline,* and the pattern itself is called the *crystal structure* of the solid. The high degree of orderliness in the structure of solids makes possible simplifications in calculations of properties of solids which would not be possible without this recurring pattern. This situation may be compared with the kinetic theory of gases, in which the complete *lack* of orderliness permits calculations based on a statistical description. The structure of liquids lies between these two extremes, having some degree of correlation between the positions of atoms with their neighbors but no long-range order such as is found in crystalline solids. For this reason, it is much more difficult to understand the behavior of liquids in terms of their microscopic structure than that of either gases or solids.

The forces that bind atoms in some crystalline solids in more or less fixed positions in the crystal lattice are exactly the same in nature as the forces responsible for molecular binding, namely, the interaction of atomic electrons. In fact, there is no essential difference between such a crystal and a large molecule. As in molecular binding, various types of bonding, such as ionic or covalent bonds, are found in crystals, depending on the electron configuration of the atoms involved. There is another type, the metallic bond, which has no direct analog in molecular structure but which is usually the most important effect in metallic crystals.

In some respects, the simplest crystal structure to understand is that of an ionic crystal, and so we begin with this structure. The most common examples of ionic crystals are found in the structures of the alkali halides (compounds of an alkali metal with a halogen), of which the most familiar is ordinary salt, sodium chloride. X-ray diffraction experiments show that the crystal structure of salt is a cubic lattice, with

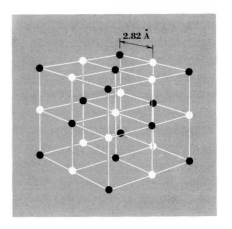

Fig. 11-1 *Face-centered cubic crystal structure of sodium chloride. Black circles represent sodium ions; white circles, chlorine ions. This structure is called face-centered cubic because eight sodium ions determine a cube, and there is an additional sodium ion at the center of each cube face. An identical position relationship holds for the chlorine ions.*

the sodium and chlorine ions occupying alternate positions in the lattice, as shown in Fig. 11-1.

It is instructive to examine in some detail the energy relationships that make such a structure stable. For the sake of simplicity, we consider first a fictitious one-dimensional crystal lattice consisting of a row of alternating sodium and chlorine ions with equal spacings, as shown in Fig. 11-2. We consider the change in potential energy of the system that results from adding one positive (sodium) ion to an end of the chain. The potential energy of this additional ion is defined as zero when it is very far from the chain. If the added ion is *positive*, its nearest neighbor

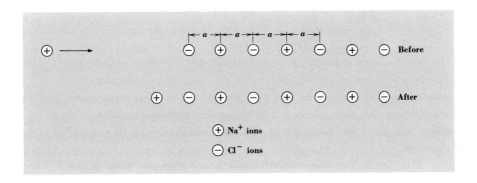

Fig. 11-2 *Fictitious one-dimensional crystal lattice of sodium chloride, used to analyze the stability of the lattice. The change in energy resulting from adding a positive ion to the left end of the chain is calculated in the text.*

is negative, and the attractive force results in a negative potential energy

$$V = -\frac{e^2}{4\pi\epsilon_0}\frac{1}{a}$$ (11-1)

when it is added, where a is the distance between adjacent ions, as shown in Fig. 11-2. The second atom in the chain, a positive ion, exerts a repulsive force on the added ion, with a corresponding potential energy

$$V = +\frac{e^2}{4\pi\epsilon_0}\frac{1}{2a}$$ (11-2)

corresponding to its distance $(2a)$ from the added ion. Proceeding down the line, we calculate the potential energy of interaction of the added ion with each ion in the original chain; the *total* interaction energy is

$$V = -\frac{e^2}{4\pi\epsilon_0 a}\left(1 - \frac{1}{2} + \frac{1}{3} - \frac{1}{4} + \cdots\right)$$ (11-3)

If the chain is very long, we can approximate the quantity in parentheses as an infinite sum and evaluate it by reference to the power-series expansion for the function $\ln(1 + x)$, which is

$$\ln(1 + x) = x - \frac{x^2}{2} + \frac{x^3}{3} - \frac{x^4}{4} + \cdots$$ (11-4)

Evaluating this series for $x = 1$, we find that the quantity in parentheses is equal to $\ln 2$, and the *total* interaction energy is

$$V = -\frac{e^2 \ln 2}{4\pi\epsilon_0 a}$$ (11-5)

The fact that this quantity is negative indicates that the configuration with the added ion attached to the end of the chain is energetically more favorable (a state of lower energy) than the state in which it is separated. Generalizing, the state in which a large number of atoms are linked together in a chain has lower energy than the state in which they are all separated.

This simple one-dimensional chain bears relatively little resemblance to a three-dimensional crystal lattice, but precisely the same argument may be used to show that a series of such chains lying side by side with alternate ions adjacent has a lower energy than a state in which the same chains are separated by great distances. If there are several planes made of such rows of chains, the state in which these planes are stacked up with alternate ions adjacent has lower energy than the state where they are separated. Hence an extension of the simple chain argument shows that the three-dimensional crystal lattice is a state with lower energy than a state in which the same ions are all separated by great distances. When this energy difference is greater than the energy expended in creating the ions initially, the structure is stable.

As observed in Sec. 9-4, the electron configurations of the ions are both filled-shell configurations which are spherically symmetric and therefore have no particular directional characteristics as far as the bonds are concerned. Thus the nature of the bond itself gives no information as to why the ions should fall into the cubic arrangement rather than other possible arrangements. The structure is determined, in fact, by energy considerations; the atoms always tend to arrange themselves in a minimum-energy configuration whose details depend on the relative sizes of the ions. Each ion exerts attractive electrostatic forces on ions of opposite charge, and so it is to be expected that in the minimum-energy arrangement each ion is surrounded by several *nearest-neighbor* ions of opposite charge. The details of the arrangement are determined by the *number* of nearest neighbors that can be fitted around the smaller of the two ions with little enough overlap of wave functions to avoid violating the exclusion principle. In the present example, the Na^+ ion is considerably smaller than the Cl^- ion because its last filled shell is the $2p$ shell, while the Cl^- ion has filled $3s$ and $3p$ shells.

In visualizing the arrangement of ions it is useful to consider a pictorial model in which each ion is represented by a hard sphere whose radius approximates that of the electron charge cloud of the corresponding ion. One conceivable arrangement is for each sodium ion to be surrounded by four nearest-neighbor chlorine ions arranged at the corners of a regular tetrahedron with the sodium ion at the center. If the radius of the chlorine ions is a, then a simple geometrical calculation (which is left as a problem) shows that the sodium ion can touch all four chlorine ions only if its radius r is at least equal to

$$r = \left(\sqrt{\frac{3}{2}} - 1 \right)a = 0.225a \tag{11-6}$$

Another scheme, illustrated in Fig. 11-3, would place the nearest neighbors at the six corners of an octahedron; in this configuration, the central ion can touch all its nearest neighbors only if its radius is at least

$$r = (\sqrt{2} - 1)a = 0.414a \tag{11-7}$$

Still another arrangement consists of eight nearest neighbors at the corners of a cube; the central ion can touch all eight if its radius is at least

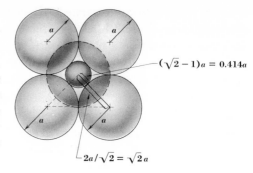

Fig. 11-3 *A sphere (represent-ing an ion in an ionic crystal) just touches six nearest neighbors, four with their centers in the same plane as the central sphere (the plane of the figure) and one each above and below, when its radius is 0.414 that of the neighbor spheres.*

$(\sqrt{2} - 1)a = 0.414a$

$2a/\sqrt{2} = \sqrt{2}\,a$

$$r = (\sqrt{3} - 1)a = 0.732a \qquad (11\text{-}8)$$

This configuration leads to the *body-centered cubic* structure shown in Fig. 11-4. Finally, a central ion can be surrounded by twelve nearest neighbors at the corners of a regular icosahedron if its radius is at least equal to a.

The actual structure of sodium chloride as revealed by x-ray diffrac-tion is the face-centered cubic lattice shown in Figs. 11-1 and 11-3, in which each ion has six nearest neighbors. The same situation is found in nearly all the other alkali halide crystals, and in all cases the reason is the small size of the alkali metal ion compared with the halogen ion. The only exceptions are the salts of cesium, whose ion is nearly the same size as halogen ions and is therefore larger than the critical size given by Eq. (11-7). Thus the cesium ion can accommodate eight nearest neighbors rather than six, resulting in the body-centered cubic structure

Fig. 11-4 *Body-centered cubic structure of cesium chloride. Each cesium ion, rep-resented by a black circle, has eight nearest-neighbor chlorine ions, represented by white circles. This structure is equivalent to two interpenetrating simple cubic lattices, one of Cs^+ ions, the other of Cl^- ions.*

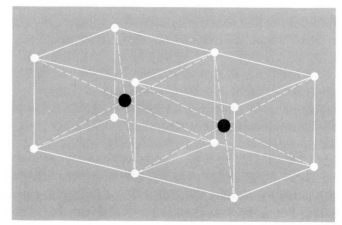

shown in Fig. 11-4.   In CsF, the situation is just the reverse of that for NaCl; the F^- ion is considerably *smaller* than the Cs^+ ion, and again the structure is face-centered cubic.

Equation (11-5) can be used to estimate the binding energy of an ion in a crystal lattice.   X-ray diffraction data show that the spacing between adjacent atoms in a crystal of NaCl is about 2.8 Å.   The associated energy is

$$\frac{e^2 \ln 2}{4\pi\epsilon_0 a} = \frac{(1.60 \times 10^{-19} \text{ coul})^2 (9 \times 10^9 \text{ m/farad}) (0.693)}{2.8 \times 10^{-10} \text{ m}}$$

$$= 7.9 \times 10^{-19} \text{ joule} = 3.4 \text{ ev} \tag{11-9}$$

This energy includes only the interaction of an ion with other ions along a single straight line in the lattice.   The effects of other ions, though not negligible, are expected to be less than this because of their greater distance.   Therefore as a rough guess we expect the binding energy of a single ion to be of the order of 5 ev.

This binding energy is related directly to the phenomenon of *melting*.   At any temperature the ions have a statistical distribution of energy; the fraction having energies of 5 ev or above is, of course, an increasing function of temperature.   The escape of these energetic ions is offset by other ions outside the lattice which collide inelastically with it, losing energy and becoming bound to the lattice.   The melting temperature is determined by the point at which these two competing processes proceed at equal rates, leading to a state of *phase equilibrium*. This equilibrium usually occurs at only one particular temperature, and so such solids usually have quite definite melting temperatures.   A similar analysis can be made of the phenomenon of boiling, and a relation between vapor pressure of a material and its temperature can be derived from statistical considerations.

The ions in an ionic crystal can also be removed or displaced by an electric field, at least in principle.   The electric field must be strong enough to produce a potential difference of a few volts over a distance of the order of 10^{-10} m.   This is an enormous electric field and one that is impossible to produce in practice.   Thus under practical electric fields the ions are not displaced; furthermore, correspondingly large fields would be required to remove individual electrons from ions because of the stability of the filled-shell configuration.   Hence there are essentially no mobile charges in an ionic crystal, and the alkali halide crystals are nonconductors of electricity.   But in a *molten* alkali halide the ions have a considerable degree of mobility, and molten alkali halides are good conductors of electricity.   Similarly, an aqueous solution of an alkali halide is a good conductor, since the ions are separated from each other so as not to be tightly bound, and can move readily through the solution.

In crystals having covalent bonds, unlike ionic crystals, the bonds are usually strongly directional in nature. As observed in Sec. 9-5, this directionality is associated with the shapes of the wave functions for electrons in the electron-pair covalent bonds. A simple example of a crystal formed by covalent bonding is the "diamond" structure, found in elements in group IV of the periodic table, including carbon, silicon, germanium, and tin. Each of these has four electrons in its outermost shell, and each tends to form four covalent bonds, one with each of four nearest neighbors. The crystal structure of these elements is characterized by an arrangement in which each atom has four nearest neighbors spaced symmetrically around it at the corners of a regular tetrahedron. Since all the electrons participate in the binding, none is particularly mobile, and we expect these materials to be poor conductors of electricity. This is in fact the case; the electrical properties of these materials classify them as *semiconductors*. The characteristics of semiconductors will be discussed in more detail in Sec. 11-6.

Covalent bonds are the usual type in many solid organic compounds, where they play the same role as in organic molecules. A familiar example is polyethylene, in which long chains of hydrocarbon groups are held together by covalent bonds.

An interesting difference in the behavior of ionic and covalent crystals is found in the dependence of the dielectric constant on frequency. As discussed in Sec. 3-6, the polarization of a dielectric material is, in general, frequency-dependent because of the inertial effects of the charged particles whose displacement provides the microscopic mechanism of polarization. In ionic crystals, motion of entire ions can contribute to the polarization but only at relatively low frequencies (e.g., less than 10^{12} cycles/sec), because at higher frequencies the mass of an ion prevents any significant displacement in response to the rapidly varying electric field. Displacement of individual electrons is important as a mechanism of polarization at much higher frequencies, since the electron mass is much smaller than that of the ions. For example, the static dielectric constant of KCl is 4.7, while the dielectric constant at optical frequencies, given according to Eq. (3-39) by the square root of the index of refraction, is 2.1. Conversely, the dielectric constant of diamond, a covalent crystal, is 5.8 at both low frequencies and optical frequencies.

In metallic crystals a new feature appears, one that has no counterpart in molecular binding. In metallic crystals the valence electrons are not tightly bound to individual atoms; instead the electrons are better described as moving in the combined potential of an array of positive ions and hence are shared by the entire crystal. The reasons for this mobility of electrons will be discussed in more detail in Sec. 11-5; here we simply state that it exists and that it is chiefly responsible for the crystal structure of many metals. As a crude pictorial model, one may think of the crystal as consisting of an array of positive ions with the spaces between ions filled with a negatively charged fluid representing the total valence-electron distribution. This fluid is often called the "electron gas"; it provides a useful model in discussing various physical properties of metallic crystals, as will be seen in the following sections.

If enough "electron gas" can occupy the spaces between adjacent ions, the attraction of this gas for each ion can more than balance the repulsion between ions and lead to a state with lower potential energy than when the atoms of metal are separated. Thus there is reason to suspect that a stable solid structure may be possible. In addition, for reasons to be discussed in Sec. 11-5, the *kinetic* energies of the valence electrons are depressed by the binding to an extended array of ions rather than to individual ions. In some metals, particularly the transition metals with partially filled $3d$ shells, there is also some covalent binding involving $3d$ electrons as well as the above effects with the $4s$ valence electrons.

Metallic binding usually occurs only when the number of valence electrons is small, since when there are several valence electrons with overlapping wave functions some are forced by the exclusion principle into higher energy states, making the metallic structure unstable. Thus the elements in groups I and II of the periodic table, and some in group III, form metallic crystals. Elements in the middle groups (III, IV, and V) sometimes form metallic crystals, but in them covalent bonding becomes competitive. An interesting example is tin, which exists in two crystalline forms. Metallic (white) tin is stable above $13°C$, while covalent (gray) tin, with its diamond crystal structure, is stable below $13°C$.

The bonding in metallic crystals can be thought of as a situation in which the atoms would form covalent bonds except for the fact that there are not enough valence electrons per atom for this. Instead, electrons are shared not just between two neighbors but among all the atoms in the solid, in accordance with the picture described above of the positive ions immersed in a sea of electrons. The bonding does not have the strongly directional character of covalent bonds, and as a result the atoms tend to come together so as to fill the available space as completely as possible. Thus the number of nearest neighbors for an atom in a metallic crystal lattice tends to be larger than in other types of solids. Two crystal lattices which are common among metallic crystals are the

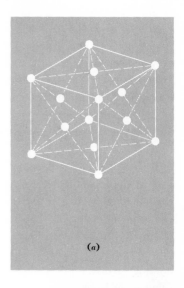

(a)

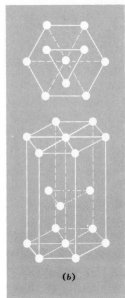

(b)

Fig. 11-5 (a) Face-centered cubic structure of a metallic element. Each atom has 12 nearest neighbors; for the atom in the center of the right face, there are 4 atoms at the corners of the face, and one each at the centers of the eight faces that adjoin this face at its edges. (b) Hexagonal close-packed structure. Again each atom has 12 nearest neighbors.

face-centered cubic lattice and the hexagonal close-packed lattice; in each of these, each atom has 12 nearest neighbors. These two structures are illustrated in Fig. 11-5.

The above discussion has centered around the concept of a crystal as a structure that is perfectly periodic. The concept of a "perfect crystal" is an abstraction; real crystals always have deviations from an ideal periodic structure. One obvious reason for this deviation is the fact that crystals have a finite extent. That is, a crystal does not extend throughout all space but must have surfaces. The peculiarities of the electron configurations near the surface of a solid are responsible for phenomena such as contact potentials, rectifying surfaces, etc. Crystal lattices may also have internal defects such as *vacant* lattice sites where an atom is missing, *interstitial* atoms which are at positions other than normal lattice sites, and impurity atoms.

There are also irregularities called *dislocations*, in which the periodic pattern of the crystal lattice is interrupted. A two-dimensional sketch illustrating a dislocation is shown in Fig. 11-6. The presence of dislocations in metallic crystals is an important factor in determining

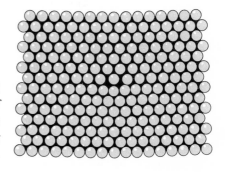

Fig. 11-6   *Two-dimensional representation of one type of crystal-lattice dislocation. The pattern is seen best by viewing the page at a grazing angle.*

their mechanical properties. The fact that some metals are *ductile* and can be deformed inelastically to a considerable degree without actual fracture is due in large measure to the presence of dislocations which can move through the crystal lattice in the course of plastic deformations.

As mentioned earlier, it is possible to make good use of the regular recurring structure of a crystal lattice in analyzing the behavior of electrons and atoms in a crystal and in understanding the relationship between various macroscopic properties of matter and its microscopic structure. Among the macroscopic properties which can be understood in this manner are specific heats, thermal and electrical conductivities, elastic moduli, and electric and magnetic properties. A detailed analysis of most of these properties requires the use of statistical techniques. The remainder of this chapter is concerned with understanding some of the macroscopic properties of crystalline solids on the basis of their microscopic structure.

In concluding this brief discussion of the structure of solids, we remark that not all materials possessing the rigid structure characteristic of solids have a definite crystal structure. A number of materials, most familiar of which is glass, exhibit a microscopic structure characterized by short-range correlations between atomic positions but without the long-range order characteristic of crystals. Such a structure is shown schematically in Fig. 11-7. These materials are said to be *amorphous,* and their behavior exhibits important differences from that of crystals.

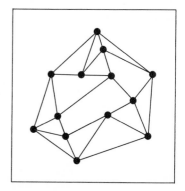

Fig. 11-7 *Schematic diagram showing the arrangement of molecules in an amorphous solid. The circles represent molecules; the lines, the intermolecular forces. Intermolecular distances are expanded for clarity.*

They never have a definite melting point but rather undergo a continuous change of mechanical and other properties as the temperature is changed. Thus glass when heated gradually softens and becomes "tacky," rather than melting suddenly as do most metals. There is no phase transition, and no latent heat of fusion, associated with such a process. Thus amorphous solids are, in principle, much more closely related to very viscous liquids than to crystalline solids.

11-2   Specific Heats

In this section we apply the considerations of the structure of solids outlined in Sec. 11-1, along with the statistical methods introduced in Chap. 10, to analysis of the specific heats of solids. The rule of Dulong and Petit, an empirical rule based on measurement of specific heats of many solid elements, states that the molar specific heat of a solid element should always be about 6 cal/mole K°. We shall see how this rule can be understood in terms of the microscopic basis of specific heat and under what circumstances departures from this rule should be expected.

In discussing the specific heats of gases, we considered the contributions of translational, rotational, and vibrational motions; the specific heat of a solid material can be understood on a similar basis. In solids, the energy is best described in terms of vibrational motion of atoms in the lattice. According to the equipartition theorem there should be, on an average, a kinetic energy $\frac{1}{2}kT$ per atom associated with motion in each of the three perpendicular directions, so that the average total kinetic energy per atom should be $\frac{3}{2}kT$. Furthermore, if it is assumed that the atoms are elastically bound by forces that obey Hooke's law, the motion is simple harmonic, and so the average potential energy is equal to the average kinetic energy.[1] Thus the average *total* energy per atom, including both kinetic and potential, should be $3kT$. The average energy per mole is $3RT$, and thus the molar specific heat should be

$$C = 3R = 6 \text{ cal/mole} \qquad (11\text{-}10)$$

in agreement with the empirical rule of Dulong and Petit.

Although this simple model accounts for the observed specific heats of solids in certain temperature ranges, it suffers from deficiencies similar to those of the corresponding theory for gases. It cannot account for the temperature dependence of specific heats observed with many solids or for the fact that some measured specific heats are *larger* than that predicted by the rule of Dulong and Petit. One source of these discrepancies is that the vibrational energy of an atom in a crystal lattice is *quantized*. The classical equipartition theorem can be expected to hold only at temperatures sufficiently high so that kT is much larger than the spacing of adjacent energy levels; otherwise the average energy per atom is *less* than that predicted by the equipartition theorem.

The simplest model that takes this discreteness of vibrational energy into account assumes that each atom is elastically bound to its equilibrium position and, as a result, executes simple harmonic motion with frequency ω about this equilibrium position. This motion can occur along any one of the three coordinate directions, and any superposition of such motions is also possible. The total energy associated with this

---

[1] H. D. Young, "Fundamentals of Mechanics and Heat," sec. 17-5, McGraw-Hill Book Company, New York, 1964.

vibrational motion is the same as that of three different harmonic oscillators with the same frequency moving in the three perpendicular coordinate directions. This is easily seen to be true in the classical case,
in which the total energy of the oscillator can be written as

$$E = \tfrac{1}{2}m(v_x{}^2 + v_y{}^2 + v_z{}^2) + \tfrac{1}{2}k(x^2 + y^2 + z^2) \tag{11-11}$$

which clearly can be separated into an energy associated with each of
the three coordinate directions. A similar separation can be made in
the quantum-mechanical treatment of the three-dimensional harmonic
oscillator. Thus in this model the N atoms in a crystal are equivalent,
as far as energy is concerned, to $3N$ harmonic oscillators, all with frequency ω.

Since each atom is bound to a definite crystal-lattice location,
we regard the atoms as *distinguishable* particles; hence the Maxwell-
Boltzmann distribution is the appropriate energy-distribution function
to use. The number n_i of oscillators with energy ϵ_i is given, just as in
Eq. (10-47), by

$$n_i = Ae^{-\beta\epsilon_i}$$
$$= Ae^{-\beta(i+1/2)\epsilon_0} \tag{11-12}$$

where $\epsilon_0 = \hbar\omega$, as previously, and the constant A is chosen to satisfy
the condition

$$\sum_i n_i = 3N$$

We now see that this problem is really identical to that of the vibrational
specific heat of a gas of diatomic molecules, discussed in Sec. 10-4, except that the number N is replaced by $3N$. Thus the average energy
per atom is just three times that given by Eq. (10-66):

$$\bar{\epsilon} = \frac{3}{2}\epsilon_0 \coth \frac{\epsilon_0}{2kT} \tag{11-13}$$

The derivative of this quantity with respect to T is, as usual, the specific
heat per atom. Replacing k by R gives the *molar* specific heat C; reference to Eq. (10-68) shows that this is

$$C = 3R\left[\frac{\epsilon_0/2kT}{\sinh(\epsilon_0/2kT)}\right]^2 \tag{11-14}$$

In the limit of very large T, this approaches the value $3R$ predicted by
the classical equipartition theorem, but at lower temperatures it deviates
from this behavior in the same manner as shown in Fig. 10-4b.

The assumption that all atoms vibrate independently of each other with the same frequency is somewhat naïve; each vibrating atom exerts forces on adjacent atoms, and these forces couple the motions of adjacent atoms. A correct description of vibrational motion of atoms in a crystal lattice must take into account the fact that a lattice vibration is a *collective* phenomenon, involving all the atoms simultaneously. The motion can be described in terms of various *normal modes* which in general have different frequencies. More detailed analysis shows that for a crystal containing N atoms there are $3N$ normal modes with various frequencies and that the energy of each mode is quantized with the same energy levels as for a simple harmonic oscillator with the same frequency. The "quanta" of energy associated with normal-mode crystal-lattice vibrations are called *phonons*; there is a close analogy between these and *photons*, which are quanta of normal-mode electromagnetic-wave energy. The total energy can still be represented as the sum of energies of a large number of harmonic oscillators, but now with a spectrum of frequencies that depends on the lattice structure. This makes possible a more precise calculation of lattice-vibration contributions to the specific heats than would be possible when using the single-frequency approximation.

We might also expect to find an additional temperature-dependent energy associated with electron energy levels and a corresponding contribution to the specific heat. In gases the excitation of electronic energy levels usually makes no noticeable contribution to specific heats at ordinary temperatures, since usually the energy levels are so much larger than kT that practically all the electrons are in the ground state. In the language of Sec. 10-4, the degrees of freedom associated with electron motion are "frozen out" at ordinary temperatures. The situation should be similar in ionic and covalent crystals, in which electrons are tightly bound in filled-shell ions or in shared-electron valence bonds. This prediction is borne out by experiment, which reveals no contribution to specific heats from electron excitation.

In metallic crystals the situation is somewhat different. As discussed in Sec. 11-1, the electrons in such a crystal behave in some respects like a gas of free or nearly free particles. Their energy levels are very closely spaced compared with kT at ordinary temperatures, unlike those of ionic or covalent crystals, and hence electrons can gain or lose small amounts of energy readily. Thus we might expect each valence electron to have an average kinetic energy $\frac{3}{2}kT$ and contribute $\frac{3}{2}k$ to the specific heat. If there is one valence electron per atom, this means an additional specific heat of $\frac{3}{2}R$ per mole; if two, $3R$ per mole, and so on.

In fact, the measured values of specific heats of metals indicate that the contributions from electron energy are very much *smaller* than this. The resolution of this discrepancy provides an interesting application of the quantum-statistical methods developed in Sec. 10-5. The equipartition theorem is based on the Maxwell-Boltzmann distribution; but we are dealing here with electron energy states of the entire crystal, and the appropriate distribution is not the Maxwell-Boltzmann but rather the Fermi-Dirac distribution, which takes into account the exclusion principle and the indistinguishability of identical particles, as discussed in Sec. 10-5.

The most striking consequence of the operation of the exclusion principle in the Fermi-Dirac distribution is that at absolute zero temperature the electrons do *not* all have zero energy, as the Maxwell-Boltzmann law would predict. Instead, they fill up the lowest available energy states, one electron in each state, up to a certain level ϵ_f called the Fermi energy. At $T = 0$ all states with energy less than ϵ_f are filled, and all those above ϵ_f are empty.

The crucial question in a specific-heat calculation is how the electron-energy distribution (and therefore the average electron energy) *changes* with temperature. This in turn depends critically on the magnitude of the Fermi energy. To understand the role of the Fermi energy, we suppose first that at ordinary temperatures ϵ_f is much *smaller* than kT. For example, at $T = 300°K$, kT has the value 0.0259 ev; let us suppose that $\epsilon_f = 0.001$ ev. Then at $300°K$ the energy levels actually occupied are, on an average, much *higher* than those occupied at $0°K$. That is, the electrons are distributed over many energy levels, the probability of occupation of any individual level is very small, the exclusion principle becomes irrelevant, and the distribution approaches the classical Maxwell-Boltzmann distribution, with its associated average kinetic energy $\frac{3}{2}kT$.

Clearly, this does not happen; otherwise electron energy would make a large contribution to specific heats of metals. In actual metals the Fermi energy is typically of the order of 2 to 10 ev, an energy much *larger* than kT at ordinary temperatures. As a consequence, at ordinary temperatures most electron energies are much *larger* than kT and are determined almost entirely by the exclusion principle and hardly at all by the temperature. Correspondingly, the average *change* in electron energy per unit temperature change is small, and so the electron contribution to the specific heat is small.

The situation is shown graphically in Fig. 11-8, which shows the Fermi-Dirac distribution function at 0, 100, and 10,000°K correspond-

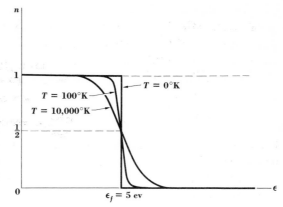

Fig. 11-8   *Fermi-Dirac distri-bution corresponding to Fermi energy $\epsilon_f = 5$ ev for several temperatures. The functions for different temperatures differ appreciably only in the small energy interval near ϵ_f.*

ing to $\epsilon_f = 5$ ev.   As the figure shows, the function changes appreciably only in the vicinity of the Fermi energy (specifically, in a region within a few kT of the Fermi energy) as the temperature changes.   But this energy range includes only a small fraction of the electrons; *most* of the electron energies do not change at all.   Hence there is a correspondingly small contribution to specific heat.

This entire discussion can be made more quantitative.   It would not be appropriate to discuss all the details here, but we shall indicate how a more precise calculation can be made.   First, the degeneracy factor g in the Fermi-Dirac distribution must be found.   Regarding electron energy ϵ as a continuous variable, we can find the number of quantum states in any energy interval $d\epsilon$ by a calculation which is essentially a generalization to three dimensions of the "particle-in-a-box" problem of Sec. 7-2.   Just as the energy levels for that problem depended on the size of the box, so in the three-dimensional analog they depend on the *volume* of the container.   In the "electron-gas" model, which treats the electrons as free particles confined to the volume V of the crystal, the number of energy levels in the interval $d\epsilon$ is found to be

$$g(\epsilon) \, d\epsilon = \frac{8\sqrt{2} \, \pi m^{3/2} V}{h} \epsilon^{1/2} \, d\epsilon \tag{11-15}$$

and the complete Fermi-Dirac function becomes

$$n(\epsilon) = \frac{8\sqrt{2} \, \pi m^{3/2} V}{h^3} \frac{\epsilon^{1/2}}{1 + e^{(\epsilon - \epsilon_f)/kT}} \tag{11-16}$$

We note that the degeneracy factor is proportional to $\epsilon^{1/2}$ just as in the Maxwell-Boltzmann case [Eq. (10-33)].

The value of the Fermi energy is found by insisting that the integral of this expression over all possible energies should be equal to the total number of valence electrons, which in turn is calculated from the atomic structure and the lattice spacing of the crystal. At temperature $T = 0$ this calculation yields a simple result:

$$\epsilon_f = \frac{h^2}{8m} \left(\frac{3N}{\pi V}\right)^{2/3}$$

(11-17)

It can be seen that ϵ_f depends on the number of valence electrons per unit volume, N/V, and is therefore independent of the dimensions of the crystal. The value of ϵ_f also varies with temperature; a more detailed calculation shows that, when $\epsilon_f \gg kT$,

$$\epsilon_f = \epsilon_{f0}\left[1 - \frac{\pi^2}{12}\left(\frac{kT}{\epsilon_{f0}}\right)^2\right]$$

(11-18)

where ϵ_{f0} is the Fermi energy at $T = 0$.

Once the Fermi energy is known, the average electron energy can be computed as a function of temperature; the derivative of this function then gives the specific heat per electron. In taking this derivative, the variation of ϵ_f with temperature must be included. We state without proof the following results: At $T = 0$, the average electron energy $\bar\epsilon_0$ is related to the Fermi energy by

$$\bar\epsilon_0 = \tfrac{3}{5}\epsilon_{f0}$$

(11-19)

The average electron energy $\bar\epsilon$ for $T > 0$ is given approximately by

$$\bar\epsilon = \frac{3}{5}\epsilon_{f0}\left[1 + \frac{5}{12}\pi^2\left(\frac{kT}{\epsilon_{f0}}\right)^2\right]$$
$$= \bar\epsilon_0\left[1 + \frac{5}{12}\pi^2\left(\frac{kT}{\epsilon_{f0}}\right)^2\right]$$

(11-20)

The specific heat per electron, which is the derivative of Eq. (11-20) with respect to T, is

$$C = \frac{\pi^2}{3}\frac{kT}{\epsilon_f}\left(\frac{3}{2}k\right)$$

(11-21)

All these results are based on the assumption that $\epsilon_f \gg kT$, which, as we have seen, is valid except at extremely high temperatures. For example, $kT = 1$ ev when $T = 11{,}700°$K. As a numerical example of Eq. (11-21), if $\epsilon_f = 5$ ev and $T = 300°$K, we find

$$C = \frac{\pi^2}{3}\left(\frac{0.0257 \text{ ev}}{5 \text{ ev}}\right)\frac{3}{2}k = (0.017)\left(\frac{3}{2}k\right)$$

which is a small fraction of the specific-heat contribution $\frac{3}{2}k$ to be expected if the electrons behaved like a classical Maxwell-Boltzmann gas. Since this is also small compared with the lattice part of the specific heat, it is usually observable only at very high temperatures, where the lattice part becomes independent of T, and at very low temperatures, where the lattice part becomes proportional to T^3 and can be separated by data analysis from the electron contribution.

11-3 *Conductivity*

Analysis of the states of electrons in solids, so useful in understanding crystal structure, also provides the key to understanding electrical and thermal conductivity of materials. Although detailed calculations of conductivities are beyond the scope of this book, we shall present here some qualitative considerations and approximate calculations based on simple models.

A striking feature of electrical conductivity is the remarkably large range of magnitudes that occur. The conductivity of good conductors such as copper is larger than that of good insulators such as quartz by a factor of the order of 10^{20}. Even more remarkably, most materials seem to fall fairly near one or the other of these extremes, although there is an important class of materials called *semiconductors* whose conductivity is intermediate between those of good conductors and good insulators. Another interesting observation is that materials that are good conductors of electricity are almost always good conductors of heat, and conversely.

The basis of electrical conduction in solids is not far to seek. The basic requirement is the presence of electrical charges that are free to move from one region of the material to another under the influence of an electric field. In ionic and covalent crystals such mobile charges are not ordinarily available, since as we have seen in Sec. 11-1 the electrons in such materials are tightly bound to individual lattice sites. To remove a valence electron from its position requires several electron volts of energy—even more for inner electrons. For an electric field to do this much work on an electron in a distance comparable to lattice dimensions it would have to have a magnitude of the order of 10^{10} volts/m, a value much larger than any available in the laboratory. Similarly, energies associated with thermal agitation at ordinary temperatures are insufficient to liberate valence electrons so that they can act as current carriers. Thus we expect ionic and covalent crystals to be insulators, and this prediction is borne out well by experiment.

In metallic crystals, on the other hand, the valence electrons are not tightly bound to individual lattice sites, and so they can move from one region of the crystal to another under the action of an electric field. To be sure, not *all* the valence electrons are free to move, even in the "electron-gas" model discussed in Sec. 11-2. To be accelerated by an electric field an electron must be able to acquire small increments of energy from the field and correspondingly to make transitions to adjacent unoccupied energy states. For an electron in one of the lowest energy states in the Fermi-Dirac distribution this is not possible at ordinary temperatures because all the adjacent levels are already occupied and the exclusion principle prevents their being doubly occupied. The nearest vacant levels may be several electron volts away, and this much energy is ordinarily not available. But electrons near the top of the distribution (with energies close to ϵ_f) *do* have nearby unoccupied levels available; it is these electrons that are accelerated by the field and can thereby contribute to the electrical conductivity.

Electrical conductivity in metals can be discussed more quantitatively on the basis of a simple semiclassical model. We assume that the electrons that contribute to the conductivity (i.e., those with energies near ϵ_f) move about at random with a speed v determined by the relation $\frac{1}{2}mv^2 = \epsilon_f$. This speed refers to the speed of the wave packets representing electrons. From time to time an electron collides elastically with an atom in the lattice and rebounds in a random direction. The average time between collisions is called the *mean free time*, denoted by τ. Similarly, the average distance traveled between collisions, denoted by λ, is called the *mean free path*. Clearly these quantities are related by

$$\lambda = v\tau \tag{11-22}$$

In the absence of an electric field, the electrons move in straight-line paths between collisions; the directions of motion are completely random, and on an average there is no net drift of electrons in one direction or another. However, when an electric field $\mathbf{E}$ is applied, each electron experiences a force $\mathbf{F}$ whose magnitude is $F = eE$. The direction is opposite to that of $\mathbf{E}$ because the electron charge is negative. According to Newton's second law, each electron thus experiences a constant acceleration a between collisions, given by

$$F = eE = ma \tag{11-23}$$

The trajectories between collisions are then no longer straight lines but rather sections of parabolas. By the end of the interval τ between col-

lisions an electron acquires an additional velocity in the direction opposite to **E**, given by $a\tau$. Since the acceleration is constant, the *average*
value of this additional velocity over the time interval is one-half this,
or $\frac{1}{2}a\tau$. This additional velocity is called the *drift velocity*, denoted
by v_d. This name is appropriate; the effect of the **E** field is to super-
impose on the random electron motion an additional velocity opposite
in direction to **E** with a magnitude given by the above equations. This
superposition is illustrated in Fig. 11-9.

(*a*)

Fig. 11-9 *Random electron motion in a metallic crystal. (a) In the absence of an electric field an electron moves in straight lines between collisions, the average velocity is zero, and there is no net drift. (b) When an electric field is applied, each path between collisions becomes parabolic, and there is an average drift velocity proportional to the applied field.*

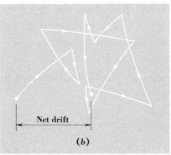

Net drift

(*b*)

Using the expression for a from Eq. (11-23), we find

$$v_d = \frac{1}{2}a\tau = \frac{1}{2}\frac{eE}{m}\tau \tag{11-24}$$

This drift velocity corresponds to a transport of charge from one region
to another, and we may calculate the magnitude of the resulting current.
This is most easily done with reference to a particular shape of specimen, as shown in Fig. 11-10. If the number of electrons participating
in conduction is N, then the conduction electron density is N/V. In a
time Δt the electrons drift a distance $v_d \, \Delta t$, and the number of electrons
flowing through a given cross section of the specimen is $(N/V)Av_d \, \Delta t$;
the total charge flow is this quantity multiplied by the charge e of each

Fig. 11-10 *Example of a specimen of material whose conductivity is to be calculated. The total charge emerging from an end in time Δt is equal to the amount of mobile charge contained in a section of specimen of length $v_d \Delta t$ and cross-section area A.   This is equal to $e(N/V)Av_d \Delta t$.*

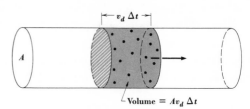

Volume $= Av_d \Delta t$

electron.   Thus the charge passing any cross section *per unit time*, which is equal to the total *current*, is given by

$$i = e\frac{N}{V}Av_d$$

$$= \frac{e^2 E\tau}{2m} A \frac{N}{V} \tag{11-25}$$

Since E is directly proportional to the potential difference between the ends of the specimen, this result shows that i is proportional to this potential difference, which is the familiar Ohm's law.

To find the electrical conductivity σ, we recall that for a material obeying Ohm's law the conductivity is defined as the ratio $\sigma = j/E$, where j is the *current density*, or current per unit area.   In the present example this is clearly given by $j = i/A$.   Dividing Eq. (11-25) by A, we find

$$j = \frac{e^2 E\tau(N/V)}{2m} \tag{11-26}$$

Finally, the electrical conductivity is given by

$$\sigma = \frac{e^2 \tau(N/V)}{2m} \tag{11-27}$$

As might be expected, σ is directly proportional to the density of current-carrying electrons, which, as explained earlier, are the electrons near the top of the Fermi distribution.   As we have seen, the Fermi distribution does not change drastically with temperature, so that the density of current-carrying electrons is expected to be nearly independent of temperature.

The conductivity is also proportional to the mean free time between collisions, τ, and thereby hangs an interesting effect.   We have spoken rather glibly about *collisions* of electrons with atoms in the lattice, and from the point of view of classical mechanics this is certainly a reasonable picture. However, a thorough analysis of the electron-wave functions corresponding to the periodic potential-energy function of the positive ions in the lattice shows that electron-wave functions whose periodicity is properly matched to that of the lattice can move through the lattice without undergoing collisions at all, so long as the lattice is perfect and free from defects. This effect is analogous to the passage of an alternating current through a series-resonant tuned circuit without any impedance effect when the frequency is equal to the resonant frequency of the circuit.

In view of this result, it may seem surprising that the electrons undergo any collisions. Why do they not accelerate constantly and without limit, leading to an infinitely great conductivity? The reason is that no crystal lattice is really perfect. Even when there are no vacancies, interstitial atoms, dislocations, or other lattice imperfections, the perfect periodicity of the lattice is still disturbed by thermal motion of atoms in the lattice. This motion, as we have seen, is also chiefly responsible for the specific heats of solids.

Thus when an atom vibrates about its equilibrium position in the lattice it becomes a target for electron collisions. The frequency of collisions is determined by the area of the target, which in turn depends on the amplitude of the oscillation. In a purely classical picture, an atom which moves a maximum distance A away from its equilibrium position presents a target area or cross section equal to the area of a circle of radius A, that is, πA^2. Furthermore, A^2 is proportional to the total energy associated with the vibration, which has been shown to be proportional to the absolute temperature T of the lattice.

The mean free time between collisions should be inversely proportional to the collision cross section for each atom and thus inversely proportional also to T. Thus the conductivity of the material, given by Eq. (11-27), should also be inversely proportional to T. From this result the *temperature coefficient of conductivity* α can be found. This is defined as the fractional change in conductivity per unit temperature change; that is,

$$\alpha = \frac{1}{\sigma} \frac{d\sigma}{dT} \qquad\qquad (11\text{-}28)$$

If σ is proportional to $1/T$, we find simply that $\alpha = 1/T$. At ordinary temperatures, say $T = 300°K$, this gives $\alpha = 0.0033/K°$. In fact, the measured values of α for many metals fall in the range 0.002 to 0.004, although there are some notable exceptions. Considering the rather crude model we have used, this agreement with experiment is gratifying.

Thus even a simple semiclassical model affords interesting insight into the mechanism of electrical conduction in solids. A number of additional remarks are in order for general clarification. First, the *magnitude* of the drift velocity can be measured directly by a variety of means, the details of which need not concern us. The drift velocity is always extremely small, typically of the order of 0.001 to 0.1 m/sec for electric fields of reasonable magnitude. This is to be compared with the speeds of random motion, which are typically of the order of 10^6 m/sec. Thus the electron drift responsible for conduction is a very small perturbation on the random motion.

Second, we have assumed that the electrons collide *elastically* with atoms in the lattice, that is, without loss of kinetic energy. In actual fact, the collisions are *not* always elastic. Because the average kinetic energy of the electrons is usually much larger than that of the lattice atoms, the electrons, on an average, lose energy in these collisions, giving energy to the lattice. The effect is to increase the lattice vibrations, which manifest themselves macroscopically as *heat*. Thus these collisions provide the microscopic mechanism by which work done on the charges by the electric field, the familiar I^2R power loss in resistors, is converted into heat.

Finally, the discussion of the distinction between conductors and insulators would seem to imply that the conductivity of insulators should be exactly zero. In fact, although conductivities are very small for good insulators, they are still measurable and are definitely *not* zero. The reason is that, although most of the valence electrons are tightly bound to individual atoms, a few fall in the high-energy tail of the statistical distribution, even at moderate temperatures, and therefore can break loose from their lattice sites and contribute to the conductivity. The number of electrons having this much energy is strongly temperature-dependent, and the increasing number of carrier electrons with increasing T completely smothers the competing effect of increased electron scattering. Thus the conductivity of insulators almost invariably increases very rapidly with temperature; an increase of a factor of 2 over a $10°$ temperature rise is typical. This effect will be discussed in more detail in Sec. 11-5 in connection with the band theory of solids.

Thus the temperature dependence of electrical conductivity has quite different origins in conductors and insulators. In conductors, σ decreases with increasing T as a result of increased scattering of a nearly constant number of current-carrying electrons; in insulators, it increases with increasing T because of the increasing number of carriers. In this respect the behavior of insulators is similar to that of *semiconductors*, to be discussed in Sec. 11-6.

Although the discussion of this section has been confined thus far to *electrical* conductivity, a parallel discussion can be made for *thermal* conductivity. The difference is that thermal conductivity involves a transport of energy rather than electrical charge, but in metals it is clear that electron motion provides the basis for both. A material containing a significant density of mobile electrons can use them to transport energy from one region of the crystal to another if the average electron energy is different in the two regions. Macroscopically, the material conducts heat from a hot region to a colder region. Just as with electrical conductivity, the thermal conductivity is expected to vary inversely with the mean free time between collisions, which has been shown to vary approximately as $1/T$, at least in the simplest model.

In thermal conductivity an additional temperature dependence enters because the average energy carried per electron increases with temperature, in contrast to the electrical situation where the charge per particle is constant. If the electrons were a Maxwell-Boltzmann gas, the average kinetic energy would be proportional to T, and this effect would exactly cancel out the $1/T$ dependence of the mean free time, leading to the result that the thermal conductivity K would be independent of temperature. For the actual Fermi gas the energy dependence on T is more complicated because we have to consider only those electrons near the top of the distribution, but proportionality to T is still a reasonable first approximation.

Detailed calculations of thermal conductivity of metals are somewhat more subtle than the corresponding calculations of electrical conductivity because the "driving force" is a temperature gradient, corresponding to different statistical energy distributions in different regions, rather than the relatively simple electric-field force. However, the same basic considerations are involved: the mean free time between electron collisions and the temperature dependence of collision cross sections. Because of these common elements, it should not be surprising that a simple relation between the two conductivities K and σ can be derived from the model discussed here. This relation, known as the *Wiedemann-Franz law*, is

$$\frac{K}{\sigma} = \frac{\pi^2}{3}\left(\frac{k}{e}\right)^2 T \tag{11-29}$$

The most remarkable aspect of this equation is that it does *not* contain any specific properties of individual materials; nevertheless, it is found to describe fairly precisely the relation of K and σ for a large number of metals at ordinary temperatures.

There is an additional mechanism for thermal conductivity, namely, lattice vibrations. Vibrations of a lattice in thermal equilibrium are characterized by standing waves in which there is no net transfer of energy in one direction or the other. Conversely, in a crystal that is *not* in thermal equilibrium the lattice vibrations correspond at least in part to traveling waves which originate in the hotter regions and propagate to the colder regions, transferring energy which is interpreted macroscopically as heat. In metals, this contribution to the thermal conductivity is usually much smaller than the electronic part, but in covalent and ionic crystals it is usually the principal mechanism for conduction of heat.

11-4   *Magnetic Properties of Solids*

Magnetic properties of solids provide yet another example of the understanding of macroscopic phenomena that can be gained by considering the microscopic structure of matter. Most materials exhibit magnetic dipole moments, either spontaneously or when subjected to an externally produced magnetic field. This property is described quantitatively by the volume density of magnetic dipole moment, that is, the magnetic dipole moment per unit volume, called the *magnetization* of the material. Magnetization is a vector quantity; its direction is that of the magnetic moment, and it is usually denoted as **M**.

Magnetic moments in a material act as a *source* of magnetic-induction field **B**, just as do current distributions. Thus the total **B** field in a material is the sum of contributions from real current distributions either inside or outside the material and the contributions from the magnetization, which can be described in terms of microscopic currents within atoms. It is customary in electrodynamics to introduce the auxiliary vector field **H** having the property that its sources are only *real* currents, not magnetization. The **H** field is defined by the equation

$$\mathbf{H} = \frac{\mathbf{B}}{\mu_0} - \mathbf{M} \tag{11-30}$$

Its role in magnetism is analogous to that of the electric-displacement vector **D**, whose sources are free charges but not polarization charges.

For some (but not all) materials the magnetization **M** is proportional to **B**, at least over certain ranges of magnitudes. For such materials, Eq. (11-30) shows that **B** is also proportional to **H**, and so all three vectors are proportional. For historical reasons it is customary to represent the proportionality of **M** to the fields in terms of **H**, not **B**, and the magnetic susceptibility of a material, denoted by χ, is defined by

$$\mathbf{M} = \chi\mathbf{H} \tag{11-31}$$

Equation (11-30) shows that **M** and **H** have the same units, and so χ is a *dimensionless* quantity. Equation (11-31) can also be expressed in terms of **M** and **B** with the help of Eq. (11-30); the result is

$$\mathbf{M} = \frac{\chi}{\mu_0(1 + \chi)}\mathbf{B} \tag{11-32}$$

When χ is much smaller than unity, as is often the case, this relation becomes approximately $\mathbf{M} = \chi\mathbf{B}/\mu_0$, from which we find approximately

$$\chi = \mu_0\frac{dM}{dB} \tag{11-33}$$

There are three principal types of magnetic behavior, called diamagnetism, paramagnetism, and ferromagnetism. Of these, ferromagnetism is the most complicated from a theoretical point of view but is also of greatest practical importance. The classification is based on the origin of magnetic moments in materials and on their interactions.

In *diamagnetism* there are no permanent magnetic dipoles in the material, but a magnetic moment is *induced* by an external field. The origin of such a moment can be understood qualitatively by considering the motion of an electron in a **B** field. An electron with speed v which would move in a straight line in the absence of **B** moves in a circular or helical path when a field is applied. The resulting circulating charge is equivalent to a current loop, which has an associated magnetic moment. Analysis of the direction of the current shows that the direction of the induced magnetic moment is always *opposite* that of **B**, so that a diamagnetic material always has a *negative* susceptibility. The above picture is naïve, of course, but a more rigorous treatment may be given, based on the changes in the quantum states of electrons in a molecule or solid which result from the magnetic force on the moving charges in the presence of a **B** field. Diamagnetic susceptibilities are always very small, typically of the order of -10^{-8} to -10^{-6}.

In *paramagnetism* the material contains permanent microscopic magnetic moments associated with electron spin or orbital electron motion, as discussed in Sec. 8-7.   In this case the action of a **B** field is not to *create* magnetic moments where none existed before but rather to tend to align the permanent dipole moments with the field by means of the torque $\boldsymbol{\tau} = \boldsymbol{\mu} \times \mathbf{B}$ which a magnetic field **B** exerts on a magnetic moment $\boldsymbol{\mu}$.   (In the following discussion care must be taken to distinguish between the electron magnetic moment $\boldsymbol{\mu}$ and the permeability of free space $\mu_0 = 4\pi \times 10^{-7}$ weber/amp m.)   The tendency of the microscopic dipoles to line up in the direction of the field under the action of this torque is partially offset by the effects of thermal motion tending to randomize the directions of the dipoles.   Thus calculating the magnetization of a material becomes a *statistical* problem and, in fact, provides an interesting illustration of some of the statistical techniques developed in Chap. 10.

Because of the two competing effects just mentioned, it is to be expected that the susceptibility of a paramagnetic material will be temperature-dependent.   At low temperatures, a relatively weak field should align most of the dipoles, since thermal motion will be insufficient to disturb this alignment when the interaction energy is large compared with kT.   At higher temperatures a stronger field should be required to maintain the same degree of alignment, and so the susceptibility should *decrease* with increasing temperature.   This temperature dependence is borne out by experiment as well as more detailed theoretical analysis and is in sharp contrast to diamagnetic susceptibilities, which are very nearly independent of temperature.   Susceptibilities of many paramagnetic materials are found to be proportional to $1/T$, a result called the *Curie law*.

Paramagnetic behavior is expected to occur in any material whose electronic structure is characterized by partly filled shells, since then electrons can change their spin orientation without altering the electron configuration.   Thus some of the transition metals, with their partly filled $3d$ shells, are paramagnetic.   Conversely, in any material where pairing of electron spins is an essential element in the structure, the spin magnetic moments cannot change directions.   For example, in ionic crystals whose ions have "filled-shell" electron configurations, each level is occupied by two electrons which are required by the exclusion principle to have opposite spins.   Similarly, the electron-pair bonds in covalent crystals require pairs of electrons with opposite spins.   Thus ionic and covalent crystals are expected to be diamagnetic but not paramagnetic, and this prediction is generally borne out by experiment. There are, however, some ionic crystals in which the ions are *not* filled-shell configurations, and there are corresponding spin and orbital magnetic moments that are free to change directions in a magnetic field. Such crystals are paramagnetic.

It is instructive to consider a simple example of a statistical calculation of paramagnetic susceptibility. We consider only the simplest possible example, in which the magnetism is due entirely to unpaired electron spins, each of which has an associated magnetic moment

$$\mu = \frac{e\hbar}{2m}$$
$$= 9.28 \times 10^{-24} \text{ joule m}^2/\text{weber} \tag{11-34}$$

(as discussed in Sec. 8-7), which must be oriented either parallel or antiparallel to the magnetic field, corresponding to the two possible orientations of spin angular momentum. The interaction energy of a magnetic dipole with a **B** field is given, in general, by $-\boldsymbol{\mu} \cdot \mathbf{B}$. Thus a dipole parallel to the field has an energy $-\mu B$, while a dipole antiparallel to the field has energy $+\mu B$.

Now we consider N unpaired electrons in a volume V. For simplicity we neglect interactions between electrons. According to the Maxwell-Boltzmann distribution, the number of electrons in a given energy state E is

$$n = Ae^{-E/kT} \tag{11-35}$$

where A is a normalization constant. Denoting by n_+ and n_- the numbers of magnetic moments parallel and antiparallel to the field, respectively, we have

$$n_+ = Ae^{\mu B/kT}$$
$$n_- = Ae^{-\mu B/kT} \tag{11-36}$$

with μ given by Eq. (11-34). The normalization constant A is determined by the requirement that the *total* number of spins is constant and equal to N; that is, $n_+ + n_- = N$. Combining this equation with Eqs. (11-36) and rearranging, we find

$$A = \frac{N}{e^{\mu B/kT} + e^{-\mu B/kT}} = \frac{N}{2 \cosh(\mu B/kT)} \tag{11-37}$$

The *total* magnetic moment in the direction of the field is

$$\mu(n_+ - n_-) = \frac{N\mu}{2} \frac{e^{\mu B/kT} - e^{-\mu B/kT}}{\cosh(\mu B/kT)}$$
$$= N\mu \tanh \frac{\mu B}{kT} \tag{11-38}$$

and finally the magnetization M is

$$M = \frac{N}{V} \mu \tanh \frac{\mu B}{kT} \tag{11-39}$$

A graph of this function is given in Fig. 11-11, which shows magnetization as a function of field. At sufficiently small values of B the magnetization is approximately proportional to B, but as B increases M asymptotically approaches the value $(N/V)\mu$, corresponding to the state where *all* the electron magnetic moments are aligned with the field. This condition is called *saturation*. The small-field susceptibility, proportional to the initial slope of the curve, is given approximately by Eq. (11-33), which, combined with Eq. (11-38), gives

$$\chi = \frac{N}{V} \frac{\mu_0 \mu^2}{kT} \tag{11-40}$$

We note that χ is proportional to $1/T$, in agreement with Curie's law.

When the temperature is reduced, the initial slope of the curve (and therefore the susceptibility) is greater, as Eq. (11-39) shows, but the saturation magnetization is the same. It is instructive to look at some numerical magnitudes. Laboratory magnets can easily produce fields of the order of 1.0 weber/m² (10,000 gauss). For such a field the interaction energy of the electron magnetic moment is

$$\mu B = \frac{e \hbar B}{2m}$$

$$= \frac{(1.60 \times 10^{-19} \text{ coul})(1.06 \times 10^{-34} \text{ joule sec})(1 \text{ weber/m}^2)}{2(9.11 \times 10^{-31} \text{ kg})}$$

$$= 0.92 \times 10^{-23} \text{ joule}$$

$$= 0.64 \times 10^{-4} \text{ ev} \tag{11-41}$$

Since at ordinary temperatures $(T = 300°\text{K})$ kT is about ¼₀ ev, the interaction energy is much *smaller* than kT at these temperatures. Even with the strongest fields that can be produced with present-day technology, of the order of 10 webers/m² or slightly higher, the interaction energy is still less than 0.3 percent of kT at 300°K. These magnitudes correspond to the region of the curves in Fig. 11-11 very close to the origin; saturation cannot be achieved at ordinary temperatures even with the strongest fields available, and it is extremely difficult experimentally even to measure departures from straight proportionality of B and M. But at very low temperatures the interaction energy can become comparable to kT at these temperatures (30 percent of kT at $T = 3°\text{K}$), and

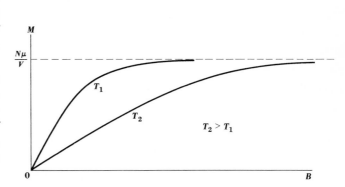

Fig. 11-11 *Graph showing magnetization M as a function of the magnetic-induction field B. At small values of B the curve is approximately a straight line, but at larger values it bends over and approaches asymptotically the saturation value of M, when all the spin magnetic moments are aligned with B.*

saturation effects *are* observed. This state of affairs is largely responsible for the great present-day interest in low-temperature magnetic properties of materials.

Equation (11-41) can be used to predict the magnitude of paramagnetic susceptibilities for typical materials. A typical density of atoms in a solid is 2×10^{28} atoms/m^3. If each of these contributes one unpaired electron, then $N/V = 2 \times 10^{28}$. Inserting the other appropriate numerical values, we find

$$\chi = \frac{(2 \times 10^{28} \text{ m}^{-3})(4\pi \times 10^{-7} \text{ weber/amp m})(9.28 \times 10^{-24} \text{ joule m}^2/\text{weber})^2}{(1.38 \times 10^{-23} \text{ joule/K}^\circ)(300\text{K}^\circ)}$$

$$= 5.2 \times 10^{-4}$$

Some materials exhibit paramagnetic susceptibilities of this order of magnitude, although many others have values smaller than this by a factor of the order of 10. In view of the rather primitive model we have used, neglecting all electron interactions except with the field, this is not surprising.

The behavior of *ferromagnetic* materials differs in several important respects from the other two types. Ferromagnetic materials exhibit very large susceptibilities, sometimes as large as 10^5, and at ordinary temperatures exhibit *saturation* at quite moderate fields, of the order of 0.1 to 2 webers/m^2. Often there is a residual magnetization even after the external field is removed. The most common ferromagnetic materials are the transition metals iron, cobalt, and nickel, although there are a number of others, including a number of compounds and alloys containing these elements.

All these phenomena are related to the basic mechanism of ferromagnetism, which is a strong electron-electron interaction which tends to line up electron spins parallel to each other even in the absence of an external field. This is intrinsically a quantum-mechanical effect without a classical analog. It is analogous to the spin-dependent interaction energy in a diatomic molecule with a covalent bond, except that in the covalent bond the lowest energy state is always one with antiparallel spins, whereas in ferromagnetic metals it is the state in which a large number of spins are parallel.

As a result of this interaction, small regions of the crystal called *magnetic domains* become spontaneously magnetized; each domain has a magnetic moment much larger than that of an individual electron. In the presence of an external field the total interaction energy of a domain with the field may be large compared with kT even at moderate fields, and the resulting reorientation of domains produces a large bulk magnetization. Roughly speaking, it is as though in Eq. (11-39) we divided N by a large numerical factor equal to the number of electrons in a domain and multiplied μ by the same factor. The effect is to increase the weak-field susceptibility by this factor and divide the field needed for saturation by the same factor.

The existence of residual magnetization is somewhat more subtle. It is associated with the fact that the magnetizing of a material by an external field is accomplished partly by changing the direction of magnetization of domains but also partly by movement of the domain boundaries. Because of lattice imperfections in polycrystalline specimens this motion is not entirely reversible, and when the field is removed the material does not return to precisely the same state it was in before the field was applied. This effect is the basis of *hysteresis*.

From the above discussion it should be clear that ferromagnetism is intrinsically a collective phenomenon, in which interelectron interactions are of primary importance. Any model that treats electrons as independent, such as the "electron-gas" model of metals, is powerless to deal with ferromagnetism. However, for every ferromagnetic material there is a critical temperature called the *Curie point*, different for different materials, above which ferromagnetic behavior disappears and the material becomes paramagnetic. Clearly this temperature is determined by the relative magnitude of kT and the interaction energy responsible for the spontaneous alignment. In the past 10 years a great deal of progress has been made in the theoretical analysis of ferromagnetism on the basis of statistical considerations and a detailed treatment of the electron-electron interactions in the material.

11-5   Band Theory of Solids

Electron states in solids play a central role in the analysis of the macroscopic properties of materials in terms of their microscopic structure, as the discussion of this chapter has shown. Detailed calculations of properties, especially those of a statistical nature, are often facilitated greatly by the concept of *energy bands*. We now introduce this concept and examine its relevance to some of the phenomena already discussed in this chapter.

When an atom is bound in a crystal lattice in close proximity with other atoms, the configurations of the valence electrons are altered significantly. The directional character of the wave functions is altered; instead of wave functions with definite total angular momentum, the electron energy states have mixtures of angular-momentum states because of the interactions with other atoms. When a valence electron is excited to an energy state higher than its ground state, its average distance from its nucleus is usually increased, and the interactions with other atoms become even more important. Such an electron becomes less localized in the vicinity of a single nucleus and becomes more and more a property of the entire crystal lattice, with a correspondingly spread-out wave function.

With the altered character of the wave functions, there are corresponding shifts in energy levels. If an isolated atom has an energy-level scheme as shown in Fig. 11-12*a*, then for *N* such atoms, far enough apart

Fig. 11-12 *Electron energy levels for sodium atoms in a crystal lattice, as a function of lattice spacing. (a) For very large spacing the levels approach those of individual isolated atoms. (b) The bands become wider as lattice spacing decreases. The broken line shows the actual equilibrium lattice spacing. At this spacing, the various bands overlap considerably.*

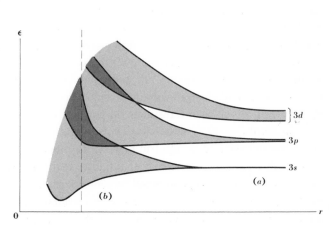

so that their interactions are negligible, each level can accommodate N times as many electrons as the exclusion principle would permit for an individual atom. When these atoms are brought together in a solid crystal structure, some of the individual atomic levels shift in one direction, and some in another, because of interactions with other atoms; the energy levels for the N atoms become spread out over a range of energies, as shown in Fig. 11-12*b*. Since the number of atoms in a crystal is usually very large, this gives virtually a continuous distribution of energies over a certain range. This range of permitted energies is called an *energy band.* Just as an electron in an isolated atom can exist only in certain definite energy levels, an electron in a solid can exist only in certain definite regions of energy, or energy bands. The regions between bands, where no electron energy levels occur in a solid, are sometimes called *forbidden bands.*

In investigating the significance of energy bands, we consider again the matter of electrical conductivity. Suppose the band structure of a certain solid is such that in the ground state all the energy levels in a certain band are occupied by electrons and that the next higher band is entirely empty. This situation can arise in a covalent crystal when the valence electrons all participate actively in the crystal binding, and a considerable amount of energy, characteristic of the energy gap between bands, is necessary to remove an electron from a bonding state.

When an electric field is applied to the crystal, completely free electrons would accelerate in the direction of the electric-field force. They would not accelerate indefinitely because of collisions, but there would be an average drift in the direction of the electric-field force. But from a quantum-mechanical point of view, an electron must gain energy to be accelerated; this means that it must move from its original energy state in the band to a new energy. If all the energy levels in a given band are occupied, then according to the exclusion principle no additional electron can move into one of these levels. In this case, the only way such an electron can gain energy is to gain an amount at least equal to the separation between the full and empty bands. This may be of the order of several electron volts and would require an impossibly large electric field; hence such transitions do not ordinarily occur.

To put the matter another way: If an electron is to be accelerated under the influence of an electric field, there must be available empty states with energies close to that of the level it originally occupies, so that it can acquire energy in small increments under the action of the field. If there are no such adjacent levels available, the acceleration does not take place, and the behavior of the material is characteristic of an insulator. Thus a material in which one band is completely full and the next higher band completely empty is expected to be an insulator. As a result of thermal motion, a few electrons have enough energy to reach the higher band, but the conductivity of such materials is extremely small compared with that of metals.

On the other hand, when an energy band is partially filled with electrons, an electron in a state near the top of the filled portion of the band can easily acquire small increments of energy by moving to one of the unoccupied levels nearby; hence such electrons can be accelerated in the presence of an external field. Thus *materials having partially filled energy bands are electrical conductors.* This band structure is characteristic of metallic crystals.

Between these two extremes is another interesting possibility. Suppose one band is completely filled and the next higher one completely empty, but the forbidden region between the two bands is relatively small, less than 1 ev. In this case, even at moderate temperatures a few electrons can make the jump from the lower band to the higher, and then they have available an abundance of energy levels to which transitions can be made when an electric field is applied. Clearly, the number of electrons in the upper band is strongly dependent on temperature, and so the electrical conductivity of such a material should increase sharply with temperature. This is also true for insulators, but the effect is much more readily observable if the energy gap is not large compared with kT at ordinary temperatures. Materials exhibiting this behavior are called *semiconductors;* they will be discussed in more detail in Sec. 11-6.

Because of the importance of the nearly full and nearly empty bands in insulators and semiconductors in determining electrical conductivity, they are usually called the *valence band* and *conduction band,* respectively. When an electron makes a transition from a normally full band to a normally empty one, it contributes to the conductivity through its ability to move into adjacent levels in the nearly empty band. At the same time, it leaves an empty energy level in the valence band, and an electron in the valence band with energy close to that of the unoccupied level can make a transition to it, thereby also contributing to the electrical conductivity. This phenomenon is most readily described in terms of the transitions of the *unoccupied* state; one speaks of transitions of electrons in the conduction band and of *holes* (unoccupied states) in the valence band. In many respects, these unoccupied energy levels behave in a manner quite analogous to charged particles. Since they correspond to the absence of an electron, they have positive rather than negative charges. They can be characterized by an effective mass, corresponding to the response of their motion to an applied electric field.

If the preceding discussion of occupied and unoccupied states in various bands has seemed somewhat abstract, a homely illustration may help to clarify the situation. The full and empty bands in an insulator or a semiconductor are comparable to a two-level parking garage. When the first floor of the garage is completely filled with cars and the second completely empty, no motion of cars can take place on either floor. But if one car is moved from the first floor to the second, then the second floor has many unoccupied spaces in which to move, and there is an empty space on the first floor which permits cars to move there as well. The two floors correspond to the valence and conduction bands in a solid.

Thus the concept of energy bands supplements the considerations of Sec. 11-3 in understanding the distinction between electrical properties of conductors and those of insulators. A similar analysis can be made in the matter of thermal conductivity, which involves the transport of energy rather than charge from one region to another. Still, the crucial factor is the ability of electrons to gain or lose small quantities of energy as a result of interactions with other electrons or with the crystal lattice. The essential condition for electron mobility is the availability of unoccupied energy levels adjacent to the occupied ones, so that in interacting with an electric field (electrical conductivity) or exchanging energy through collisions (thermal conductivity) an electron can gain or lose energy in any required amount. Thus the metals, characterized by partially filled bands, are good electrical and thermal conductors, whereas nonmetals, characterized by filled bands, are poor conductors.

Following is a simple application of the band concept, together with some statistical considerations, to a calculation of the temperature dependence of electrical conductivity of a crystalline solid having a filled band separated by an energy gap from a normally empty band, as shown in Fig. 11-13. In the limit of very low temperatures there are no electrons in the empty band, but at any finite temperature a few electrons have enough energy to reach this band. The electron-energy distribution is given by the Fermi-Dirac distribution function, and it is clear that at least at low temperatures the Fermi level lies somewhere in the forbidden region between bands. The conductivity is directly proportional to the number of electrons that have enough energy to reach the conduction band.

As a simple numerical example, let us suppose that the top of the valence band is at $\epsilon = 0$, the Fermi level is at $\frac{1}{2}$ ev, and the beginning

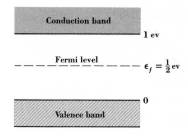

Fig. 11-13 *Band structure for a material having a filled valence band separated by an energy gap from an empty conduction band. The position of the Fermi energy at low temperatures is shown.*

of the next allowed band is at 1 ev. At $T = 300°$K, kT is about 0.0259 ev, and the occupation index for a level near the bottom of the conduction band is approximately

$$n_i = \frac{1}{e^{(1 \text{ ev} - 1/2 \text{ ev})/0.0259 \text{ ev}} + 1} \simeq e^{-19.3}$$

If the temperature is increased 10K° to 310°K, then $kT = 0.0268$ ev, and the occupation index is

$$n_i \simeq e^{-18.7}$$

The *ratio* of the conductivity at $T = 310°$ to the value at 300° is equal to the ratio of the two occupation indices:

$$\frac{\sigma_{310}}{\sigma_{300}} = \frac{n_{310}}{n_{300}} = \frac{e^{-18.7}}{e^{-19.3}} = e^{0.6}$$
$$= 1.82$$

That is, the conductivity nearly doubles with a $10°$ temperature rise. This effect is offset in part by the increased electron scattering at the higher temperature, as discussed in Sec. 11-3, but the increase in carrier density is by far the predominant effect. Thus, as already pointed out, the conductivity of insulators and semiconductors always increases sharply with temperature, and the band theory of solids provides a useful picture of the mechanisms involved. It is possible to make more detailed calculations, taking into account the shift of the Fermi level with temperature, the degeneracy factor in the conduction band, and the temperature dependence of scattering; considerable progress has also been made in calculating the spacings of the energy bands themselves, and the degeneracy factors, on the basis of the electron configuration of the crystals. However, such calculations are beyond the scope of this book.

11-6 Semiconductors

The semiconductors comprise the class of solids whose electrical properties are intermediate between the good metallic conductors and the good insulators. A few properties of semiconductors have already been mentioned, such as the temperature dependence of the electrical conductivity, increasing with temperature rather than decreasing as with most metals. The semiconductors are of considerable theoretical interest, inasmuch as they provide an interesting illustration of several of the principles discussed in this chapter. They are also of enormous practical interest, forming the basis for a wide variety of devices used in electronic circuitry, including diodes, transistors, photocells, and particle detectors.

The semiconductors with the simplest structure are elements in group IV of the periodic table: carbon, silicon, and germanium. These elements have several features in common; each has four valence electrons which in the solid state are used to form four covalent bonds, one with each of four nearest-neighbor atoms. In the resulting crystal structure, called the "diamond" structure, each atom lies at the center of a regular tetrahedron with four nearest neighbors at the corners.

Because of covalent bonding, the valence electrons are all fairly tightly bound to individual atoms; correspondingly, the band structure consists of a valence band completely filled at low temperatures, separated by an energy gap from a normally empty conduction band, as shown in Fig. 11-14. This description also fits many good insulators; the distinguishing feature of a semiconductor is that the energy gap separating the filled band from the empty one is relatively small, 1.1 ev in the case of silicon and only 0.7 ev for germanium. Thus these materials are insulators at sufficiently low temperatures, but at increasing temperatures increasing numbers of electrons are thermally excited to empty levels in the conduction band. Thus the conductivity is a strongly increasing function of temperature. Conductivity resulting in this way from thermal excitation is called *intrinsic conductivity*, to distinguish it from another type of conductivity due to impurities, to be discussed later.

In addition to thermal excitation, there are other mechanisms by which electrons can be excited from the conduction band to the valence band. One such mechanism is by absorption of light whose photons have energies greater than that of the energy gap. Thus the conductivity of germanium is increased by illuminating it with light photons of energy greater than 0.7 ev; materials exhibiting this property are said to be *photoconductive*. Another mechanism is collisions of the electron with

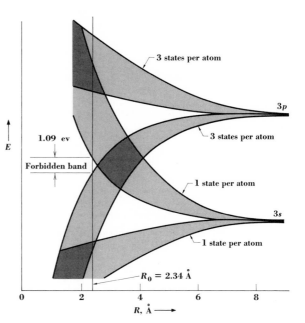

Fig. 11-14 *Band structure of silicon crystal, as a function of interatomic spacing R of nearest neighbors. At the actual value R_0 the 3s and 3p bands have crossed, and there is an energy gap of 1.1 ev. The structure of the 4s and 4p bands of germanium is similar, but the energy gap is 0.72 ev.*

energetic charged particles. A charged particle passing through a crystal lattice, such as a high-energy proton or α particle, excites electrons from the valence to the conduction band, producing an increase in conductivity.

In both these cases, the effect is a temporary departure from thermal equilibrium, so that there are temporarily more electrons in the conduction band than would be indicated by the Fermi-Dirac distribution for the thermal equilibrium state. When the source of excess energy is removed, some of the electrons drop from the conduction band back to the valence band with subsequent loss of energy. The process of excitation and deexcitation of electrons, also described as the creation of electron-hole pairs and their subsequent recombination, is a continuous process but one in which creation and recombination occur at equal rates in a thermal equilibrium state.

Some of the most interesting and useful properties of semiconductors are associated with the dramatic changes in conductivity produced by the presence of extremely minute quantities of impurities. Suppose that an atom of arsenic finds its way into a germanium crystal; arsenic lies in group V of the periodic table, adjacent to germanium, and has five valence electrons rather than four. When one of these electrons is removed, the configuration of the remaining electrons is very similar to that of germanium, being simply scaled down in size by an insignificant factor (32/33) because the nuclear charge is $+33e$ instead of $+32e$. Thus an arsenic atom can masquerade in a crystal lattice as a germanium atom; four of the five valence electrons form covalent bonds with four germanium atoms, and the remaining electron is very loosely bound to the atom. Only a very small addition of energy, about 0.01 ev (much less than the energy gap between valence and conduction bands), is required to excite it into the conduction band, and at ordinary temperatures practically *all* these extra electrons are in the conduction band, where their behavior is much like that of electrons in metals. Hence the conductivity of the material increases in direct proportion to the number of arsenic atoms present. Since at ordinary temperatures only a very small fraction of the valence electrons of germanium are in the conduction band the presence of arsenic atoms, even to the extent of 1 part in 10^{10}, changes the conductivity quite drastically and is, in fact, the determining factor for conductivity.

The presence of these loosely bound electrons associated with the arsenic impurity atoms is represented in the energy-band scheme as a set of additional levels lying just below the beginning of the conduction band, as shown in Fig. 11-15a. Because electrons in these levels can readily be excited into the conduction band, they are called *donor levels,* and the arsenic atoms are called *donor impurities,* or *n*-type impurities; a semiconductor containing donor impurities is called an *n*-type semiconductor. Other group V elements such as phosphorus or antimony are also *n*-type impurities. The conductivity associated with *n*-type impurities is due entirely to electrons. Unlike the case of excitation of valence electrons of germanium, there is no corresponding motion of the "holes" left in the valence band, since the corresponding positive charges are associated with individual impurity atoms and are not free to move.

The presence of an impurity atom with only three valence electrons has an analogous effect. Suppose we include some atoms of gallium, an element in group III, adjacent to germanium. Gallium tends to form four covalent bonds, one with each of four neighboring germanium atoms, but it lacks one electron for this. It can, however, steal an electron from a neighboring germanium atom to complete the four-bond crystal structure. When this theft is accomplished, one of the germanium atoms is left with a missing electron, or *hole*. Then, just as a donor electron is free to migrate in the conduction band, this hole in the valence band is also free to migrate. The resulting conductivity consists solely in the motion of holes, or regions of positive charge each corresponding to a missing electron; there is no contribution from the

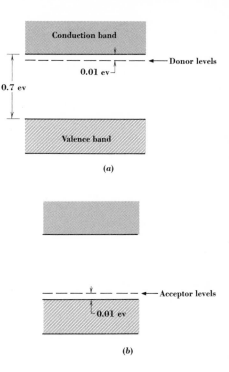

Fig. 11-15 (*a*) *Band structure of germanium with donor impurities, showing the donor levels lying just below the conduction band. At T = 0 these levels are occupied, but with only a small addition of energy from thermal agitation the electrons are excited to the conduction band. (b) Band structure of germanium with acceptor impurities, showing the acceptor levels lying just above the valence band. Electrons excited to these levels leave holes in the valence band which contribute to conductivity.*

associated electron, since it is now bound to the impurity atom just as a vacancy is bound to an individual donor atom.   An atom containing only three valence electrons is called an *acceptor* impurity.   Correspondingly, a semiconductor containing such impurities is called a *p*-type semiconductor, indicating that the current is carried by positive "charges."   Other elements in group III, such as boron, aluminum, and indium, are also acceptor impurities.

Ordinary measurements of electrical conductivity cannot distinguish between the various types of conductivity, intrinsic, *n*-type, and *p*-type.   However, there is an experiment which may be used to determine whether the current is being carried by positive or negative charges, making use of the *Hall effect*.   This effect is produced by imposing a magnetic field perpendicular to the direction of current flow in the sample whose conductivity is being studied, in an arrangement similar to that shown in Fig. 11-16*a*.   We suppose first that the conductivity is due to the motion of positive charges, as shown in Fig. 11-16*b*.   These charges move, on an average, in the direction of the current, and the magnetic field exerts, on an average, a force $q(\mathbf{v} \times \mathbf{B})$.   The direction of this force, labeled **F** in the figure, is such as to tend to push the posi-

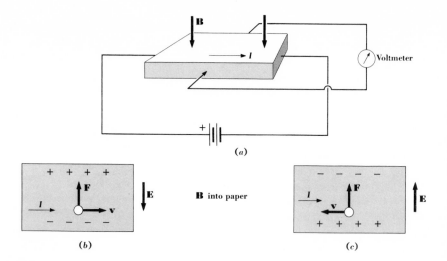

Fig. 11-16 (a) *Apparatus for observing the Hall effect;* (b) *current carried by positive charges (holes);* (c) *current carried by negative charges (electrons) moving oppositely to the direction of conventional current flow I.*

tive charges to one side in the sample. This transverse drift cannot continue indefinitely because charge accumulates on the sides, creating a transverse electric field just large enough to cancel the transverse magnetic-field force. Corresponding to this transverse electric field is a potential difference whose magnitude and sign may be measured.

Now we consider the situation when the current is carried by negative charges, which move in the direction opposite to that of conventional current flow, as shown in Fig. 11-16c. The signs of both q and **v** are reversed with respect to the positive-charge case, the direction of **F** is the same as before, and the transverse potential difference has the opposite polarity in this case. Thus the *sign* of the Hall-effect potential determines whether the conductivity is due to electrons or holes. More detailed measurements of the Hall effect may be used to obtain further information regarding the behavior of electrons and holes in semiconductors.

Some of the most interesting practical devices using semiconductors make use of a crystal which has n-type impurities in some regions and p-type impurities in other regions. The most straightforward although not always the most practical way to make such a semiconductor crystal is to "grow" a crystal by pulling a small seed crystal very slowly out of a container of melted semiconductor.   By varying the concentration of the various impurities in the melt while the crystal is being grown, one can make a crystal containing alternate n and p regions.   The boundary layer separating an n region from a p region is called a *p-n junction;* most of the interesting properties of semiconductor diodes, transistors, and other devices are determined by the properties of these junctions.

When a potential difference V is imposed between the terminals of a p-n junction and the current I measured as a function of V, the result is similar to that shown in Fig. 11-17.   This behavior is in striking contrast to that of ordinary conducting materials obeying Ohm's law, in which the current I is proportional to the potential difference V.   Furthermore, the device conducts much more readily in one direction than in the other; it acts as a *rectifier.*

This directional characteristic of the device can be understood roughly as follows: When the p region is at higher potential than the n region, the electric field is such as to cause holes in the p region to flow into the n region and electrons in the n region to flow into the p region.   When the polarity is reversed the fields are in such a direction as to tend to cause electrons to flow from the p to the n region and holes from the n to the p region.   But at ordinary temperatures there are relatively few electrons in the p region and relatively few holes in the

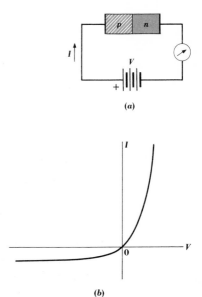

Fig. 11-17 (a) *A semiconductor p-n junction in a circuit;* (b) *graph showing the asymmetric voltage-current relationship, in agreement with the theoretical prediction given by* Eq. (11-42).

n region, only those contributed by thermal excitation of valence electrons. Thus the resulting current flow is much smaller.

A more detailed theoretical analysis of the action of a p-n junction takes into consideration the fact that in each region hole-electron pairs are constantly being generated by thermal excitation. These, along with the holes and electrons contributed by the acceptor and the donor impurity atoms, respectively, can diffuse from one region to the other. In an equilibrium state when no net current is flowing, the total diffusion current of holes and electrons across the junction is zero. When an external electric field is imposed, both the diffusion rate and the rate of thermal generation of holes and electrons are altered, and the net current flow is different from zero. For a simple p-n junction the relationship between current and applied voltage is given approximately by

$$I = I_0(e^{eV/kT} - 1) \tag{11-42}$$

where I_0 is a constant characteristic of the device. This equation is the function corresponding to the graph in Fig. 11-17b.

Other devices can be constructed from p-n junctions. A *transistor* is a sandwich containing at least two p-n junctions, in the configuration n-p-n or p-n-p. The simplest possible circuit employing such a device is shown in Fig. 11-18. The three regions are termed the emitter, the base, and the collector. In the absence of current in the emitter part of the circuit, relatively little current flows from collector to base, as with the simple p-n junction. However, when a voltage between emitter

Fig. 11-18 *An n-p-n transistor and associated circuit. With no voltage applied to the emitter, little current flows in the collector circuit. When a potential difference is applied between emitter and base, as shown, electrons travel from the emitter region to the base, and for sufficiently large collector voltage most of them continue into the collector. Thus a small amount of power into the emitter circuit can control a larger power in the collector circuit, and the device operates as an amplifier.*

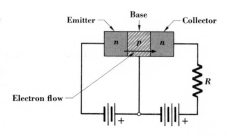

and base is applied in the direction shown, the result is that some of the conduction electrons in the emitter travel into the base region, in which they come under the influence of the potential difference between base and collector and so pass on to the collector.

Thus a current in the emitter circuit is used to control a current in the collector circuit. Furthermore, the voltage source in the collector circuit may be considerably larger than that in the emitter circuits so that, although the currents are of comparable magnitudes, the *power* dissipated in the resistor R in the collector circuit may be considerably larger than the power input in the emitter circuit. Thus the device acts as a power amplifier. In other kinds of circuit connections, transistors can be used as voltage or current amplifiers as well.

Semiconductor electronics is a spectacular example of how research in fundamental physics (in this case, the physical properties of semiconductors) leads to practical applications of widespread importance. The development of semiconductor devices in the past 15 years has entirely revolutionized the field of electronics engineering. In many applications they have almost completely replaced vacuum tubes, as a result of smaller size, greater efficiency, and greater reliability.

PROBLEMS

11-1   In a simple cubic crystal lattice, each atom is at the center of a regular octahedron with six nearest neighbors at the corners. Show that in the "hard-sphere" model the central atom just touches six nearest-neighbor spheres of radius a if its radius is $(\sqrt{2} - 1)a$.

11-2   Show that, in a body-centered cubic crystal structure, a central sphere just touches each of eight nearest-neighbor spheres of radius a if its radius is $(\sqrt{3} - 1)a$.

11-3   Show that in a "close-packed" crystal structure an atom of radius a can accommodate twelve nearest neighbors of radius a if six are placed in a plane hexagonal arrangement around it, with three each above and below the plane. Show that all twelve neighbor spheres touch the central sphere in this arrangement, which is called the hexagonal close-packed structure.

11-4   Show that in a face-centered cubic lattice each atom has 12 nearest neighbors. This is most easily seen by considering the neighbors of an atom at a face-centered position.

11-5 Derive the electronic specific-heat formula [Eq. (11-21)] from the expression for the average electron energy [Eq. (11-20)].

11-6 For a metal with Fermi energy $\epsilon_f = 5$ ev, find the rms speed of electrons with energy in the vicinity of ϵ_f.

11-7 For any system consisting of N identical parts (molecules, atoms, or electrons) each with a set of energy levels ϵ_i with degeneracies g_i, governed by the Maxwell-Boltzmann distribution, the *partition function* is defined as

$$Z = \sum_i g_i e^{-\epsilon_i/kT}$$

Show that the average energy $\bar{\epsilon}$ of each part is given by

$$\bar{\epsilon} = kT^2 \frac{\partial}{\partial T} \ln Z = -\frac{\partial}{\partial \beta} \ln Z$$

where $\beta = 1/kT$, and that the specific heat per part is

$$C = T \frac{\partial^2 (kT \ln Z)}{\partial T^2}$$

independent of the details of the energy levels or their degeneracies.

11-8 Compare the predicted value of the temperature coefficient of conductivity given by Eq. (11-28) and the following paragraph with measured values listed in a handbook. Values usually listed are temperature coefficients of *resistivity*; show that this coefficient has the same magnitude as the quantity α defined in the text.

11-9 Check the validity of the Wiedemann-Franz law [Eq. (11-29)] for three metals, using handbook values of K and σ.

11-10 Derive the relation between **M** and **B** given by Eq. (11-32), from Eqs. (11-30) and (11-31).

11-11 In the magnetization calculation preceding Eq. (11-39), show that the partition function for the system, as defined in Sec. 10-4, is given by

$$Z = 2 \cosh \frac{\mu B}{kT}$$

and that the magnetization is given by

$$M = \frac{N}{V} kT \frac{\partial}{\partial B} \ln Z$$

11-12 For a semiconductor with n-type impurities and a band scheme as shown in Fig. 11-15a, suppose the donor levels are 0.01 ev below the bottom of the conduction band. For relatively low temperatures and small impurity concentrations, the Fermi level is approximately the same energy as the donor levels. Explain why this should be so. At what temperature are one-half the electrons from the donor states excited to the conduction band? At what temperature are 99 percent in the conduction band?

11-13 Suppose a piece of very pure germanium is to be used as a photocell by making use of the increase in conductivity resulting from electron-hole pair generation by absorption of radiation. What is the longest wavelength radiation that can be detected? In what region of the spectrum does this radiation lie? Could a device be made sensitive to longer wavelengths by using a *p-n* junction instead?

11-14 What elements are suitable to use as impurities in silicon to make it an *n*-type semiconductor? A *p*-type?

11-15 As a very simple model, suppose a pure semiconductor crystal has N valence electrons and that their energy-band structure may be represented as N levels in the valence band, all with very nearly the same energy, and N more levels in the conduction band, also very close together but separated from the valence band by an energy V.
  a. Show that for sufficiently low temperatures the Fermi energy is approximately halfway between these two narrow bands.
  b. Find, in terms of V and other relevant quantities, the temperature at which 10^{-10} of the valence electrons are excited to the conduction band. Is there any temperature at which the populations in the two bands are equal? Explain.

11-16 Draw a circuit diagram similar to Fig. 11-18 except using a *p-n-p* transistor. Explain carefully the reasons for the polarities of the various voltage sources.

11-17 Semiconductor devices are intrinsically rather temperature-sensitive; for example, a *p-n* junction is not an effective rectifier above a certain temperature. Discuss how the maximum temperature limit depends on the relative concentrations of impurity current carriers and carriers resulting from thermal electron-hole generation.

IN THIS CHAPTER we discuss phenomena directly related to the structure and properties of the atomic nucleus.   The most important properties of nuclei are introduced, and it is shown how some of them can be understood in terms of the structure of the nucleus.   Not all nuclei are stable; several kinds of instability resulting in radioactivity and nuclear disintegration are discussed.   Nuclei can also participate in a variety of reactions, in which the constituent parts are rearranged and new nuclei formed.   These processes are analogous to the rearrangement of electrons and atoms in molecules in the course of chemical reactions.   Two particular classes of reactions, fission and fusion, are of considerable practical importance.

12-1   *Properties of Nuclei*

In the discussion of atomic structure in the past several chapters the nucleus of the atom was usually represented as a *point*, containing most of the mass of the atom and a charge exactly equal in magnitude to the total negative charge of all the electrons in a neutral atom.   In this chapter, we shall discuss the properties and structure of the nucleus in more detail.

The most obvious physical property of a nucleus is its *size.* We have already discussed in Sec. 8-1 the experiments of Rutherford and his collaborators, which established in 1911 the fact that the atomic nucleus is much smaller than the overall dimensions of the atom. Rutherford established that the positive electrical charge in the atomic nucleus is concentrated in a region no larger than 10^{-14} m in diameter, less than $1/10,000$ of the overall diameter of the atom; as far as the electronic structure of an atom is concerned, representing the nucleus as a point is a very good approximation. Since these pioneering experiments, many investigators have made other scattering experiments with α particles, protons, and electrons, to measure nuclear dimensions and charge configurations in more detail. Although the "surface" of a nucleus is not a sharply defined boundary, an approximate radius for each nucleus can be determined; it is found that the nuclear radius is a smoothly varying function of its mass, as shown in Fig. 12-1. In this figure nuclear radii determined from high-energy electron-scattering experiments are plotted as a function of the *nuclear mass number A,* defined as the total number of protons and neutrons in the nucleus. This number is very nearly (but not exactly) equal to the mass of the nucleus expressed in *atomic mass units* (amu), to be discussed later in this section.

Fig. 12-1   *Radii of nuclei, measured by electron-scattering experiments.   The radius varies smoothly with nuclear mass number A.   The nuclear volume is directly proportional to A, showing that the density of nuclear matter is nearly constant, independent of A.*

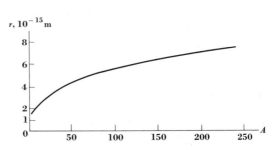

The curve in Fig. 12-1 can be described well by the empirical equation

$$r = r_0 A^{1/3} \qquad \text{with} \qquad r_0 = 1.2 \times 10^{-15} \text{ m} \tag{12-1}$$

This equation may be used to compute the volume V of a nucleus, and from that its density, which in terms of atomic mass units is approximately A/V. We find

$$V = \tfrac{4}{3}\pi r^3 = \tfrac{4}{3}\pi r_0{}^3 A$$
$$\frac{A}{V} = \frac{3}{4\pi r_0{}^3}$$

(12-2)

The significance of this result is that the density is independent of A; thus all nuclei have approximately the same density. This observation is important in understanding the stability of nuclei, as will be shown later.

The fact that an atom with its normal complement of electrons is electrically neutral shows that the electric charge of the nucleus is in magnitude an integer multiple of the electron charge e; it is usually denoted as Ze. Furthermore, since the electronic structure of an atom determines its chemical behavior, the identification of a nucleus as belonging to a particular element is determined by the nuclear charge. Thus the hydrogen nucleus has $Z = 1$, helium $Z = 2$, lithium $Z = 3$, and so on. Z is also equal to the number of electrons in a neutral atom and is therefore equal to the *atomic number* of an element, which is the number used to arrange the elements in sequence in the periodic table; in nuclear physics Z is also called the *charge number.*

As mentioned previously, measurements of the mass of the electron show that the electrons in an atom account for only a small fraction of its total mass; most of the mass is associated with the nucleus. The total mass of a neutral atom can be determined from its *atomic mass;*[1] for example, the atomic mass of hydrogen is usually given as 1.008 g/mole, which means that 1 mole of hydrogen atoms has a total mass of 1.008 g. Now a *mole* of anything is N_0 atoms or molecules, where N_0 is Avogadro's number, equal to

$$N_0 = 6.022 \times 10^{23} \text{ molecules/mole}$$

(12-3)

Thus the mass of a hydrogen atom is

$$M_H = \frac{1.008 \text{ g/mole}}{6.022 \times 10^{23} \text{ molecules/mole}} = 1.673 \times 10^{-27} \text{ kg}$$

(12-4)

This value includes the mass of an electron, $m_e = 0.00091 \times 10^{-27}$ kg. Thus the mass of the hydrogen nucleus, which is a proton, is

$$M_P = 1.672 \times 10^{-27} \text{ kg}$$

(12-5)

---

[1] The term *atomic weight* is sometimes used; since the fundamental physical quantity referred to is always *mass*, not weight, the term *atomic mass* is to be preferred. The latter term is used throughout this text.

Nuclear masses are often most conveniently expressed in terms of the *atomic mass unit*, abbreviated amu.   By definition, an atomic mass unit is one-twelfth the mass of a neutral carbon atom.   That is, by definition, the mass of one atom of the stable isotope of carbon is 12 amu. On this scale, the mass of a neutral hydrogen atom is 1.008 amu.   From the above discussion it is clear that

$$6.022 \times 10^{23} \text{ amu} = 1 \text{ g} = 10^{-3} \text{ kg} \qquad (12\text{-}6)$$

Atomic masses can be measured directly by means of an instrument called a mass spectrometer; one type of mass spectrometer is shown schematically in Fig. 12-2.   Atoms of the element under study are partially ionized in an oven and then accelerated by two electrodes to a

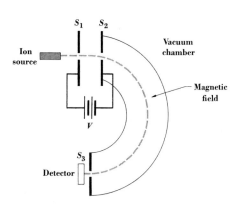

Fig. 12-2   *A mass spectrometer of the type invented by Dempster about* 1920.   *Ions created by electron bombardment are accelerated by the potential difference V and then pass through beam-defining slits into a region of uniform magnetic field directed into the plane of the paper.   Ions are detected by a photographic film or a sensitive electrometer at the detector position shown.   The radius of curvature of the ion trajectories can be measured directly.*

kinetic energy directly proportional to the accelerating voltage.   They are then permitted to travel into a region containing a uniform magnetic field, which exerts a force $q\mathbf{v} \times \mathbf{B}$, where q is the net charge of the ionized atom, $\mathbf{v}$ its velocity, and $\mathbf{B}$ the magnetic field.   Under the action of this force, always perpendicular to $\mathbf{v}$, the ion describes a circular path with a radius R determined by the condition that the force, whose magnitude is qvB, is equal to the mass times the centripetal acceleration v^2/R.†   That is,

$$qvB = \frac{mv^2}{R} \qquad (12\text{-}7)$$

† H. D. Young, "Fundamentals of Mechanics and Heat," sec. 8-5, McGraw-Hill Book Company, New York, 1964.

By appropriate design of the ion source one can obtain singly ionized atoms (i.e., atoms with one electron missing) so that the net charge of each atom is simply the electron charge e. Furthermore, the *speed v* of the ions emerging from the accelerating electrodes is determined by the energy relationship

$$\tfrac{1}{2}mv^2 = eV \tag{12-8}$$

where V is the potential difference. Combining this with Eq. (12-7), we find

$$m = \frac{B^2R^2e}{2V} \tag{12-9}$$

Thus by measuring the accelerating voltage, the magnetic field, and the radius of curvature of the path of the ion in the magnetic field, one can measure the mass of the ion quite precisely.

All the masses of the light nuclei are found to be very nearly integer multiples of the mass of the proton. This fact was observed from chemical measurements many years before the mass spectrometer was developed and suggests strongly that protons are one of the fundamental building blocks of all nuclei. An apparent exception is chlorine, which from chemical observations appears to have an atomic mass of about 35.5 amu. It is now known that chlorine as it exists in nature is a mixture of atoms with two kinds of nuclei, 75 percent having a mass of 35 amu and the other 25 percent, 37 amu. The electrical charges of these two nuclei are equal, so that the electronic structure and chemical behavior of atoms containing them are very nearly identical.

Atoms containing two nuclei with the same nuclear charge number Z but different masses are called *isotopes* of an element. Two isotopes of a given element have the same positive charge in their nucleus and the same electronic structure but different masses. As we shall see in the next section, the two nuclei differ only in the number of *neutrons* they contain.

Two additional properties of nuclei which are of importance are *angular momentum* and *magnetic moment*. For electrons in atoms, these two quantities are closely related, and there is a similar relationship for nuclei. The mutual interactions among particles in a nucleus permit a relative motion analogous to the orbital motion of electrons in an atom; associated with this motion are angular momentum and, because of the circulating charge, also magnetic moment. In addition, just as with electrons, the constituent particles of a nucleus, protons and neutrons, have an intrinsic or *spin* angular momentum and associated magnetic moment.

The earliest direct evidence for the existence of nuclear angular momentum and magnetic moment came from spectroscopy. Even before 1900, it was known that the "fine structure" of spectra due to spin-orbit interactions does not exhaust all the possibilities of details of spectrum lines but that some lines possess a still finer structure, known as *hyperfine* structure. A number of distinct effects are responsible for hyperfine structure; one of the important ones is interaction of electrons with the magnetic field of the nuclear magnetic moment, leading to an interaction energy that depends on the relative orientations of nuclear spin, electron spin, and electron orbital angular momentum.

On the assumption that the nuclear angular momentum, like all other angular momenta, is quantized, the number of lines into which a given spectrum should be split by the hyperfine interaction is determined by the number of possible values of the component of nuclear angular momentum in a given direction. For example, hyperfine splitting of a single energy level into five sublevels indicates a total angular-momentum quantum number of 2, with corresponding components ± 2, ± 1, 0 in the direction of a specified axis. Furthermore, spectroscopic measurement of the *magnitude* of the energy shifts associated with this interaction makes possible a determination of the magnitude of the magnetic moment of the nucleus.

The angular momentum of a nucleus has come to be called *nuclear spin*; this is something of a misnomer, inasmuch as it is made up of contributions from both spin angular momentum of particles and orbital angular momentum due to their motions with respect to each other. In order to account for hyperfine splitting due to nuclear spin, it is necessary to permit both integer and half-integer values of the nuclear angular-momentum quantum number. Thus, certain nuclei have a spin quantum number of $\frac{3}{2}$, with possible components $\pm\frac{3}{2}$, $\pm\frac{1}{2}$ in a given direction, leading to a fourfold hyperfine splitting. All nuclei with *even* values of the mass number A are found to have *integer* nuclear spin, while all those with *odd* values of A have *half-integer* spins. This observation provides a valuable clue as to the constituents of nuclei, to be discussed in Sec. 12-2.

The ratio of magnetic moment to angular momentum is called the *gyromagnetic ratio*. For orbital motion of electrons, this ratio is $e/2m$, although for spin angular momentum and magnetic moment of the electron, it has very nearly twice this value. The gyromagnetic ratio of nuclei is conveniently expressed as

$$g\,\frac{e}{2M} \tag{12-10}$$

where g is a pure number, typically between 1 and 3, and M is the proton mass. Thus, while the spin angular momentum of a nucleus has the same order of magnitude as that for orbital motion of electrons, both being proportional to $\hbar$, the magnetic moments of nuclei are typically smaller than those associated with electron motion by the factor of the ratio of electron to proton masses, $m/M \simeq 1/1{,}840$.

In 1946, two groups of physicists, working independently at Harvard and Stanford Universities, developed a method of measuring nuclear magnetic moments which is much more precise than the spectroscopic determinations outlined above. This method is called *nuclear magnetic resonance;* it makes use of measurements of the frequency of precession of the nuclear angular momentum, analogous to the precession of a gyroscope, in an external magnetic field. This technique is discussed in Appendix H.

12-2 Nuclear Structure

The nuclear properties outlined in Sec. 12-1 can be observed without any probing into the details of nuclear structure; we shall now examine this structure in more detail. What are the fundamental building blocks of nuclei? To experimenters in the early years of the present century, the fact that many nuclear masses are integer multiples of that of the lightest nucleus (a single proton) suggested strongly that the total mass is made up simply of the appropriate number of protons. For the heavier nuclei, this would lead to an electrical charge greater than that actually observed, and so it was proposed to neutralize some of the proton charge by adding electrons to the nucleus. For example, the helium nucleus has a mass about four times that of the proton but a charge only twice as great; perhaps it contains four protons and two electrons. The fact that some radioactive nuclei emit electrons in the course of their decay seemed to lend further support to this explanation.

Although this hypothesis appears attractive at first, there are several reasons why it cannot possibly be correct. One is that it is not possible to understand nuclear spins on this basis. Since both proton and electron have spin ½, any nucleus with an even total number of particles (protons plus electrons) should have a spin that is an *integer* multiple of $\hbar$, whereas those with an odd number of particles should have half-integer spins. There are, in fact, many nuclei that do not follow this rule. The simplest example is the nucleus of deuterium, the isotope of hydrogen with mass number $A = 2$. If this nucleus consisted of two protons and an electron, it should have a spin of either $\frac{1}{2}$ or $\frac{3}{2}$; instead, its spin is found to be 1. Many other examples can be cited. Magnetic moments pose an even more serious problem. The electron magnetic moment is of the order of a thousand times greater than that of the proton; yet the observed magnetic moments of nuclei are characteristic of the magnitude of the magnetic moment of the proton, not of the electron, casting further doubt on the existence of electrons in the nucleus. Still other evidence might be cited.

About 1925 it was proposed that one of the nuclear building blocks might be a *neutral* particle (no electric charge) having a half-integer spin and a mass about equal to that of the proton. This particle, even before it was discovered experimentally, was named the *neutron*. The detection of a neutral particle posed serious experimental problems, inasmuch as none of the usual techniques for observing charged particles would work successfully with a particle having no charge. Such a particle would not be deflected by an electric or magnetic field, would not make its presence known by creating ions, and therefore would have no effect on photographic emulsions.

Finally in 1932 James Chadwick, one of Rutherford's associates, made a series of observations which could be interpreted as demonstrating the existence of the neutron. It had been discovered earlier that, when a beryllium target is bombarded by α particles from a heavy radioactive element such as polonium, radiation is produced which does not consist of charged particles but which penetrates matter more readily than any other known radiation (α, β, or γ rays). This radiation in turn was observed to knock protons out of hydrogen-rich substances such as paraffin. Although it had originally been thought to consist of high-energy γ rays, Chadwick showed that a much more natural interpretation was that of a neutral particle with a mass approximately equal to the proton mass.

Further experiments confirmed Chadwick's hypothesis, and it was recognized that protons and neutrons are the fundamental building blocks of nuclei. The observed angular momentum of nuclei could then be understood on the assumption that the neutron spin is $\frac{1}{2}$. Deuterium, for example, was assumed to be a proton and a neutron bound together, so that a spin of 0 or 1 was to be expected. As pointed out above, the observed spin is 1.

The mass of the neutron is slightly greater than that of the proton; the two masses are, respectively,

$$M_N = 1.675 \times 10^{-27} \text{ kg} = 1.00866 \text{ amu}$$
$$M_P = 1.672 \times 10^{-27} \text{ kg} = 1.00728 \text{ amu}$$

$$(12\text{-}11)$$

The generic term *nucleon* is often used to describe either a proton or neutron; both proton and neutron are nucleons. Any nucleus is identified by the numbers of protons and neutrons that it contains. As already observed, the number of protons is equal to the atomic number Z. The number of neutrons is usually denoted by N, and the total number of nucleons, called the *nucleon number* or the *mass number*, is A. Clearly,

$$A = Z + N$$

$$(12\text{-}12)$$

The various nuclear species can also be identified by the notation $_ZX^A$, where X is the chemical symbol of the corresponding element. For example, the atomic number of chlorine is 17. The notation for the isotope of chlorine whose nucleus has mass number 35, corresponding to 17 protons and 18 neutrons, is $_{17}Cl^{35}$. This notation is somewhat redundant, inasmuch as the atomic number identifies the element uniquely. That is, the notation Cl^{35} conveys the same information as does $_{17}Cl^{35}$.

We mentioned in Sec. 12-1 the existence of *isotopes*, various species of the same element, whose atoms have the same nuclear charge but somewhat different nuclear mass. The assumption that protons and neutrons are the basic building blocks of nuclei provides a natural explanation for this difference; two isotopes of an element have nuclei with the same number of protons but different numbers of neutrons. For example, the nucleus of Cl^{35} has 17 protons and 18 neutrons ($Z = 17$, $N = 18$, $A = 35$), while that of Cl^{37} has 17 protons and 20 neutrons ($Z = 17$, $N = 20$, $A = 37$). Individual nuclear species, each identified by values of Z and N (or alternatively Z and A) are called *nuclides*.

The neutron, like the proton, has a spin angular momentum of $\frac{1}{2}\hbar$. It also has a magnetic moment, with a direction opposite to that of the angular momentum. Its gyromagnetic ratio is thus a negative quantity and has the value $-1.913(e/M)$. It may not be immediately obvious how a particle with no electrical charge can have a magnetic moment, since in all the cases considered thus far the two have been inseparable. The explanation is to be found in the internal structure of the neutron, which in some respects is not an indivisible particle. We defer further discussion of this matter to Chap. 13, where we shall discuss the nature of fundamental particles in more detail.   Both protons and neutrons, like all other particles having spin ½, obey the Pauli exclusion principle.

The most immediate question concerning nuclear structure is what holds the constituents of a nucleus together.   Protons, having like electrical charges, repel each other.   The observed radii of nuclei are less than 10^{-14} m.   The amount of energy necessary to overcome the electrical repulsion and push two protons within 10^{-14} m of each other is

$$E = \frac{e^2}{4\pi\epsilon_0 r} = \frac{(9 \times 10^9 \text{ nt m}^2/\text{coul}^2)(1.6 \times 10^{-19} \text{ coul})^2}{10^{-14} \text{ m}}$$

$$= 2.3 \times 10^{-14} \text{ joule}$$

$$= 1.44 \times 10^5 \text{ ev} \tag{12-13}$$

or about 10^4 times the ionization potential of the hydrogen atom.   Yet despite this very strong electrical repulsion, protons are somehow bound together in a nucleus, along with neutrons.   Gravitational attraction cannot account for the stability of nuclei; the gravitational attraction between two protons is *smaller* than their electrostatic repulsion by a factor of the order of 10^{-38}.   Thus gravitational interactions are of no importance in the understanding of nuclear structure, although they are of primary importance in the structure of stars.

The forces responsible for the stability of nuclei are not of any familiar nature but instead are a manifestation of a new kind of force, which for lack of a better name is called the *nuclear force*.   Not only must the nuclear force between two protons be much stronger than the electrical repulsion at short distances, but it must be a *short-range* force; otherwise protons would be attracted no matter how far apart they are. We might therefore expect that the potential energy due to the nuclear interaction should be proportional not to e^2/r, as in the case of the electrostatic force, but to a function which drops off more quickly with increasing r, such as

$$V(r) = -f^2 \frac{e^{-r/a}}{r} \tag{12-14}$$

where f is a constant whose role is analogous to that of the electrical charge in characterizing the strength of the interaction, and a is a constant with units of length which describes the *range* of the interaction, that is, how rapidly it drops off with increasing r.   Figure 12-3 illustrates the behavior of this function.

Equation (12-14) is not just a guess; it has some theoretical foundation.   For the present, however, we regard it as an empirical rule which

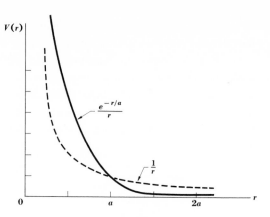

Fig. 12-3 *Graph of the Yukawa potential function, given by Eq. (12-14), and, for comparison, a Coulomb (1/r) potential function having the same value at r = a. The Yukawa potential drops off much more rapidly with increasing r than the Coulomb potential.*

helps to visualize the nature of nuclear forces. This potential-energy function is called the *Yukawa potential,* in honor of the Japanese theoretical physicist H. Yukawa, who first proposed such a potential-energy function in 1935 on the basis of a meson-exchange theory. We shall return briefly to the Yukawa theory of nuclear forces in Sec. 13-3. Experiments have shown that the potential energy associated with the attractive force between two nuclear particles is of the order of 10^7 ev and is the same for neutron-neutron interactions as for proton-proton interactions. Thus the nuclear force is not directly connected with electrical charge.

The magnitudes of nuclear interaction energies are such that it is convenient to measure them in *million electron volts,* abbreviated Mev, with the definition

$$1 \text{ Mev} = 10^6 \text{ ev} \tag{12-15}$$

Another peculiar property of nuclear forces, not shared by more familiar forces such as electrical or gravitational interactions, is that of *saturation.* An individual nucleon does not interact simultaneously with an unlimited number of other nucleons but only with a small number. This is in contrast to electrical interactions, in which a given electrical charge interacts with *all* other charges in its vicinity. Instead, the nuclear force seems to involve only interactions of an individual nucleon with at most three others. For example, the α particle, or helium nucleus, contains two protons and two neutrons in a stable structure with total nucleon number $A = 4$. This structure, however, exerts virtually no attractive force toward an additional proton or neutron, and there is *no* stable nucleus with $A = 5$.

Additional evidence for the saturation of nuclear forces is provided by the observation that nuclear matter has roughly constant density. That is, the volume of a nucleus is approximately proportional to the nucleon number A, as shown by Eq. (12-2) and the accompanying discussion. The term "approximately" is necessary because measured values of nuclear radii depend somewhat on the techniques used for the measurement. Nuclear radius and nuclear volume are not precisely defined quantities, just as the diameter of an atom is not a precisely defined quantity. Nuclear particles, like electrons, must be described in quantum-mechanical language by wave functions; when we say that a nucleus has a certain radius, we mean that the wave function describing its configuration is confined mostly within this radius, but the boundaries of a nucleus are not completely sharply defined.

Information concerning the interaction energies of nucleons in a nucleus can be obtained from precise measurements of nuclear masses. The simplest example is deuterium, the nucleus of the $A = 2$ isotope of hydrogen. This nucleus, the simplest of all nucleon bound states, contains one proton and one neutron. This combination is usually called a *deuteron.* It might be thought that the mass of the deuteron would be simply the sum of proton and neutron masses,

$$M_P + M_N = 1.00728 \text{ amu} + 1.00866 \text{ amu} = 2.01594 \text{ amu} \tag{12-16}$$

Instead, the observed value of the deuteron mass M_D is somewhat *less* than this, about 2.01356 amu. On the basis of relativistic considerations, this result is to be expected, since the total energy of the system when the two particles are bound is less than when they are separated. The amount by which the mass of the deuteron is less than the sum of proton and neutron masses should be related to the potential energy associated with the bound state. The magnitude of this energy is usually called the *binding energy*, abbreviated E_B. Thus we expect to find

$$E_B = (M_P + M_N - M_D)c^2 \tag{12-17}$$

In calculations of this sort, a useful conversion factor is that a mass of 1 amu is the equivalent of an energy of 931 Mev. Using this conversion factor, we find that the binding energy of the deuteron is

$$E_B = (0.00238 \text{ amu})c^2 = 2.22 \text{ Mev} \tag{12-18}$$

This binding energy can also be *measured* directly by a technique analogous to that used in measuring ionization potentials of atoms: bombardment with high-energy particles or electromagnetic radiation. It is observed that the minimum energy necessary to dissociate the deuteron, in the frame of reference where the total momentum is zero, is 2.22 Mev, in agreement with the above calculation.

Similar calculations have been made for other nuclei; as expected, the total mass of a nucleus is always somewhat less than the sum of masses of its constituent parts, and the difference is ascribed to the mass equivalent of the binding energy. It is of interest to calculate the binding energy *per nucleon* for various atoms. Except for nuclei with very small mass numbers, the binding energy per nucleon is very nearly the same for all nuclei, about 8 Mev. Figure 12-4 shows a graph of binding energy per nucleon as a function of the nucleon mass number. This observation is further evidence of the fact that nuclear forces exhibit saturation and is in sharp contrast to the binding of electrons in atoms, where

Fig. 12-4 *Binding energy per nucleon, as a function of nucleon number. Except for very small values of A, the binding energy per nucleon is nearly independent of A. The "spike" at A = 4 shows the unusual stability of the α-particle structure.*

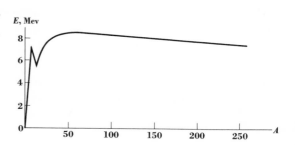

the average binding energy per electron increases sharply as the atomic number Z increases. The slight decrease of the binding energy per nucleon at large values of A is due chiefly to the increasing importance of the electrostatic repulsion of protons. This effect, which always tends to *decrease* the binding energy, is of longer range than the nuclear force and does not saturate; hence it becomes relatively more important at large A. In fact, electrostatic effects are primarily responsible for the fact that no nucleus with A greater than 209 is stable. Stability of nuclei will be discussed in the next section.

The foregoing has been a very incomplete description of what is usually called a *phenomenological* theory of nuclear forces, a description of nuclear forces which does not attempt to analyze their fundamental nature. There are still many unanswered questions regarding the fundamental nature of nuclear forces, but all models that have achieved any success in understanding nuclear forces make use of additional unstable particles called *mesons,* which are created and destroyed by the protons and neutrons in a nucleus, in much the same way that photons are created and destroyed in transitions in electronic energy levels in atoms. The interaction between two nucleons can be described in terms of a game of catch in which the two particles toss mesons back and forth at each other. The meson-exchange theory of nuclear forces will be discussed in somewhat more detail in Sec. 13-3.

12-3 Unstable Nuclei

A number of heavy elements have nuclei that are not stable but disintegrate spontaneously. In fact, no nucleus with $Z \geq 84$ *or* $A \geq 210$ is stable. The most famous examples of unstable nuclei are uranium, thorium, and radium, although there are many others. The history of the investigation of radioactivity is an exciting tale with many of the characteristics of a good mystery story. It began in 1896 with the accidental discovery by Henri Becquerel that salts of uranium emit spontaneously a radiation with penetrating properties akin to those of x-rays, such as the ability to affect a photographic plate even when it is wrapped in black paper or thin sheets of metal. In the subsequent investigation of the phenomenon of radioactivity, many of the most famous physicists of the age were involved, including Becquerel himself, Roentgen (the discoverer of x-rays), Pierre and Marie Curie, Rutherford, and many others.

The emissions from radioactive nuclei were classified into three categories, which were labeled alpha, beta, and gamma (α, β, and γ) rays. By studying the deflections of these particles in electric and magnetic fields, it was shown that α rays consist of a stream of particles having a mass of 4 amu and a charge of $+2e$. Subsequent work has shown conclusively that these particles are identical with the nuclei of helium atoms.

By similar techniques the β rays were identified as high-energy electrons. It was discovered early that they have considerably greater penetrating power than α particles and can pass through thin sheets of metal, whereas α particles are stopped even by a few centimeters of air at ordinary pressures. The nature of γ rays was in doubt for a considerable time; it was discovered that they are not deflected by electric or magnetic fields, and so they cannot be charged particles. It has now been established definitely that they are quanta of electromagnetic radiation, similar to x-rays but usually with higher energies. The penetrating power of γ rays of energies typical of nuclear disintegrations is much greater than that of α or β rays with comparable energies.

Why should heavy nuclei be unstable? We recall that, because of the saturating property of nuclear forces, the average binding energy per nucleon is nearly independent of the total nucleon number A, so that the total attractive potential energy due to the nuclear force is approximately proportional to A. Conversely, however, the electrical repulsions of the particles continue to increase with Z, the atomic number. In fact, since each proton experiences an electrical repulsion due to *all* the other protons, the *total* electrostatic potential energy increases approximately as Z^2. Thus it is not surprising that, as the number of particles in the nucleus increases, a point is finally reached where the electrostatic repulsion with its longer range and lack of saturation overcomes the short-range saturating attractive nuclear forces. The critical point comes at $A = 210$; there are no known stable nuclei with mass numbers greater than this.

Why should an unstable nucleus emit an α particle? Why not individual protons or neutrons? Although there is no one-sentence answer to this question, the explanation is to be found in the peculiar stability of the α-particle structure. Just as two protons and two neutrons in this bound state can have considerably less total energy than when they are all separated, so it is energetically more favorable for an unstable nucleus to emit this combination of particles bound together than an individual particle. In fact, there is reason to believe that even in stable nuclei there is a short-range correlation among the various particles which can be described in terms of groups of particles resembling α particles in their structure.

On this basis, one may think of α emission, often called α *decay*, as a process in which an α particle within the nucleus moves about under the average influence of the other nucleons; associated with this interaction is a potential-energy function which varies with its distance r from the center of mass of the other nucleons in the general way shown in Fig. 12-5a. At sufficiently great distances r, so that the nuclear force is no longer effective, the potential varies as $1/r$, characteristic of the electrostatic repulsion. But at sufficiently small r, when the nuclear forces become operative, the potential energy must decrease, corresponding to an attractive interaction; otherwise the α particle would not be bound even temporarily.

Assuming this generally plausible form for the interaction potential energy, we picture an α particle as trapped in the central potential well. In terms of classical mechanics, there is no way for it to escape from this well except by somehow acquiring enough additional energy to surmount the potential-energy barrier, and so there is no way to understand α emission on the basis of classical mechanics. Quantum

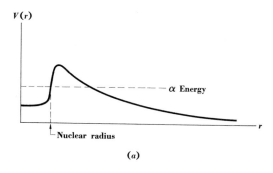

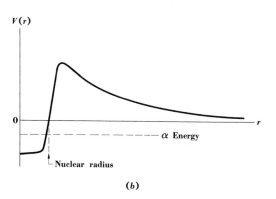

Fig. 12-5 (a) *General form of the α-particle potential-energy function in a heavy unstable nucleus. Quantum mechanics predicts that there is a certain probability that the particle will be found outside the potential well, despite the fact that classical mechanics provides no way for it to escape from the well.* (b) *In a stable nucleus, the α-particle energy in the potential well is less than it is outside, and α emission is energetically impossible.*

mechanics, however, provides a natural explanation for α decay. In fact, when the theory of α emission was developed in 1928 it was regarded as an important confirmation of the newly born quantum mechanics. At a potential-energy barrier, beyond which the particle cannot pass according to classical mechanics, the wave function for the particle does not drop suddenly to zero but rather decreases asymptotically to zero. That is, there is some *penetration* of the wave function into regions which classically would be described as regions of negative kinetic energy, just as in the situations discussed in Sec. 7-4.

Thus if the wave function of the particle is initially confined entirely within the potential well, there is a certain finite probability at any time that it will be found *outside* this potential well, despite the fact that classically there is no way for it to get out. This effect has been described pictorially as "tunneling," referring to the fact that the particle, in a manner of speaking, tunnels through the potential barrier rather than climbing over it. This general point of view regarding α emission can be developed into a detailed theory, and α emission by nuclei is now fairly well understood.

When a nucleus emits an α particle, the neutron number N and the charge number Z both decrease by 2, and the total nucleon number A by 4. For example, a nucleus of radium, $_{88}\text{Ra}^{226}$, emits an α particle and becomes a nucleus of radon, $_{86}\text{Rn}^{222}$. This in turn emits another α particle and becomes a nucleus of polonium, $_{84}\text{Po}^{218}$. A different series contains, as one of its elements, actinium, $_{89}\text{Ac}^{225}$. This emits an α, decaying into francium, $_{87}\text{Fr}^{221}$, which decays into astatine, $_{85}\text{At}^{217}$, which decays into bismuth, $_{83}\text{Bi}^{213}$, and so on.

The radioactive-decay process in which an electron (a β ray) is emitted, usually called β *decay*, seems even harder to understand than α decay, since it has already been concluded that there are no electrons in the nucleus. We are forced to assume that somehow the constituent particles of the nucleus are transformed so that an electron is produced. The simplest assumption is that a neutron is converted into an electron and a proton:

$$n \rightarrow p + e \tag{12-19}$$

Investigation of the masses as given by Eqs. (12-11) shows that this is a possibility, since the neutron mass is greater than the proton mass by 0.00134 amu, whereas the electron mass is only 0.00055 amu. However, in this process it would be impossible to conserve angular momentum, inasmuch as all three particles have spin ½; the proton and electron each can have a component of angular momentum of $\pm\frac{1}{2}$ in a given direction, implying that the neutron initially had a component of zero or ± 1, which disagrees with the observed spin of ½ for the neutron.

The way out of this dilemma was shown by Pauli, who postulated that a third particle is produced in the process, a particle having no electrical charge and therefore not readily observable. Such a particle could carry away energy, momentum, and angular momentum. This particle was christened the *neutrino*, the Italian equivalent of "little neutral one." Thus, using the symbol ν for a neutrino, we tentatively describe the β-decay reaction as

$$n \rightarrow p + e + \nu \tag{12-20}$$

The angular-momentum considerations just mentioned indicate the neutrino must have spin ½. Investigations of the energy and momentum relationships for this reaction suggested that the neutrino, if it exists, has zero rest mass and therefore an energy-momentum relationship given simply by $E = pc$. This is the same energy-momentum relationship as that for the photon, which, however, is a quite different particle, with

different angular momentum and other properties.   It has become cus-
tomary to call the new particle in the right side of Eq. (12-20) an *anti-neutrino* ($\bar{\nu}$).   The neutrino will be discussed in more detail in Chap. 13.

The process of transforming one particle into several others, described rather glibly above, is a new concept.   We are accustomed to
processes which *rearrange* particles, combining or separating them, but
here is a process in which particles are actually *created* and *destroyed.*
There are, in fact, many examples of such processes; we have already
seen one of them, the creation and destruction of *photons* in electromagnetic interactions.   The principles underlying the creation and destruction of particles will be discussed in more detail in Chap. 13.

The production of γ rays (high-energy photons) in radioactive disintegrations is not very surprising.   Just as atoms have various energy
levels corresponding to different electron configurations, it is perfectly
reasonable to suppose that nuclei also have various energy levels.   If an
unstable nucleus undergoes a radioactive disintegration, the residual
nucleus may be left not in its ground state but in an excited state.   In
some cases, it may then decay to the ground state with the emission of a
photon.   As we have seen, energies associated with nuclear interactions
are typically of the order of several Mev, in contrast to energies associated with atomic interactions, typically of the order of a few electron
volts.   Thus the energies of typical γ-ray photons are much larger than
for visible light or x-rays.

We have referred briefly to the existence of radioactive decay series,
in which a succession of decays occurs.   Such decay series, as well as
various other phenomena involving nuclear reactions, are conveniently
representd by means of a chart called a Segre chart, named for its inventor Emilio Segre, a collaborator of Fermi.   In this chart, the atomic
number Z is plotted on the horizontal axis, and the neutron number N
on the vertical axis.   Any nuclide is represented on this chart by a point
whose coordinates are the number of protons and the number of neutrons, respectively.   Nuclides having the same mass number $A = N + Z$
lie along diagonal lines oriented at $45°$.

Figure 12-6c shows the uranium decay series as represented on a
Segre chart.   In any α-decay transition, N and Z each decrease by 2, and
the transition is represented by a diagonal line as shown.   Similarly, any
transition corresponding to β decay, in which Z increases by 1 and N
decreases by 1, is also represented by a diagonal line.   The first element
in this particular series that occurs in nature is U^{238}; the final member
of the chain, that is, the only one that does not undergo further radio-

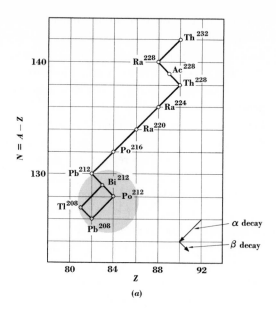

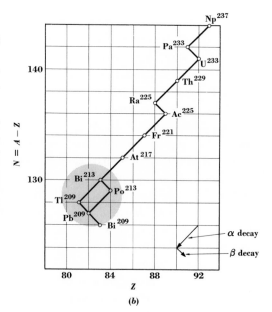

Fig. 12-6 *Segre chart showing four decay series. (a) Thorium decay series; (b) neptunium decay series; (c) uranium decay series; (d) actinium decay series. In each series, A decreases in steps of r. Each nuclide in the thorium series has A = 4n, where n is an integer. Each nuclide in the neptunium series has A = 4n + 1, each in the uranium series A = 4n + 2, and each in the actinium series A = 4n + 3. Branching occurs at least once in each series.*

active decay, is Pb^{206}. An interesting feature of this chart is the branching at Bi^{214}, which decays into Pb^{210} by an α and a β decay which can occur in either order, as shown.

Three other decay series are known. Two of them, starting with thorium 232 and uranium 235, respectively, occur in nature; the other,

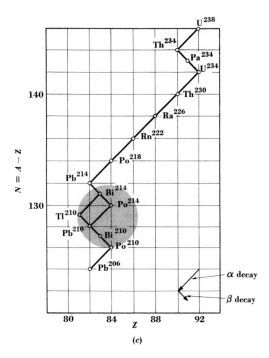

(c)

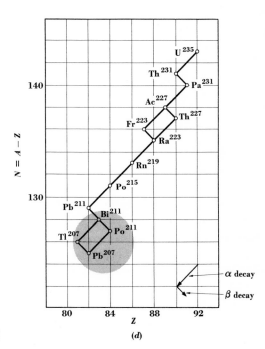

Fig. 12-6 *Continued*   (d)

starting with neptunium 237, begins with nuclei produced artificially in nuclear reactors, by means of processes to be discussed in Sec. 12-6. In most cases, α or β decay leaves the residual nucleus in an excited state rather than the ground state, and so α or β emission is often followed by emission of one or more γ-ray photons. These decay series are also shown in Fig. 12-6.

Another interesting feature of the decay series illustrated in Fig. 12-6 is that they indicate the existence of unstable isotopes of nuclei which also have stable isotopes. For example, Pb^{206} is stable, but Pb^{210} and Pb^{214} are unstable, containing four and eight more neutrons, respectively, than the stable isotope. This phenomenon occurs not only with heavy nuclei but with practically *all* nuclei. For any given number of protons, there is a certain optimum number of neutrons for maximum stability. This balance between numbers of protons and neutrons needed for a stable structure can be understood at least qualitatively on the basis of saturation of nuclear forces and the Coulomb repulsion of protons. If there were no electrostatic effects, the most stable nuclei would be those containing equal numbers of protons and neutrons, paired off into α-like structures. This actually occurs for the light elements, such as the stable nuclides $_2He^4$, $_6C^{12}$, $_8O^{16}$, $_{10}Ne^{20}$, $_{12}Mg^{24}$, $_{14}Si^{28}$, $_{16}S^{32}$, and $_{18}Ar^{36}$. An interesting exception is $_4Be^8$, which is *not* stable.

With increasing A, the repulsive electrical interactions become relatively more important, and the most stable structure for a given Z contains a few *more* neutrons than protons. The value of N needed for maximum stability is shown as a function of Z in Fig. 12-7. As this figure shows, any nucleus containing either too many or too few neutrons for its number of protons is not stable. An example is the radioactive nuclide Co^{60}, which contains one more neutron than the stable Co^{59}, and undergoes β decay into the stable nuclide Ni^{60}.

Another example, and one which introduces a new feature, is the unstable nuclide Na^{22}. The stable isotope of sodium has $A = 23$, so that Na^{22}, comparatively speaking, has one neutron too few—just the opposite difficulty from that of Co^{60}. One is tempted to think that, if there were such a thing as a positive electron, this nucleus would undergo decay in which it emits a positive electron, thereby decreasing Z and increasing N by one unit each. The resultant nucleus would be Ne^{22}, which is stable. As a matter of fact, this is precisely what happens. Positive electrons do exist; they were first discovered in cosmic rays in 1932 by the American physicist Carl Anderson. They do not have a permanent existence, since whenever a positive electron collides with an

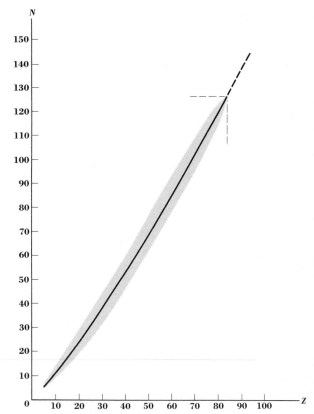

*Fig. 12-7 Graph
showing values of N
for maximum stability,
as a function of Z.
All stable nuclei fall
within the shaded area
shown.*

ordinary electron, both particles disappear and γ rays are produced. The properties of positive electrons will be discussed in more detail in Sec. 13-2. A nuclear disintegration in which a positive electron is produced is referred to as β^+ emission. Commonly, however, *β decay* is taken to mean emission of either an ordinary (negative) electron or a positive electron, also called *positron*.

An interesting variation of the β-decay process occurs with nuclei having too few neutrons for stability but insufficient energy to make β^+ emission possible. In some such cases it is energetically possible for a nucleus to *capture* an orbital electron from one of the inner shells, transforming a proton in the nucleus into a neutron according to the scheme

$$p + e^- \rightarrow n + \nu$$

Usually the residual nucleus is in an excited state, and one or more γ photons are emitted in addition to the neutrino. Because electrons in the K shell, being closest to the nucleus, are most likely to be captured, this decay mode is called *K capture;* the more general term *orbital-electron capture* is also used.   An example of this process is

$$_4\text{Be}^7 + e^- \rightarrow _3\text{Li}^7 + \nu$$

If a *K* electron is absorbed by the Be nucleus, the result is an Li atom with the proper number of electrons, but in a *K* x-ray energy state.

It is of interest to examine the *rates* at which nuclear decay processes take place.   Energies involved in nuclear interactions are so large compared with those associated with thermal agitation, photons of visible light, and other ordinary influences that rates of nuclear decays are very nearly independent of their environment.   If at times *t* there are *N* radioactive nuclei, then the number of decays occurring in a short time interval following this time, say Δt, is expected to be proportional to *N* and to the time interval.   That is,

$$\Delta N = -\lambda N \Delta t \tag{12-21}$$

or, in the limit as Δt approaches zero,

$$\frac{dN}{dt} = -\lambda N \tag{12-22}$$

where λ is a constant characteristic of the decay process for a given nuclide, called the *decay constant* for the process.

If there are N_0 nuclei at time $t = 0$, the number $N(t)$ at any later time *T* can be found by integrating this differential equation.   This is most easily accomplished by separating variables and integrating both sides directly, as follows:

$$\int_{N_0}^{N} \frac{dN}{N} = \int_{0}^{t} -\lambda \, dt$$

$$\ln \frac{N}{N_0} = -\lambda t \tag{12-23}$$

$$N = N_0 e^{-\lambda t}$$

On both sides of the first equation, the lower limits represent the initial values of *N* and *t*, respectively, and the upper limits the final values. The number of nuclei surviving at time *t* decreases exponentially from the initial value N_0 and asymptotically approaches zero after a very long time.

The decay rate of a nucleus can also be characterized by the *half-life,* which is defined as the time required for the number of nuclei to decrease by a factor of 2.   Clearly, the half-life is closely related to the decay constant λ in Eqs. (12-23).   To obtain the relationship, we observe that the time $T_{1/2}$ at which the number of nuclei has decayed to $\frac{1}{2}N_0$ is given by

$$\frac{1}{2}N_0 = N_0 e^{-\lambda T_{1/2}} \tag{12-24}$$

from which we find

$$T_{1/2} = \frac{\ln 2}{\lambda} = \frac{0.693}{\lambda} \tag{12-25}$$

Half-lives observed for decay processes cover an extremely wide range, from the shortest time intervals that can be measured in the laboratory (of the order of 10^{-11} sec) to at least 10^{15} years.

An interesting practical application of radioactivity which has been developed in recent years is the dating of archeological specimens by means of the content of a long-lived radioactive isotope of carbon, C^{14}, which the specimens contain. This unstable isotope of carbon, with a half-life of 5,568 years, is produced in the atmosphere by bombardment of N^{14} nuclei by cosmic rays. Living plants and animals which obtain their carbon from carbon dioxide in the atmosphere contain C^{14} in the same proportion as it is found in the atmosphere. When the organism dies, the intake of C^{14} stops, and the C^{14} that has already been deposited decays, with a half-life of 5,568 years. Thus by measuring the relative concentrations of C^{14} and C^{12} in the remains of a once-living organism, one can deduce how long ago it died. This technique has been of great importance in recent years in evaluating archeological research. Similar techniques with several other isotopes are used in dating rock formations.

In radioactive decay chains, several successive decay processes proceed simultaneously; as a nucleus in the chain decays, it is replenished simultaneously by decay from the previous member in the chain. In each case, the rate of decay of a given element in the chain is proportional to the amount of that element present, with a different characteristic decay constant for each. Finding the number of nuclei of each element in the chain as functions of time requires solution of a set of simultaneous differential equations, one for each element in the chain. Although the details of this calculation are more complicated than the simple case discussed here, the statistical description of the decay rate in terms of the number of nuclei present and the decay constant is exactly the same.

Finally, in concluding this brief discussion of unstable nuclei we remark that the study of the various kinds of instabilities provides valuable insight into the *stability* of those nuclei that do *not* undergo decay processes. To be stable, a nucleus must satisfy several criteria, including stability against the possibilities of both α and β emission, as discussed above. Another possibility is a decay in which the nucleus splits into two or more pieces in a process called *fission*. For a stable nucleus this too must be energetically impossible. Fission will be discussed in more detail in Sec. 12-6.

12-4   *Instruments of Nuclear Physics*

In this section we shall survey very briefly some of the instruments used for research in nuclear physics. They fall into two categories: techniques for observing particles and measuring their properties, and instruments for accelerating charged particles to high velocities for use in collision experiments.

Historically speaking, the earliest means for detecting the presence of particles was photographic emulsion. Photographic plates were responsible for the discovery of both x-rays and radioactivity in the last decade of the nineteenth century. A photographic emulsion consists of a suspension of a silver halide in a gel, which is dried after preparation. The silver halides have the property that when exposed to any kind of ionizing radiation, either photons or charged particles of sufficiently high energies, the molecules are excited to metastable states; this makes them susceptible to a chemical reaction in which the silver ions are reduced by a developing solution to metallic silver, which because of its colloidal nature appears black. This process is used in practically all ordinary black-and-white photography.

When a charged particle passes through an emulsion, it loses energy along the way, leaving a track which, when developed, shows as a black line along the trajectory of the particle. Furthermore, the blackness of the line depends on the rate at which the particle is losing energy, which in turn depends only on its speed and charge. Thus detailed examination of tracks on photographic emulsions provides information about not only the trajectory of the particle but also its speed and therefore its energy. Even more detailed information can be obtained if, during the passage of the particle through the emulsion, a magnetic field is imposed. When a particle with mass m and charge q moves with a speed v perpendicular to a uniform magnetic field **B**, the field exerts a force perpendicular to the direction of the velocity, resulting in a circular trajectory whose radius R is given by

$$R = \frac{mv}{qB} \tag{12-26}$$

provided the speed is sufficiently small that relativistic considerations do not enter.[1] Appropriate corrections can be made for relativistic speeds. Thus, if the charge of the particle is known, detailed observations of the trace in a photographic emulsion, under the influence of a magnetic field, can be used to determine both its energy and momentum and thus its mass. Although this technique is the oldest of all methods of detecting radiation, it is still of great importance, especially in cosmic-ray work and the search for new particles.

Another general category of devices for observing particles employs a phenomenon called *scintillation*. Various materials, when bombarded by charged particles or high-energy electromagnetic photons, absorb energy through excitation of electronic energy levels and subsequently reradiate this energy as visible light. The phenomenon is very similar in principle to that of fluorescence, in which a material exposed to ultraviolet radiation emits visible light of a color that is nearly independent of the wavelength of the initial radiation. In the early twentieth century, thin sheets were coated with fluorescent materials and used to detect beams of x-rays, α particles, and other radiation. More recently, it has been discovered that for some kinds of radiation certain transparent crystals are more efficient scintillators. Present-day scintillation counters typically use a transparent crystal, often an alkali halide or one of various organic materials, in conjunction with a vacuum phototube or a similar device called a photomultiplier, both of which operate on the principle of the photoelectric effect discussed in Chap. 5. These are used to generate an electrical pulse in an external circuit resulting from the passage of ionizing radiation through the scintillation crystal. These so-called *scintillation counters* are used both with γ photons and with charged particles.

Another general class of particle detectors makes direct use of the ionizing property of energetic charged particles. These devices had their genesis with the observation that a charge electroscope placed in the vicinity of a radioactive material gradually becomes discharged; α and β particles produce ions in the surrounding air, thereby increasing its conductivity and permitting the charge of the electroscope to leak off. One of the most commonly used forms of ionization detectors is the Geiger-Müller tube, shown in Fig. 12-8. Two electrodes are sealed in a glass tube containing any one of various gases under low pressure, and a potential difference is applied between the electrodes. The potential difference is adjusted so that it is not large enough to initiate a glow dis-

---

[1] *Ibid.*, sec. 8-5.

Fig. 12-8   *Schematic diagram of a Geiger tube used for the detection of charged particles. If the voltage V is sufficiently large, a charged particle which creates ions in the gas between the electrodes initiates an ion avalanche that results in a pulse of current in the circuit, nearly independent of the initial amount of ionization. If V is reduced sufficiently so that the avalanche effect does not occur, the voltage pulses are much smaller, but they are then proportional to the initial ionization, which is directly related to the particle energy and may be used to measure energy.*

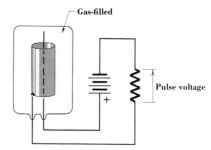

charge in the tube.   When a charged particle passes through, it creates a number of ions which are accelerated under the action of the potential difference.   Some of these ions acquire enough kinetic energy before their first collision so that further ionization is produced by collision. The result is an avalanche effect, in which many more ions are produced than those resulting from the original charged particle.   Because of the electrode configuration, the electric field is more intense near the central wire electrode than elsewhere; the avalanche effect occurs only in a region relatively close to this electrode, and so the discharge does not continue indefinitely.   Again, the result is an electrical pulse in the external circuit, which can be used to trigger any of various electronic devices that count pulses.   There are many variations on this basic theme, some of which are constructed in such a way that they can also be used to measure particle energies.

More recently, instruments have been made which operate on a principle similar to that of the Geiger counter but use solid-state devices instead.   The use of semiconductors as photocells was mentioned in Sec. 11-6.   Similarly, semiconductor devices may be used as detectors of radiation, and by proper design it is possible to produce avalanche effects exactly analogous to those in the Geiger counter.   Because of their versatility, reliability, and mechanical ruggedness, solid-state particle detectors are used increasingly in nuclear physics research.

Still another class of devices for observing particles shares with photographic emulsion the possibility of observing the *trajectory* of a particle, not simply its presence in a device. One of these is a *cloud chamber,* which makes use of a chamber containing a vapor which can be supercooled, that is, cooled below the temperature at which it would ordinarily begin to condense. Condensation of a vapor into the liquid phase always involves a phenomenon called nucleation, associated with the fact that a droplet of pure liquid must attain a certain critical size to be thermodynamically stable. The formation of droplets out of the vapor phase is facilitated by the presence of irregularities such as dust particles or ions, which serve as "nucleation centers." Thus, when a charged particle passes through a supercooled vapor, it provides along its path a series of nucleation centers, around which the vapor begins to condense. Visually, the effect is of a thin cloudy streak in an otherwise transparent vapor. As with photographic emulsions, a magnetic field can be used to produce curvature of the paths, and the energy and momentum of the particle can be measured. The trajectories can be recorded photographically, and present-day cloud chambers often use stereoscopic photography to record a three-dimensional picture.

A related device operating on the same general principle is the bubble chamber, which uses a superheated liquid, often liquid hydrogen or propane, rather than a supercooled vapor. The passage of a charged particle through the liquid creates nucleation centers which become small bubbles of vapor; hence the particle produces a track of vapor bubbles in an otherwise transparent liquid. Bubble chambers have one great advantage over cloud chambers in experiments where the incident particle collides with another particle in the chamber; the matter in a bubble chamber is ordinarily much more dense than that in a cloud chamber, and collisions are much more likely. A typical bubble chamber is shown in Fig. 12-9.

All these methods make use of the fact that the particle being detected has an electrical charge. Thus none of these devices is directly usable for detecting *neutral* particles such as neutrons or neutrinos. Neutrons are most commonly detected by means of a nuclear reaction in which the neutron is absorbed by a nucleus, which then emits a charged particle. An example is boron 10, which absorbs a neutron and emits an α particle, according to the reaction

$$_5B^{10} + n \rightarrow {}_2He^4 + {}_3Li^7 \tag{12-27}$$

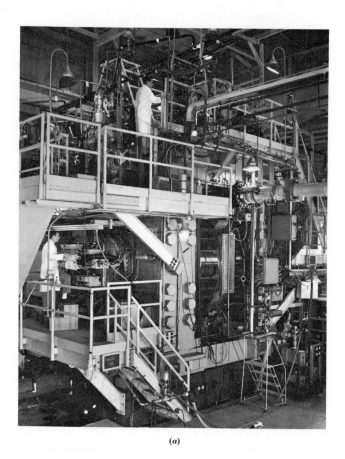

(a)

Fig. 12-9 (a) A
hydrogen bubble
chamber. (b) Photo-
graph made with this
bubble chamber.
Several particle tra-
jectories can be seen.
(c) Diagram identifying
some of the trajectories
in the photograph.
Broken lines show
trajectories of neutral
particles, which leave
no tracks.

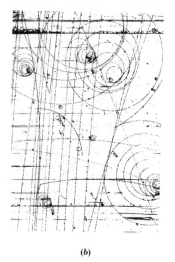

(b)

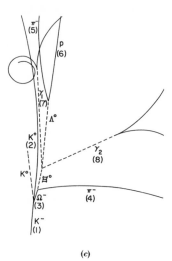

(c)

The charged particles that result can be detected by any of the means outlined above. Detecting neutrinos is much more difficult, since they interact only very weakly with other particles. To observe their very unlikely collisions with other particles, it is necessary to build scintillation counters of heroic dimensions, several meters on a side.

In the early days of nuclear physics, experiments involving collisions of particles with nuclei always made use of particles emitted by naturally radioactive nuclei. Using these sources, however, imposes a severe limitation on the variety of experiments that can be performed, particularly with respect to the upper limits of energies available from nuclear disintegrations, typically 1 to 5 Mev. Various devices have been developed which accelerate charged particles to energies much larger than any available from natural radioactivity and which can be controlled precisely. In some of these machines, the particles are simply accelerated in a straight line; in others they are accelerated in a circular or other closed path.

In the former category, the class of machines known as *linear accelerators*, the original model was an ordinary x-ray tube, in which electrons are accelerated by a large potential difference, producing x-rays when they strike the target anode. These high-energy electrons can be used for various other kinds of experiments in which such electrons can be useful. By a simple modification, such a machine can be made to accelerate protons, α particles, or other charged particles. All that need be added is a source of ions, which in the case of hydrogen might be supplied simply by a source of hydrogen gas with an electric arc to ionize it. Since an α particle has twice the charge of a proton, accelerating an α particle through a potential difference of 50,000 volts produces an α-particle energy of 100,000 ev. Even so, the energy limitation of this type of accelerator is determined by the maximum dc potential difference that can be developed. For reasons associated with the technology of rectifiers, dielectric breakdown problems, and so on, this is usually limited to the order of 1,000,000 volts.

Larger potential differences can be developed by using electrostatic machines, such as a Van de Graaff generator, with which potential differences greater than 10^6 volts can be obtained. A Van de Graaff accelerator built by Westinghouse Electric Corp. near Pittsburgh was used for the first experiments in which bombardment of nuclei with high-energy protons actually resulted in changes in the structure of the nuclei.

A variation of the linear accelerator which makes possible great increases in maximum energy is shown schematically in Fig. 12-10. The accelerating electrodes are shaped in the form of tubes, and alternate

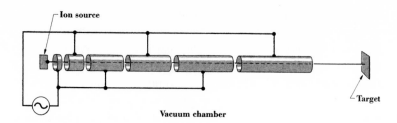

Fig. 12-10 *A linear accelerator. The alternating-voltage source reverses polarity in synchronism with the passage of bursts of particles through successive electrodes, so that they are accelerated at each gap. The entire electrode configuration and ion source are enclosed in a vacuum chamber to prevent collision of particles with air molecules.*

electrodes are connected to the two poles of an alternating potential difference, as shown. Within each tube, there is essentially no electric field; the potential differences and therefore the fields appear chiefly in the gaps between electrodes, and so these are the regions where acceleration occurs. It is possible to arrange the polarities so that a particle is accelerated in the first gap and then, while it is within the second electrode, to reverse the polarity so that it is accelerated again at the second gap. By properly timing the reversals of polarity, the particle can be given an additional push at each gap. Thus, if the accelerating potential is 100 kv and there are 10 gaps, the total energy is 1 Mev. One practical way of achieving the synchronization is to make the potential difference a periodically varying function, often simply sinusoidal, and to make successive electrodes longer and longer, so that the particle spends equal times in successive electrodes. A new linear accelerator at Stanford University accelerates particles to energies of 20×10^9 ev = 20 Bev, where Bev stands for *billion electron volts*. This machine is about 2 miles long.

Still another class of machines uses a uniform magnetic field to make a charged particle move in a circular path. A typical *cyclotron* is shown schematically in Fig. 12-11. As pointed out in Eq. (12-26), the radius of curvature of the path of a particle is proportional to its speed, and so the angular velocity

$$\omega = \frac{v}{R} = \frac{qB}{m} \tag{12-28}$$

is independent of radius. Between the magnet poles is a vacuum cham-

Fig. 12-11 *Schematic diagram of a cyclotron. The accelerating electric field which appears across the gap between the dees is periodically reversed by the alternating-voltage source, in synchronism with the charged particles moving in arcs of circles. As they gain energy, the particles spiral outward until they reach the outer edge of the magnetic field, when they fly off at tangents. The dees are enclosed in a vacuum chamber, not shown.*

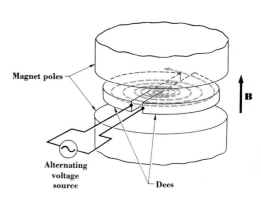

ber enclosing two D-shaped electrodes, called *dees*. An accelerating potential is applied between these two dees, just as in the linear accelerator. The polarity of this voltage is reversed twice each cycle, so that each time a particle arrives at the gap between the dees it is accelerated and moves into a segment of a circular orbit of slightly larger radius than previously. Correspondingly, at each passing of a gap it acquires an energy equal to the potential difference between the dees. The cyclotron was invented in 1932 by E. O. Lawrence of the University of California (Berkeley) and almost immediately was used to produce energies of several million electron volts, considerably larger than any that had been obtained previously. Since then, cyclotrons have been built which accelerate protons to about 20 Mev.

The fundamental limitation on the operation of an ordinary cyclotron is a relativistic effect. Relativistically, the momentum of a particle is given not simply by $m\mathbf{v}$ but by

$$\mathbf{p} = \frac{m\mathbf{v}}{\sqrt{1 - v^2/c^2}} \tag{12-29}$$

The orbit radius becomes

$$R = \frac{mv}{qB\sqrt{1 - v^2/c^2}} \tag{12-30}$$

and the angular velocity

$$\omega = \frac{v}{R} = \frac{qB}{m}\sqrt{1 - \frac{v^2}{c^2}} \tag{12-31}$$

Thus ω is no longer constant but *decreases* as the particle energy increases. To compensate for this, the frequency of the oscillator supplying the potential difference to the dees must be decreased in synchronization with the acceleration of the particles. This frequency variation is carried out in a cyclic manner, so that the particles are accelerated in bunches rather than continuously. A machine having this modification is called a *synchrocyclotron* (see Fig. 12-12); the largest such machine yet built accelerates protons to an energy of about 700 Mev.

For larger energies it would be necessary to make an electromagnet so huge as to be prohibitively expensive. Another type of accelerator has been developed in which the radius of the orbit is constant but the magnetic field is increased as the particle speeds increase. Thus the magnets must establish a magnetic field only in a ring-shaped region,

Fig. 12-12   *Part of the 450-Mev synchrocyclotron at Carnegie-Mellon University. The large cylindrical surfaces are the covers for the magnet coils, surrounding the magnet pole pieces. The vacuum chamber is between the poles; one panel of the vacuum chamber has been removed, and the interior of the chamber can be seen.*

not over an entire disk as in the case of the cyclotron. Correspondingly, the vacuum chamber need not be a large disk but can be a doughnut-shaped enclosure. Such a machine is called a *synchrotron*. The magnetic field and the accelerating electric field are varied periodically to keep pace with a certain group of particles, so that the particles are again accelerated in bunches rather than continuously.

The first two synchrotrons built in the United States were the bevatron (6.2 Bev) at the University of California in Berkeley and the cosmotron (3.0 Bev) at Brookhaven National Laboratory. The two highest-energy synchrotrons now in operation are at Brookhaven National Laboratory in New York (33 Bev), shown in Fig. 12-13, and at CERN (European Council for Nuclear Research) in Geneva, Switzerland. The United States Atomic Energy Commission is planning a

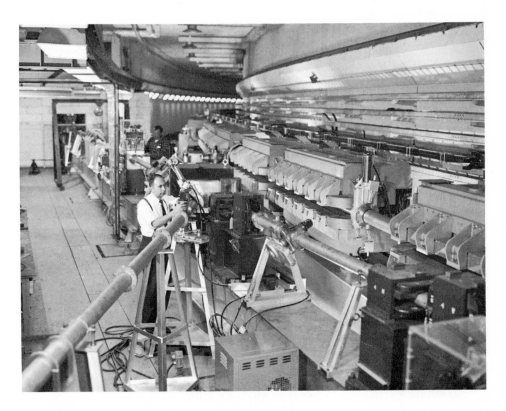

Fig. 12-13 *Part of the 33-Bev alternating-gradient synchrotron (AGS) at Brookhaven National Laboratory on Long Island, New York. (Photo courtesy of Brookhaven National Laboratory.)*

200-Bev machine, to be built near Weston, Illinois. Construction of this machine is tentatively planned to begin in 1968 and will require about 6 years. The estimated total cost is $350,000,000.

Still higher-energy machines are contemplated, and the practical limit for this kind of machine is not yet in sight. It should be pointed out, however, that the definition of "practical limit" has been drastically altered in the past 20 years. In the early days of nuclear physics an expenditure of $1,000 for physics laboratory equipment was a sizable investment; nowadays a high-energy accelerator costs many millions of dollars. This shift in viewpoint reflects a rapidly changing attitude of society as to the importance of scientific research.

It is not evident from the above discussion of high-energy particle accelerators *why* it is of interest to produce particles with such high energies. The reasons for this interest will emerge in the following section and in Chap. 13.

12-5   *Nuclear Reactions*

A nuclear reaction is any encounter between nuclei or between a nucleus and a particle that results in a rearrangement of their constituent parts. The term *reaction* is used in the same sense as in chemical reactions, in which molecules of two substances are changed into molecules of other substances by rearrangement of their constituent parts (atoms). The same notations are used in both cases. If nucleus A is bombarded by an α particle, resulting in the formation of a new nucleus B and a proton, the reaction is symbolized by the equation

$$A + \alpha \rightarrow B + p \tag{12-32}$$

Various schemes are used for labeling protons, neutrons, and α particles:

$$
\begin{aligned}
&\text{Proton} = p = {}_1p^1 \\
&\text{Neutron} = n = {}_0n^1 \\
&\text{Alpha} = \alpha = {}_2\text{He}^4 \\
&\text{Electron} = \beta^- = {}_{-1}e^0 \\
&\text{Positron} = \beta^+ = {}_1e^0
\end{aligned}
\tag{12-33}
$$

There are several *conservation laws* which are believed to be obeyed universally in all nuclear reactions.[1] Some of them are identical with

---

[1] This is not to imply that violation of any of these rules is entirely outside the realm of possibility. But at the present time there is no evidence for the violation of any of these laws, and it seems very likely that they are universally applicable.

corresponding principles of classical mechanics and electrodynamics; others are unique to nuclear physics. In the former category are conservation of energy (including energies associated with mass), momentum, angular momentum, and electric charge. In the latter category is the conservation of the number of nucleons. That is, there is no reaction in which a proton disappears unless a neutron appears in its place, and conversely.

Reactions are classified as *exothermic* or *endothermic*, according to whether the final total kinetic energy is greater than or less than the initial total kinetic energy. Just as an exothermic chemical reaction is one that evolves heat, an exothermic nuclear reaction is one that "evolves" kinetic energy. An increase in total kinetic energy must be accompanied by a corresponding decrease in total mass. If M_1 is the *total* initial mass of all reacting particles, M_2 the total final mass, T_1 the initial total kinetic energy, and T_2 the final total kinetic energy, then conservation of energy requires that

$$T_1 + M_1c^2 = T_2 + M_2c^2 \tag{12-34}$$

In any endothermic reaction, there is always a certain minimum initial kinetic energy required for the reaction to occur. This minimum is called the *threshold energy*. As a simple example of the threshold for an endothermic reaction, we consider the reaction

$$_3\text{Li}^6 + {}_2\text{He}^4 \rightarrow {}_4\text{Be}^9 + {}_1p^1 \tag{12-35}$$

produced by bombarding a solid lithium target with α particles.

Reference to a table of nuclear masses shows that the total mass on the left side is

6.01513 amu + 4.00260 amu = 10.01773 amu

while that on the right side is

9.01219 amu + 1.00782 amu = 10.02001 amu

Thus the final mass is greater than the initial mass by 0.00228 amu. Using the conversion factor $(1 \text{ amu})c^2 = 931$ Mev, we find that the energy equivalent of this mass is 2.12 Mev. Thus the total initial kinetic energy must be greater than the total final kinetic energy by about 2.1 Mev.

It would *not* be correct to conclude from this calculation that the reaction indicated by Eq. (12-35) can be produced by bombarding a lithium target with α particles of any energy greater than 2.12 Mev.

The reason is a fundamental one and merits further discussion. The problem is that the α particle cannot give up *all* its kinetic energy in the collision; if all the final particles were at rest after the collision, conservation of *momentum* would be violated. In order to conserve momentum there must be some residual kinetic energy after the collision; thus the initial α-particle energy must be considerably *greater* than 2.12 Mev.

It is instructive to calculate in detail the relationship between the minimum kinetic energy T necessary for the reaction and the energy Q (in the present example, 2.12 Mev) obtained from the mass difference. This calculation is greatly facilitated by the use of the *center-of-mass coordinate system*,[1] a frame of reference moving with respect to the laboratory so that in this system the total momentum is zero. In this coordinate system it *is* possible for the kinetic energy after the collision to be zero, and in fact the minimum initial energy corresponds to the case when both final particles are produced with essentially zero kinetic energy. Their common final velocity with respect to the laboratory frame of reference is then simply the velocity of the center-of-mass coordinate system with respect to the laboratory system.

We now proceed with the details of the calculation. For simplicity we use nonrelativistic mechanics, justified by the fact that the kinetic energy of each particle in the present example is much smaller than its rest energy. The relativistic generalization of this formulation is straightforward but more involved in its details. We let m_1 be the mass of the bombarding particle, m_2 that of the target particle, and let their initial speeds relative to the center of mass be v_1 and v_2, respectively. Since m_2 is stationary in the laboratory coordinate system, the center-of-mass velocity has magnitude v_2, both before and after the collision, and the initial speed of m_1 in the laboratory coordinate system is $v_1 + v_2$. The situation is illustrated in Fig. 12-14.

The threshold situation, viewed in the center-of-mass system, occurs when the total initial kinetic energy is just Q, so that the two particles collide head on and are stopped completely, leaving two new particles with no appreciable kinetic energy. Thus

$$Q = \tfrac{1}{2}m_1v_1{}^2 + \tfrac{1}{2}m_2v_2{}^2 \tag{12-36}$$

Also, the total momentum is zero at all times, by definition of the center-of-mass coordinate system, and so we have the additional relationship

$$m_1v_1 = m_2v_2 \tag{12-37}$$

[1] *Ibid.*, sec. 11-3.

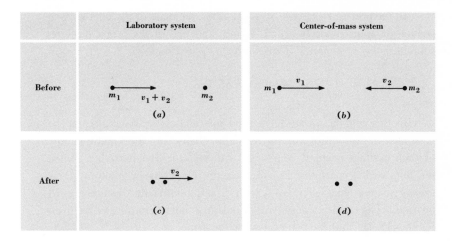

Fig. 12-14   (a) *Bombarding particle m_1 and target particle m_2 as seen in the laboratory coordinate system.* (b) *Particles as seen in the center-of-mass coordinate system.* (c) *Motion of particles with common velocity after the collision, as seen in the laboratory coordinate system.* (d) *In the center-of-mass coordinate system, both final particles are at rest after the collision.*

In the laboratory coordinate system the bombarding particle's speed is $v_1 + v_2$, and its kinetic energy T is

$$T = \tfrac{1}{2}m_1(v_1 + v_2)^2 \tag{12-38}$$

We may now use Eq. (12-37) to eliminate v_2 from Eqs. (12-36) and (12-38):

$$Q = \tfrac{1}{2}m_1\left(1 + \frac{m_1}{m_2}\right)v_1^2 \tag{12-39}$$

$$T = \tfrac{1}{2}m_1\left(1 + \frac{m_1}{m_2}\right)^2 v_1^2 \tag{12-40}$$

Finally, combining these two equations, we find

$$T = \left(1 + \frac{m_1}{m_2}\right)Q \tag{12-41}$$

which shows that the threshold kinetic energy of the bombarding particle in the laboratory coordinate system must always be greater than the threshold energy Q in the center-of-mass system, by a factor depending on the ratio of the masses.

In the previous example [Eq. (12-35)], the mass of the bombarding particle is approximately $m_1 = 4$ amu, and that of the target particle, lithium, is $m_2 = 6$ amu.   Thus we have approximately

$$T = \left(1 + \frac{4}{6}\right)(2.12 \text{ Mev}) = 3.53 \text{ Mev} \tag{12-42}$$

In this calculation we have used nonrelativistic dynamics, on the basis that the velocities are much smaller than c and the kinetic energy of each particle is small compared with mc^2 for that particle.   When the bombarding particles are high-energy electrons or photons, their speeds are *not* small compared with c, and relativistic dynamics must be used.   The resulting energy relationship is not as simple as that given by Eq. (12-41), but the principles are the same.

In experiments involving nuclear collisions and reactions, it is often useful to describe the *probability* of occurrence of a certain reaction under specified experimental conditions.   For example, many nuclear reactions are found to be more likely for certain energies of bombarding particles than for others.   The probability of occurrence of any reaction is conveniently expressed in terms of a *cross section* for the reaction, which is simply the effective target area presented by each target nucleus to the bombarding particle.   The cross section, denoted by σ, is defined by specifying that, when a target nucleus is placed in a *beam* of bombarding particles containing N particles per unit area perpendicular to the direction of the beam, the number of events (collisions, reactions, or whatever is being described) *per target nucleus* is given by $N\sigma$.

As a simple example, suppose that in the reaction described by Eq. (12-32) a beam of α particles containing 10^{10} particles/cm^2 impinges on a target whose area is 1 cm^2 and contains 10^{16} target nuclei and that 10^2 reactions are found to occur.   The probability for any one α particle to undergo a reaction is then $10^2/10^{10} = 10^{-8}$.   The probability for any one α particle to undergo a reaction with a *particular* target nucleus is $10^{-8}/10^{16} = 10^{-24}$.   Thus the effective target area per nucleus is smaller than the total target area (1 cm^2) by 10^{-24}, and the cross section for the reaction is therefore $\sigma = 10^{-24}$ cm$^2 = 10^{-28}$ m^2.

Since nuclear dimensions are typically of the order of 10^{-15} to 10^{-14} m, it is not surprising that cross sections for nuclear reactions are often of the same order of magnitude as cross-section areas of nuclei themselves.   It is convenient to introduce a unit of area called the *barn*, defined by

1 barn $= 10^{-24}$ cm$^2 = 10^{-28}$ m^2

Reaction cross sections are not necessarily related directly to the actual geometrical cross section of the nuclei participating in the reaction. For example, the cross section for the reaction

$$Be^9 + p \rightarrow Li^6 + \alpha \tag{12-43}$$

for 0.1-Mev protons is 5×10^{-5} barn, while the cross section for the neutron-capture reaction in which a cadmium nucleus absorbs a thermal neutron (a neutron whose energy is about equal to $\frac{3}{2}kT$ for the material in which it is moving) is of the order of 3,000 barns. A nucleus can have a reaction cross section much *larger* than its geometrical cross section, because particles always have wave functions that extend over considerable regions of space; the wavelength of a thermal neutron is much larger than nuclear dimensions and certainly cannot be described as a point interacting with a nucleus.

There are many cases where a particular combination of target nucleus and bombarding particle can participate in a variety of reactions, each leading to a different set of final particles and nuclei. In such cases, there is, in general, a different cross section for each reaction, and in general each cross section depends on the energy of the bombarding particle. In addition, the concept of cross section can be extended to provide a more detailed description of the characteristics of a reaction. For the same example as above, it is of interest to describe the *directions* of the emergent α particles relative to the direction of the incident proton beam; in general, some directions are more likely than others. This behavior is conveniently described by introducing a *differential cross section*, defined as the cross section $d\sigma$ per unit solid angle $d\Omega$ of emergent particle direction. This quantity is denoted by $d\sigma/d\Omega$; it is usually a function of emergent angle, bombarding particle energy, and spin orientation of bombarding and target particles.

Measurements of cross sections for nuclear reactions, as well as cross sections for various elastic scattering processes, have played an extremely important role in research in nuclear physics and, in fact, have provided the great preponderance of evidence on which present understanding of nuclear structure is based.

12-6 Fission and Fusion

We conclude this chapter with a brief discussion of two classes of nuclear reactions which, although not different in principle from those considered in the previous section, are of such importance that it is of interest to single them out for special attention.   The first is *nuclear fission*, first observed in 1939 by Hahn and Strassmann.

Nuclear fission, as the name implies, is a reaction in which a nucleus splits into two smaller nuclei.   Fission is most commonly observed with the heavy radioactive elements which can also undergo other forms of radioactive disintegration.   It is customary to distinguish between *spontaneous fission*, in which a nucleus spontaneously divides without any external stimulus, and *induced fission*, in which the fission is a result of bombardment by another particle, usually a neutron.   The most familiar element that undergoes spontaneous fission is uranium 235. There are many possible fission reactions; usually the products are two smaller nuclei called *fission fragments* and a few free neutrons; an example of a spontaneous fission is

$$_{92}U^{235} \rightarrow _{56}Ba^{140} + _{36}Kr^{93} + 2n \tag{12-44}$$

Why is fission of heavy nuclei energetically possible?   The answer is contained in Fig. 12-4, which shows that the binding energy per nucleon is less in heavy nuclei than in those of moderate size, say $A = 100$ or so.   It has already been pointed out that the electrical repulsion of protons is chiefly responsible for this decrease at large A.   The result is that a heavy nucleus can achieve a state of lower total energy (greater total binding energy) by dividing into two smaller pieces.   There are usually competing processes, particularly α and β decay; for some nuclei these are the predominant mechanisms for achieving stable structures. In some others induced fission resulting from neutron absorption is possible but the absorption cross section is very small.   However, U^{235} is one of several nuclides in which both spontaneous and induced fission are important modes of decay.

Investigation of the various nuclear masses involved shows that fission is most favorable, energetically speaking, when the two fragments are of unequal size.   Figure 12-15 shows the distribution of fission-fragment mass members from induced fission of U^{235} with thermal neutrons.   There is a strong peak in the vicinity of $A = 95$ and another around $A = 140$, and the curve is symmetric around $A = 235/2$. (Why?)

The appearance of free neutrons can be understood on a similar basis.   With increasing nuclear mass, the number of neutrons in a stable nucleus increases faster than the number of protons, as explained in Sec. 12-3 and illustrated by Fig. 12-7.   For example, for $_{26}Fe^{57}$ the neutron/proton ratio is about 1.2 while for $_{82}Pb^{206}$ it is about 1.5.   Thus when a heavy nucleus divides in two, the fragments have too many neu-

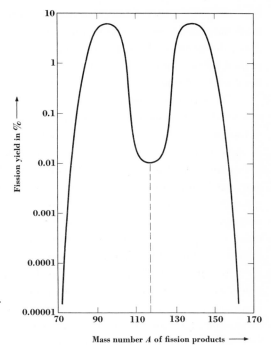

Fig. 12-15 *Graph showing the mass distribution of fission fragments from fission of* U^{235} *induced by absorption of thermal neutrons. The vertical scale is logarithmic.*

trons for stability.   The situation is adjusted in two ways: by the libera-
tion of free neutrons at the time of fission and by subsequent β decays
of the fission fragments, in which Z increases and N decreases until a
stable configuration is reached.   In the fission described by Eq. (12-44),
each fission fragment undergoes several successive β decays following
fission.   In *induced fission*, the reaction is stimulated by the absorption
by the nucleus of another particle, usually a neutron; in other respects
the reaction is similar to spontaneous fission.

One of the most interesting features of fission reactions is that the
neutrons resulting from the fission of one nucleus can, in turn, trigger
the fission of other nuclei.   On an average, each fission of a U^{235} nucleus
produces about 2.5 neutrons.   Thus, if sufficient numbers of these neutrons can be made to induce further fission, a self-sustaining *chain reaction* can occur.   The first successful chain reaction was produced in
1942 by Fermi and his collaborators at the University of Chicago.

Not all the neutrons are successful in producing further fission;
some of them escape from the region where the uranium nuclei are contained, and others participate in other reactions.   The cross section for
neutron absorption followed by fission is much larger with slow neutrons
than with energetic neutrons.   In fact, this energy dependence is so great

that ordinarily a successful chain reaction with a sample of material of moderate size is possible only when some means is provided to slow down the neutrons by collision with other nuclei before they are absorbed by uranium nuclei. This slowing down is the function of the *moderator* material in a nuclear reactor.

The chain reaction resulting from a series of nuclear fissions of the type just described is an important practical source of energy. It is of interest to compare the magnitudes of the energies involved with those in typical chemical reactions. The average kinetic energy associated with a single nuclear fission is of the order of 200 Mev; typical energies associated with combustion of ordinary fuel such as coal or gasoline are typically of the order of 10 ev per molecule, so that, on an "energy per unit mass" basis, the fission of uranium produces about 10^7 times as much energy as the burning of ordinary fuels. Fission chain reactions are also used in bombs, but perhaps the less said about them, the better.

An interesting by-product of the development of nuclear chain reactions is the development of new elements with $Z > 92$, the transuranic elements. Here is an example: U^{235} is a relatively rare isotope of uranium; the most common isotope is U^{238}, which is not readily fissionable. But if some U^{238} is included in a reactor in which U^{235} is undergoing fission, some of the U^{238} nuclei absorb neutrons, becoming U^{239}. This in turn undergoes β decay, forming a new nucleus with charge number $Z = 93$, which does not occur in nature. This new element has been named *neptunium*. It in turn undergoes another β decay into an element with $Z = 94$, *plutonium*. This series of reactions is represented symbolically as

$$_{92}U^{238} + {}_0n^1 \rightarrow {}_{92}U^{239}$$
$$_{92}U^{239} \rightarrow {}_{93}Np^{239} + \beta^- + \nu \qquad (12\text{-}45)$$
$$_{93}Np^{239} \rightarrow {}_{94}Pu^{239} + \beta^- + \nu$$

Plutonium 239 is also susceptible to fission, just as is U^{235}. Thus the effect of this series of reactions is to convert the nonfissionable U^{238} into a fissionable material which then serves as further fuel for the reactor. In such a reactor, called a *breeder reactor*, it is actually possible to produce more new fuel than is consumed.

Variations on this theme have provided a large number of additional elements which do not occur naturally on earth. Examination of the products of chain reactions in nuclear reactors has revealed the existence of elements with atomic numbers up to 104. Another amusing sidelight is the fulfillment of the alchemists' dream of transmutation of the elements. In one experiment, it was necessary to convey an extremely corrosive solution through a pipe in the presence of a high neutron flux. To avoid corrosion, the pipe was lined on the inside with gold. Alas, the gold, $_{79}Au^{197}$, absorbed neutrons and β-decayed into mercury, $_{80}Hg^{198}$, which was promptly eaten away by the solution. Such are the dreams of the philosophers!

The detailed mechanism of nuclear fission can be understood at least qualitatively on the basis of a model which is also useful in the analysis of other nuclear phenomena, the *liquid-drop model.* This model makes use of the close analogy between the binding of nucleons in a nucleus by their short-range attractive nuclear forces and the binding of molecules in a liquid by short-range attractive forces, both mainly with nearest neighbors. In both cases there are "surface-tension" effects resulting from the fact that particles near the surface of the structure are pulled toward its center by the asymmetric distribution of other particles near them.

In the absence of any disturbing influence, a drop of water is spherical; this configuration minimizes the surface-to-volume ratio and therefore the energy associated with surface tension. Similarly, heavy nuclei would be spherical if it were not for the disturbing effect of the electrical repulsion of protons. In all cases, the spherical configuration is an equilibrium state, but it may sometimes be an *unstable* equilibrium. That is, if an external influence, such as an incoming neutron, distorts the nucleus more than a certain critical amount from its spherical shape, the resulting electrical forces may be such as to tend to distort it further, to the point where it breaks in two.

A slightly more sophisticated point of view is that when the normally spherical nuclear surface is disturbed by some outside influence, the result is a wave on the surface which can be visualized as a pulsation of the surface. These pulsations increase the probability that two sections of the nucleus can separate far enough so that their electrical repulsion can overcome the nuclear attraction and push them completely apart, resulting in fission.

The inverse of nuclear fission is *nuclear fusion,* in which two light nuclei combine to form a single heavier one. Fusion reactions are exothermic only for light nuclei. A simple example is the fusion of two deuterium nuclei to form an α particle:

$$_{1}H^2 + _{1}H^2 \rightarrow _{2}He^4 + Q \tag{12-46}$$

The total mass of the two deuterium atoms is 4.02820 amu, while that of the helium atom is 4.00260 amu; thus the reaction is exothermic by 0.02560 amu, or about 23.8 Mev.

In order for fusion to occur, the two nuclei must be brought together within the range of the nuclear force, of the order of 10^{-15} m. For this to occur, the repulsive Coulomb force must be overcome; the potential energy associated with Coulomb repulsion of two charges of magnitude e at a separation of 10^{-15} m is about 1.4 Mev, and this is therefore the order of magnitude of the threshold energy (in the center-of-mass system) for fusion in the above example. One conceivable way of producing fusion reactions is somehow to make deuterium gas very hot, so that a sizable fraction of the atoms in the high-energy tail of the Maxwell-Boltzmann distribution have energies of the order of 1 Mev. Since at room temperatures ($T = 300°$K) kT is about $\frac{1}{40}$ ev, it is clear that enormously high temperatures are necessary. Temperatures of the necessary magnitude (10^6 to 10^8°K) are found in the interiors of stars; in fact, fusion reactions are believed to be entirely responsible for the energy production of stars.

In series of fusion reactions, helium nuclei and various heavier nuclei can be built up successively from individual protons and neutrons. By calculating the probabilities of various fusion reactions, it is possible to make a theoretical prediction of the relative abundance of various elements. Some physicists think of the universe as we know it as having originated as a great swarm of neutrons, from which fusion reactions and β decays led to the evolvement of heavy nuclei and electrons and thus to atoms of the various elements.

Because of the very high temperatures involved in producing fusion reactions, such reactions are also called *thermonuclear* reactions. The first man-made thermonuclear reaction occurred in the hydrogen bomb; intensive efforts are currently under way to develop controlled thermonuclear reactions that can be used for the generation of power in a manner similar to the fission reactors currently in use. Deuterium, one of the likely "fuel" materials for such a thermonuclear reactor, occurs on the earth in much greater abundance than any of the fissionable heavy elements, such as uranium, and hence potentially constitutes an energy source of enormous abundance.

PROBLEMS

12-1 Compute the approximate density of nuclear matter, and compare your result with typical densities of ordinary solid materials.

12-2 Find the mass of the electron, in amu, to three significant figures.

12-3 A mass spectrometer of the Dempster type is used to separate the two isotopes U^{235} and U^{238}. The radius of curvature of the particles is to be approximately 1 m, and the accelerating potential difference is 100 volts. Assuming the ions are singly ionized, what magnetic field B is needed?

12-4 Using the Bohr model of the hydrogen atom, find the magnetic field at the position of the nucleus resulting from the "current" associated with the moving charge. From this, together with the magnetic moment of the proton, calculate approximately the magnitude of the hyperfine splitting of energy levels resulting from the interaction of the nuclear magnetic moment with this field.

12-5 In a magnetic field $B = 1.0$ weber/m^2, what frequency is necessary for nuclear magnetic resonance with protons?

12-6 The mass of the α particle, without electrons, is 4.00151 amu. Find the total binding energy (in Mev) and the binding energy per nucleon.

12-7 How much electrical potential energy (in Mev) is required to add a proton to a nucleus with $Z = 91$ and $A = 234$?

12-8 Discuss the possibility of existence of electrons in the nucleus on the basis of the uncertainty principle. For example, for an electron to be localized in a region of nuclear dimensions, how much momentum must it have? How much energy? How does this energy compare with nuclear binding energies?

12-9 The total binding energy of $_{17}Cl^{35}$ is 289 Mev.
a. What is the binding energy per nucleon?
b. Find the mass of this nuclide in amu, to five significant figures.

12-10 Derive an expression for the *force* corresponding to the Yukawa potential function [Eq. (12-14)]. If $a = 10^{-15}$ m and $f^2/a = 10$ Mev, at what distance is this force equal in magnitude to the Coulomb repulsion of two protons?

12-11 Radium 226 undergoes α decay, leading to radon 222. The masses, including all electrons in each atom, are 226.0254 amu and 222.0163 amu, respectively. What is the maximum-energy α particle that can be emitted?

12-12   Sodium, Na^{22}, undergoes β^+ decay to the stable isotope Ne^{22}. The masses of the neutral atoms are 21.99444 and 21.99138 amu, respectively. Find the energy of the β^+ on the assumption that it accounts for the entire energy difference. Is this assumption realistic?

12-13   A carbon specimen from a certain archeological find was found to contain 0.20 as much C^{14} per unit mass of C^{12} as currently living organic matter. What is the approximate age of the specimen?

12-14   The radioactive isotope Sr^{90} has a half-life of 25 years.
  a.   What is the decay constant?
  b.   After what time has 99 per cent of the original amount decayed?

12-15   Nuclei that undergo α decay usually emit α particles with definite energy or at most a discrete spectrum of energies, while β-decay energy spectra are often continuous. Why?

12-16   The radioactive isotope of potassium, $_{19}$K^{40}, occurs with an abundance of about 0.01 per cent relative to the common, stable isotope $_{19}$K^{39}, and its half-life is 1.3×10^9 years. Assuming that these two isotopes were produced with equal abundance at the time of formation of the elements, calculate the age of the universe.

12-17   A certain Van de Graaff generator develops a potential difference of 1,000,000 volts. If it is used to accelerate α particles, what energy do the particles have?

12-18   In a cyclotron, the maximum energy attainable is determined by the magnetic field B and the radius R of the vacuum chamber between the poles of the magnet. If the field is $B = 2$ webers/m^2, what radius is necessary for 10-Mev protons? What frequency should the oscillator which supplies the alternating potential difference to the dees have?

12-19   The cyclotron in Prob. 12-18 is to be modified to accelerate α particles.
  a.   What is the maximum-energy α particle that can be obtained?
  b.   What frequency should the oscillator have?

12-20   The Carnegie Tech synchrocyclotron accelerates protons to 450 Mev. The magnetic field is 2.0 webers/m^2. Find the maximum and minimum oscillator frequencies.

12-21   A β-ray spectrometer is an instrument similar in design to a mass spectrometer but used to measure energies of β-decay electrons. Calculate the radius of curvature of the path of a 1-Mev electron in a magnetic field $B = 1.0$ weber/m^2. Is it necessary to use relativistic dynamics to compute this radius? Explain.

12-22　The reaction $_8O^{16} + n \rightarrow {}_6C^{13} + {}_2He^4$ is endothermic by 2.20 Mev. If a target of $_8O^{16}$ is bombarded by neutrons, what minimum neutron energy is necessary for the reaction to occur?

12-23　The radioactive isotope of cobalt, $_{27}Co^{60}$, is produced by irradiating the stable isotope $_{27}Co^{59}$ with thermal neutrons in a reactor. The cross section for neutron absorption is about 20 barns. A sheet of Co^{59} with a total mass of 0.010 kg is placed in a reactor where the neutron flux is 10^{16} neutrons/m^2 sec for a period of 10 hr. How many Co^{60} nuclei are produced? (The half-life is sufficiently long so that the decay during irradiation is negligible.)

12-24　In photodisintegration of deuterons, a deuteron absorbs a γ-ray photon and splits into a proton and a neutron. The deuteron binding energy is about 2.23 Mev. What minimum energy must the photon have?

12-25　Consider the hypothetical fusion reaction

$$H^3 + Li^6 \rightarrow Be^9 + Q$$

The masses are 3.01605, 6.01513, and 9.01219 amu, respectively. Calculate the energy liberated in this reaction, and the energy per unit mass of fuel consumed.

12-26　A fusion reaction which is believed to be of importance in some stars is the fusion of three α particles to form a $_6C^{12}$ nucleus. The masses of the corresponding neutral atoms are 4.002604 and 12.000000 amu, respectively. How much energy is released in each fusion?

THE CONCEPT OF fundamental particles represents an attempt to understand the constitution of all matter on the basis of a few basic building blocks. The status of these building blocks in 1930 is reviewed, and then it is shown how a relativistic theory of the electron leads to a model in which particles can be created and destroyed. This in turn opens the door to an understanding of nuclear forces in terms of the exchange of unstable particles between nucleons. Particles having the necessary properties have been observed in cosmic radiation and in laboratory experiments with high-energy accelerators. The quest for the understanding of these particles has also led to the discovery of still other particles, known as "strange particles." Some of the symmetry and conservation laws introduced in an attempt to understand the interactions of these new particles are discussed, and finally a few of the most important unsolved problems in the theory of fundamental particles are reviewed.

13-1   Atomic View of Matter

The word *atomic* is derived from two Greek words meaning *not divisible*. In this section, *atomic* is used not in the narrow sense of atoms as the smallest units of chemical elements but in a broader sense, as a representation of all matter, including the constituents of nuclei, in terms of fundamental building blocks.   The atomic concept is a very ancient one, having been stated by the Greek philosophers Leucippus and Democritus in about 400 B.C.   Since that time, the atomic concept has played a central role in attempts to understand the behavior and structure of matter.

During the nineteenth century, evidence for the existence of atoms and molecules grew so overwhelming that it was no longer possible to debate their existence, and it was established beyond doubt that atoms and molecules are the smallest units of chemical elements and compounds, respectively, that can exist.   During the opening years of the present century it became clear that atoms of an element are not indivisible but have internal structure, implying that there are still more fundamental building blocks of which atoms are made.   The first to be identified positively was the *electron;* its existence was suspected as early as 1870 and was established conclusively by the fundamental experiments of J. J. Thomson in 1897.   By the mid-1930s the existence and most important properties of the proton, neutron, and positron had been put on an equally firm footing.

In the furious development of physical theory which took place in the 1920s and early 1930s, the preponderance of effort was directed toward applying the newly discovered quantum-mechanical principles to these particles in an effort to understand phenomena pertaining to atomic and molecular structure, such as energy levels, specific heats, and so on. By 1930, it appeared that the problems of *atomic* physics were essentially solved, inasmuch as the new quantum mechanics was believed to provide all the necessary principles.   At this point, then, the atomic physicists could rest on their laurels, confident that all that remained was to clean up calculational details.

With respect to the structure of the nucleus, however, the problems were far from solved.   In fact, in 1930 virtually nothing was known about the details of nuclear structure.   It was known that the dimensions of nuclei are smaller by a factor of 10^5 than those of atoms and that energies associated with interactions of nuclear particles are larger by the same factor, but there was virtually no understanding of the nature of the interaction by which nuclear particles are held together.

Even more profound problems loomed on the horizon.   What is the nature of the interactions of fundamental particles?   Classical physics provides only two basic interactions, electromagnetic and gravitational. The stability of nuclei suggests the existence of another strong interaction between nuclear particles.   Does this third kind of interaction complete the list, or are there still others, waiting to be discovered?

What about the masses of the particles? Why should there be two particles, one charged and one neutral, with approximately equal masses, and a third with opposite charge and much less mass? Should a complete theory be able to *predict* these masses? What is the status of the *photon*, the quantum of electromagnetic radiation? Should it be classified as a fundamental particle? If so, how can one understand the fact that photons can be created and destroyed in atomic processes, while the other particles seem to have a permanent existence?

In summary, while the main features of atomic structure were well understood by 1930, the corresponding problems of nuclear structure had just begun to be investigated. And there was not even the beginning of a comprehensive theory of fundamental particles that would enable the prediction of masses and other properties of the particles and the nature of their interactions. In short, the mystery of atomic structure in 1900 has its counterparts in the mystery of nuclear structure in 1930 and the mystery of the properties and interactions of the fundamental particles in the mid-1960s. Some of the questions raised in the preceding paragraphs have been answered fairly completely by subsequent investigations; others remain only partially answered or completely unanswered. Thus the discussion of fundamental particles and their interactions takes us to one of the present-day frontiers in theoretical physics.

13-2   *Relativistic Electron Theory*

One of the most successful theories for describing the behavior of a certain class of fundamental particles, in terms of the agreement of its predictions with experimental observations, is the relativistic theory of the electron. This theory had its genesis in 1928, when a young English theoretical physicist named Dirac developed a wave equation for the electron which was a relativistic generalization of the Schrödinger equation. To understand the need for such a generalization, we recall that, in developing the Schrödinger equation in Chaps. 6 and 7, we made use of the relationship $E = p^2/2m$ for the kinetic energy E and the momentum p of a particle of mass m. This relationship is valid only when the speed is much smaller than c and when the energies involved are all much smaller than mc^2. Just as newtonian mechanics is a special case of relativistic mechanics, so quantum mechanics as expressed by the Schrödinger equation is a special case of a more general formulation based on relativistic considerations. This generalization is just what the Dirac equation provides.

Although this equation and its solutions cannot be developed in detail here, we can discuss some of its most important general features. First, Dirac discovered that the requirement that the equation be compatible with the theory of relativity, together with the requirement that in the nonrelativistic limit it should reduce to the Schrödinger equation for a particle with spin ½, was sufficient to specify *uniquely* the form of the equation. Even more important, in including interactions with an electromagnetic field, the form of this *interaction* is also specified uniquely by requirements of relativistic invariance.

One of the most significant features of the interaction is the fact that part of it can be identified as the interaction of a magnetic dipole with a magnetic field, and the magnetic moment μ is related to the spin angular momentum S by

$$\mu = \frac{e}{m} S = \frac{e\hbar}{2m} \tag{13-1}$$

This shows that the gyromagnetic ratio for the intrinsic magnetic moment of the electron is e/m, rather than $e/2m$ as for orbital motion of charged particles. This, we recall, was the same conclusion indicated by the fine structure of atomic spectra, discussed in Sec. 8-7. But in the Dirac equation the magnetic moment of the electron comes out automatically, without having to be introduced as an additional assumption; this represents a major triumph of the Dirac theory of the electron and is a beautiful example of the function of scientific theory in giving unity to a variety of observations. The Dirac equation thus synthesizes in one body of theory the various assumptions that led to the original Schrödinger equation, the concept of electron spin, and the different gyromagnetic ratios for spin and orbital magnetic moments.

An equally significant result from the Dirac equation is the prediction of energy levels of electrons. For a free particle without interactions there are solutions of the equations corresponding to all energies greater than mc^2. This is to be expected, since the *rest* energy of the particle is mc^2. But the equation also permits solutions corresponding to energies which are *negative*, in fact less than $-mc^2$, as shown in Fig. 13-1. It was not clear at first what physical significance, if any, these negative energy levels had, yet neither was it clear how one could justify simply ignoring them. Worse yet, there seemed to be nothing to prevent a particle in a positive energy state from making a transition to a negative energy state with the emission of a photon of energy greater than $2mc^2$; this made the stable existence of electrons difficult to understand.

Fig. 13-1 *Energy levels for a free particle, as predicted by the Dirac equation. An electron can have any energy greater than mc². Transitions from positive to negative energy states are prevented by assuming that what is called "vacuum" is actually a state in which all the negative energy levels are occupied and the positive levels all empty. Thus the exclusion principle prevents transitions to negative energy levels.*

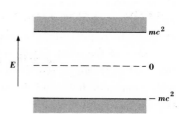

Dirac proposed to circumvent this difficulty by an ingenious but somewhat artificial scheme. He supposed that what is customarily called "vacuum" actually corresponds to a state of affairs in which all the negative energy levels are filled and all the positive energy levels empty. In this case, an additional electron in a positive energy level cannot make a transition to a negative energy level, since the latter levels are already filled and the exclusion principle prevents their being occupied by more than one electron each. Electrons in the negative energy states would not be observable in any ordinary low-energy interaction because of the fact that *all* the negative energy levels are occupied. To be observed, a negative energy electron must interact with its surroundings; in the course of this interaction its quantum state is altered. But if there are no nearby unoccupied states available, its state cannot change unless an energy of at least $2mc^2$ is available; otherwise it is unobservable. Clearly this proposal requires a drastic, although perhaps necessary, revision of the concept of what empty space is.

If this picture is correct, what physical meaning has a situation in which one of the normally filled negative energy states happens to be empty? Dirac proposed that this "hole" in the negative energy states, since it represents the absence of a negative charge, should be physically observed as a positively charged particle. Attempts were made to show that the observed mass of such a particle might be different from that of an electron, so that conceivably it might be identified as a proton. These attempts were not entirely convincing, and Dirac himself tended to believe that there should be some other basis on which to understand such states.

The key to this understanding came in 1932, when C. D. Anderson, using a cloud chamber for the investigation of cosmic-ray particles, observed a particle which appeared to have the same mass as that of the electron but a positive charge, as indicated by a deflection in a magnetic field opposite to that expected for a negative particle. Subsequent investigation disclosed that this particle, which was soon christened the *positron,* was identical to the electron in all its properties except that its charge was *positive* and its magnetic moment and angular momentum were in the *same* direction rather than opposite directions, as for a negatively charged particle. Furthermore, it was soon established that positrons are actually *created* in collisions involving high-energy cosmic-ray particles. This process is illustrated by the cloud-chamber photograph of Fig. 13-2.

This creation can be understood on the basis of the Dirac theory as a transition in which an electron in a negative energy state gains enough

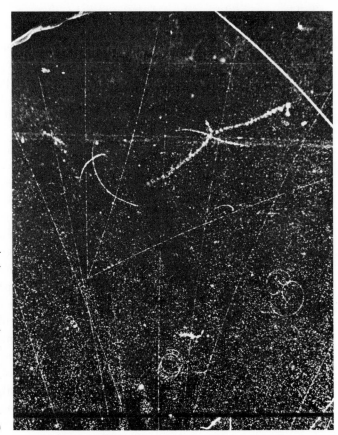

Fig. 13-2 *Photograph of cloud-chamber tracks produced by a cosmic-ray shower. Several electron-positron pairs, forming V-shaped tracks, are produced by one original high-energy particle. (Photo courtesy of Brookhaven National Laboratory.)*

energy (at least $2mc^2$) to reach a positive energy state in which it becomes physically observable, leaving a hole in the negative energy states that is observed as a positively charged particle or positron. Conversely, it was observed that a positron may undergo a collision with an electron in which both particles disappear and a corresponding amount of electromagnetic energy appears, usually as two or three γ photons with total energy $2mc^2$. This process is called *annihilation* of positrons.

Although Dirac's original theory was formulated in terms of energy levels for electrons, it was soon recognized that it could be reformulated in a manner which puts electrons and positrons on an equally fundamental basis and eliminates the necessity for filling all the negative energy states. Conceptually, this amounts simply to saying that if filled negative energy states are unobservable, and only holes in these states are observable, then it is physically more realistic to describe the state of the system directly in terms of the numbers of electrons and positrons.

Thus in the reformulated Dirac theory the *state* of a system is described in terms of the numbers of electrons and positrons in various energy, momentum, and angular-momentum states. Not only are transitions in states of individual particles permitted, but allowance is also made for processes in which the *number* of particles changes, corresponding to production or annihilation of electron-positron pairs. The relativistic electron theory is intrinsically a *many-particle* theory; no longer is it possible to speak of a system which can be said with certainty to contain only one particle.

The fact that the number of particles in a state can no longer be regarded as constant is a major departure from the point of view of the Schrödinger quantum mechanics; yet in a sense it is a welcome departure, since it tends to put electrons and photons on a similar footing. We recall that photons are created and destroyed in various kinds of atomic processes. We have noted various similarities in behavior of electron and photon, particularly their dual wave-particle nature; it seems natural that they should also share the property of being able to be created or destroyed. One fundamental difference is that, whereas photons are created and destroyed singly, electrons and positrons are created or destroyed only in pairs, so that in any interaction the number of electrons minus the number of positrons is constant. The complementary nature of electrons and positrons with respect to creation and destruction is often described by the statement that one is the *antiparticle* of the other, which simply means that a particle and its antiparticle are always associated in a creation or destruction process. Neither electrons nor positrons may be created or destroyed singly.   In Sec. 13-4 we shall cite several other examples of antiparticles.

Closely related to this property is the fact that electrons and positrons obey the exclusion principle, whereas photons do not.   There is nothing to prevent an electromagnetic field from containing a large number of photons of the same energy, momentum, and polarization, and in fact the limiting case where there are very many photons present and quantum effects can be ignored is simply classical wave optics, described by the Maxwell electromagnetic field equations.   There is *no* corresponding "classical limit" for electrons and positrons, since each possible state can accommodate only one particle.

In this unified theory of electrons and the electromagnetic field, a *state* of a system is described by the number of electrons, positrons, and photons with each of the various possible energies and momenta.   Similarly, a transition of the system from one state to another is described in terms of the creation or destruction of any of these particles.   For example, an electron with initial momentum $\mathbf{p}_1$ which undergoes an electromagnetic interaction and emerges with momentum $\mathbf{p}_2$ is described as a process in which the initial electron is destroyed and a new one is created.   Similarly, if this process involves electromagnetic waves, we speak of the emission or absorption of a photon of a certain energy and momentum.

It is convenient to represent electron-photon interactions by means of schematic space-time diagrams or graphs in which one axis is a space coordinate for each particle; the other is time.   These are known as *Feynman diagrams*, in honor of Richard P. Feynman, who introduced them in 1949, and who has made many of the most important contributions to the understanding of electron-photon interactions (including demonstrating the usefulness of these graphs).   In such a diagram, an electron is represented by a solid line, and a photon by a broken line.

Several elementary Feynman diagrams are shown in Fig. 13-3. Figure 13-3*b* is particularly significant, since it shows that a collision of two electrons (either positive or negative) can be described in terms of exchange of a photon; the photon acts as the mechanism for transfer of energy and momentum from one particle to another, by means of which the motions of the two particles are altered.   Thus the interaction is described not as a force but as the emission and absorption of an intermediary particle.   The situation is analogous to that of two basketball players exerting a repulsive force on each other by tossing a ball back and forth.   In the interaction with an electron and a positron, ordinarily

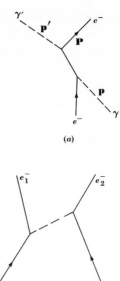

(a)

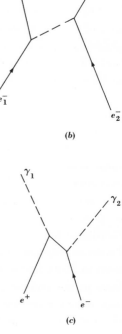

(b)

Fig. 13-3   *Three simple Feynman diagrams.   In each, solid
lines represent electrons or
positrons, and broken lines,
photons.   The diagrams are
schematic; no attempt is made
to relate directions of lines
with particle speeds.   (a) Compton scattering.   An electron at
rest absorbs a photon with
momentum* **p**, *leading to a
virtual intermediate state.
Then the electron emits a photon
with momentum* **p′**; *the final
electron momentum is* **P**.   *(b)
Electron-electron scattering by
exchange of a virtual photon.
(c) Electron-positron annihilation, with production of two
photons.*

(c)

described as an *attractive* force, we may think of the players as alter-
nately snatching the ball away from each other.

One additional feature of the above scheme deserves mention.   In
the Feynman diagrams shown in Fig. 13-3, each corner, or *vertex*, includes two electron lines and one photon line, corresponding to an electron emitting or absorbing a photon.   But such a process violates the
classical principles of conservation of momentum and energy, as can
be seen by considering an electron at rest.   When it emits a photon, it
must recoil in the opposite direction in order to conserve momentum;

but then both the photon and the electron have energy, and so energy conservation has been violated. The resolution of this apparent paradox is the fact that, according to the uncertainty principle, a state which lasts a very short time interval Δt has an uncertainty ΔE in its energy, related by

$$\Delta E \, \Delta t \geq \hbar \qquad (13\text{-}2)$$

Thus a transition in which an electron emits a photon is possible, provided the resulting state lasts a sufficiently short time so that Eq. (13-2) permits the necessary temporary energy nonconservation. In the diagrams in Fig. 13-3, the intermediate states of the system during a transition are not states of well-defined energy, but if the initial and final states both last a long time their energy must be well defined; in fact, initial and final energies must be equal. The principle of conservation of energy must be interpreted in this slightly generalized sense.

Particles that exist temporarily in violation of energy conservation, as permitted by the uncertainty principle for energy, are often called *virtual* particles, to emphasize their transitory nature. Correspondingly, a state in which such particles are present is called a virtual state. In Fig. 13-3*b*, the photon exchanged in the electron-electron scattering diagram is a *virtual photon*.

The theory described briefly above is called *quantum electrodynamics*. Since its initial development starting in about 1949 it has become one of the most highly developed of all physical theories; in problems where only electromagnetic interactions are present, its predictions agree with experimental observations with an accuracy sometimes as great as 1 part in 10^9. In this sense, there is reason to believe that our understanding of the interaction of electrons with the electromagnetic field is nearly complete. But there are also electromagnetic interactions with other particles whose behavior is not nearly so well understood. Some of them will be discussed in the next sections.

13-3 Mesons and Nuclear Forces

We return now to the interactions of nuclear particles. In 1930 virtually nothing was known about this interaction. Observations of the dimensions and binding energies of nuclei indicated that, unlike electromagnetic forces, the nuclear force has a very short range, of the order of 1.5×10^{-15} m, but that within this range it is of the order of a hundred times as strong as the electrical repulsion between two protons at corresponding distances. It was speculated that the interaction between two nucleons could be described by a potential-energy function having the general form

$$V(r) = -f^2 \frac{e^{-r/a}}{r} \tag{13-3}$$

or something similar. Aside from this very general picture, however, information about the nuclear force was mostly negative. It could not possibly be electromagnetic or gravitational in nature. Its behavior was unlike that of any other known interaction. In short, the nuclear force was a mystery.

In 1935 the Japanese physicist H. Yukawa made a bold hypothesis. Suppose that nucleons can emit and absorb some kind of particle, in a manner similar to the emission and absorption of photons by atomic electrons. This game of catch with particles would be accompanied by transfer of energy and momentum, resulting effectively in an interaction force between the two nucleons. To appreciate the magnitude of Yukawa's conjecture, we must realize that it, like de Broglie's hypothesis regarding the wave nature of electrons, was advanced entirely in the absence of any experimental evidence to support such a hypothesis. In 1935 there had been not the slightest shred of evidence that such a particle existed. Yet, as with de Broglie's wave hypothesis, it was clear that nothing less than a radical idea offered any hope of illuminating the mystery of nuclear forces, and the world of physics was receptive to Yukawa's suggestion.

Just as with the emission of a photon by an electron, the emission of an intermediary particle by a nucleon is forbidden by energy and momentum conservation, but again we are saved by the uncertainty principle; a transition that violates energy conservation by an amount ΔE is not forbidden, so long as the resulting virtual state lasts a sufficiently short time $\Delta t = \hbar/\Delta E$. This observation can be used to estimate the mass such a particle must have. In the particle-exchange picture of nuclear forces, the *range R* of the force must be related to the distance the virtual particle can travel during the time Δt of its temporary existence. Since the speed of the particle can never be greater than c, the range can be at most

$$R = c \, \Delta t \tag{13-4}$$

Furthermore, the uncertainty in energy ΔE of the state necessary for such a particle to be produced must be at least as great as mc^2, where m is the mass of the particle. Combining this and Eq. (13-4) with the fundamental uncertainty relation given by Eq. (13-2), we find that the mass of the particle should be of the order of

$$m = \frac{\hbar}{Rc} = \frac{1.0 \times 10^{-34} \text{ joule sec}}{(1.5 \times 10^{-15} \text{ m})(3.0 \times 10^8 \text{ m/sec})} = 2.5 \times 10^{-28} \text{ kg} \quad (13\text{-}5)$$

or about 250 times the electron mass.

Accordingly, Yukawa postulated the existence of an unstable particle with a mass between 200 and 300 times that of the electron, which can be emitted or absorbed by a nucleon. In proton-neutron interactions, the particles can be either neutral or charged. For example, a proton may emit a positively charged particle, becoming a neutron. This particle is then absorbed by the neutron, which then becomes a proton, leaving one proton and one neutron as in the initial state. These particles were soon given the name mesotrons, from the Greek prefix meso-, meaning "in between," referring to the fact that their masses are intermediate between those of the electron and the nucleons. This name has since been shortened to *meson*. At the time of Yukawa's proposal in 1935, there was no *direct* experimental evidence that these particles existed.

In 1937, only 2 years after Yukawa's original hypothesis, a flurry of excitement was created by the discovery in cloud-chamber tracks of charged particles with masses of about 200 times the electron mass. It was immediately suspected that they were the particles Yukawa had predicted. They exhibited some very puzzling behavior, however. Because of the role these particles supposedly play in the nuclear interaction, they themselves should have strong interactions with nuclei. That is, a meson should be strongly scattered by a nucleus with which it collides, much more so than if only the electromagnetic interaction were present. Correspondingly, the range of these particles in matter should be very small. It turned out, however, that the observed particles behaved exactly as though their interaction with the nucleus was entirely electromagnetic; there was no indication of a strong "nuclear-force" interaction. Thus the initial excitement was followed immediately by a period of confusion and frustration. The meson was supposed to be the nuclear glue; yet it appeared not to interact with nuclei at all.

No appreciable progress was made in the solution of this mystery until 10 years later when in 1947 *another* kind of meson was discovered. These mesons are somewhat heavier than the first, having masses of about 270 times the electron mass, and scattering experiments show that they *do* interact very strongly with nucleons. To distinguish the two kinds of particles, the strongly interacting particles discovered in 1947 are called π mesons or *pions,* while the weakly interacting particles discovered 10 years earlier are called μ mesons or *muons.*

Further investigation of the mesons, mostly with cloud chambers and photographic emulsions, revealed various additional features. There are three kinds of pions, with positive, negative, and zero charge, and two kinds of muons, positively and negatively charged. In each case, the charge has the same magnitude as the electron charge. The masses are shown in Table 13-1, which also shows that the pions have zero spin (and therefore no intrinsic magnetic moment) while the muons have spin ½.

Table 13-1   *Properties of Mesons*

Particle	Charge	Mass, m_e	Spin	Decay products	Mean life, sec
π^+	+	273	0	$\mu^+ + \nu$	2.5×10^{-8}
π^-	−	273	0	$\mu^- + \nu$	2.5×10^{-8}
π^0	0	264	0	$\gamma + \gamma$	2.2×10^{-15}
μ^+	+	207	½	$e^+ + \nu + \bar{\nu}$	2.2×10^{-6}
μ^-	−	207	½	$e^- + \nu + \bar{\nu}$	2.2×10^{-6}

All the mesons are *unstable;* each decays spontaneously into other particles. Experiment shows that a charged pion always decays into a muon with the same charge; furthermore, if the pion is initially at rest the resulting muon always has the same energy. Energy and momentum conservation require that at least one additional particle must be produced, but since it is not observed in cloud-chamber tracks it must be neutral. The fact that the muon always has the same energy shows that there is *only* one additional particle, since if there were two or more they could share the energy and momentum in various ways and the muons would be observed to have a spectrum of energies. Angular-momentum conservation shows that the neutral particle has spin ½; energy and momentum relations show that it has zero rest mass, and so it is assumed to be a neutrino. Thus the decay scheme of the charged pions is represented as

$$\pi^\pm \rightarrow \mu^\pm + \nu \tag{13-6}$$

The *lifetime,* or average time between production and decay, is about 2.5×10^{-8} sec, as shown in Table 13-1. There is now reason to believe that the neutrino associated with π decay is not the same as that associated with β decay, but that there are two kinds of neutrinos. We return to this point briefly in Sec. 13-5.

The neutral pion, which cannot decay into a muon because of charge conservation, decays instead into two γ photons, represented symbolically as

$$\pi^0 \to \gamma + \gamma \tag{13-7}$$

The muons always decay into electrons with a continuous spectrum of energy, showing that at least two neutral particles are produced in each decay. It has been established that the decay process is

$$\mu^\pm \to e^\pm + \nu + \bar{\nu} \tag{13-8}$$

where $\nu + \bar{\nu}$ represents a neutrino-antineutrino pair. The lifetime for this process is 2.2×10^{-6} sec.

Because of the role played by pions in nuclear interactions, it should be possible to *produce* π mesons in the laboratory in sufficiently energetic nucleon collisions. Artificial pion production was first accomplished in 1948, using protons accelerated in the synchrocyclotron of the University of California (Berkeley). The energy equivalent of the mass of the charged pions is

$$\begin{aligned}
m_\pi c^2 &= (273)(9.11 \times 10^{-31} \text{ kg})(3.00 \times 10^8 \text{ m/sec})^2 \\
&= 2.24 \times 10^{-11} \text{ joule} \\
&= 140 \text{ Mev}
\end{aligned} \tag{13-9}$$

The bombarding particle must have more energy than this, for reasons discussed in Sec. 12-5. The proton cannot give up *all* its kinetic energy in a collision; otherwise all the particles would be at rest after the collision, violating conservation of momentum. Thus the minimum energy for the bombarding particle is the energy required to produce a pion in a state in which the bombarding particle, the target particle, and the pion all move off with a common velocity. In the center-of-mass coordinate system this corresponds to the bombarding particle and the target particle approaching each other with zero total momentum, leaving all three particles at rest after the collision.

In a sense, the most fundamental kind of collision process is that between two nucleons, since this is the prototype situation for all nuclear interactions. Therefore, it is instructive to calculate the amount of energy required for pion production in a collision between two protons, one accelerated in a synchrocyclotron, and the other in a stationary target such as liquid hydrogen. Because of the large energies involved, it is necessary to use relativistic dynamics; the energy E and momentum p

of a particle of mass m are related by

$$E^2 = (mc^2)^2 + (pc)^2 \tag{13-10}$$

For a system which initially contains two protons of mass M, one with momentum p and the other at rest, the *total* energy is

$$E = Mc^2 + \sqrt{(Mc^2)^2 + (pc)^2} \tag{13-11}$$

which may be rewritten

$$E^2 = 2EMc^2 + p^2c^2 \tag{13-12}$$

After the collision, if the bombarding particle has the minimum energy for meson production, all three particles move off with a common final velocity, so that the energy-momentum relation is exactly the same as for a single particle of total mass $2M + m$, where m is the pion mass. The *total* energy and momentum are the same as before the collision. Thus we have

$$E^2 = (2M + m)^2c^4 + p^2c^2 \tag{13-13}$$

Comparing this with Eq. (13-12), we find

$$2EMc^2 = (2M + m)^2c^4$$
$$E = 2Mc^2 + 2mc^2 + \frac{m^2}{2M}c^2 \tag{13-14}$$

The first term in this expression represents the rest energy of the two protons, and so the remaining two terms are the kinetic energy of the bombarding proton. This energy must be somewhat larger than twice the rest energy of the π meson; the minimum energy is about 290 Mev. By 1952, there were several cyclotrons in the world capable of accelerating protons to these energies, and it became possible to produce pions in the laboratory. There ensued an intensive investigation of the properties of these particles as well as the muons produced in their decay. The precision of the numerical values in Table 13-1 results from experiments with artificially produced pions.

In addition to their contributions to the understanding of interactions between nucleons, pions also are helpful in understanding some anomalous properties of individual nucleons. One such anomaly is the magnetic moment of the proton which, if it behaved in accordance with the Dirac equation, should have a gyromagnetic ratio e/M, as discussed in Sec. 13-2. Instead, the measured value of the gyromagnetic ratio is found to be $2.79\, e/M$. Moreover, the neutron, which has no charge and therefore according to the Dirac theory ought to have no magnetic moment, has a magnetic moment of $(-1.91e/M)(\frac{1}{2}\hbar)$. Both these anom-

protons and antineutrons are produced and destroyed only as part of a *pair* interaction. Just as it is impossible to create or destroy a single electron (+ or −), it is also impossible to create or destroy a single nucleon or antinucleon. Creation or destruction invariably involves a nucleon-antinucleon *pair*. This phenomenon is related to a new conservation law to be discussed in the next section.

All the hyperons mentioned above have spin ½, and each one has an associated antiparticle. There is an anti-Λ^0, denoted as $\overline{\Lambda^0}$, three anti-Σ's (+, −, and neutral), and two anti-Ξ's (+ and neutral). Each antiparticle is produced only in association with a nucleon or hyperon and annihilates similarly.

A quick check over the above list shows that the total number of elementary particles discussed thus far is up to about 30. In the next section we shall describe some of the attempts to find orderly relationships among them.

13-5 Symmetry and Conservation Laws

In this section we shall discuss a scheme for classifying the fundamental particles and their interactions and for relating the interactions to various conservation principles. This area represents a branch of theoretical physics in which understanding is still far from complete; some of the following discussion is necessarily more empirical than fundamental, and it is sometimes necessary to make *ad hoc* assumptions regarding the behavior of particles. In this sense, particle physics at the present time is in much the same state as the Bohr theory of the hydrogen atom, which in 1915 provided a partially successful representation of the energy levels of the atom but no real fundamental understanding of the nature of its structure.

The trend of the discussion in the few preceding sections has been increasingly to associate *interactions* between particles with the *creation* and *destruction* of particles. The nuclear "force" representing the interaction between two nucleons was described in terms of the creation of a meson by one nucleon and its absorption by the other. This description is completely analogous to representing the electromagnetic interaction of two charged particles in terms of the emission of a photon by one particle and its subsequent absorption by the other. In terms of this picture, it is also clear that the *strength* of a given interaction is determined by the likelihood of the emission and absorption of the particles responsible for the interaction. The fact that within its range the nuclear force between two protons is much stronger than the electromagnetic interaction indicates that at least at short distances the likelihood of emission and absorption of mesons by the nucleons is much greater than for photons.

As pointed out in Sec. 13-3, particles associated with interactions, such as mesons and photons, are *virtual* particles; their emission and absorption would not be in accordance with the principle of conservation of energy except that the virtual states in which they are created live for a sufficiently short time so that the uncertainty principle permits the required uncertainty in energy. Such particles cannot be observed directly unless they are given enough additional energy so that the state can live an indefinitely long time without violating energy conservation. A rough calculation shows that pions exchanged between nucleons have lifetimes of the order of 10^{-24} sec, while pions observed in the laboratory have lifetimes of the order of 10^{-8} sec. In the latter case, the lifetime is determined not by the close proximity of the particles but by the probability of spontaneous decay. This probability in turn is governed by the likelihood of destruction of one particle and the associated creation of others, just as in the processes determining the interactions between particles.

We are thus led to the conclusion that the very same processes responsible for *interactions* between particles are also responsible for the *production* and *decay* of particles. Furthermore, particles that interact very strongly should have relatively short lifetimes, and particles that interact weakly should have correspondingly longer lifetimes. For example, the free π^0 meson decays according to the scheme

$$\pi^0 \rightarrow \gamma + \gamma \tag{13-18}$$

with a lifetime of the order of 10^{-15} sec, while the decay of the free neutron occurs according to

$$n \rightarrow p + e^- + \nu \tag{13-19}$$

with a lifetime of the order of 15 min, longer than that for the π^0 by a factor of 10^{18}. Thus the interaction corresponding to the β decay of the neutron must be very much *weaker* than that corresponding to the decay of the π^0 meson.

The electromagnetic interaction between two particles of charge e is proportional to e^2. For some purposes it is more convenient to express this interaction strength in terms of the dimensionless quantity

$$\frac{e^2}{4\pi\epsilon_0\hbar c} = \frac{(1.60 \times 10^{-19} \text{ coul})^2 (9.00 \times 10^9 \text{ m/farad})}{(1.06 \times 10^{-34} \text{ joule sec})(3.00 \times 10^8 \text{ m/sec})} = \frac{1}{137} \tag{13-20}$$

Stated in other terms, the probability of absorption or emission of a photon by a particle with charge e is proportional to e, so that an interaction involving both emission and absorption must be proportional to e^2. The corresponding parameter used to characterize the strength of meson-nucleon interactions is usually called g, and the quantity $g^2/\hbar c$, which is analogous to the quantity expressed by Eq. (13-20), is found experimentally to have values of the order of 1 to 10, depending on the details of the particular theory used. This again corresponds to the observation that, within their range, nuclear interactions between two protons are stronger by a factor of the order of 100 than electromagnetic interactions.

Thus there is evidence for at least four different classes of interactions: the strong interactions (the interactions of mesons with nucleons), the electromagnetic interactions, the weak interactions associated with β decay, and the still weaker gravitational interactions, which are believed to be of no consequence in particle interactions. Before proceeding with a more systematic classification of the various interactions, we make one additional observation. Experiment shows that particles having spin zero or an integer are created and absorbed singly. Particles in this category are the pions, the K mesons, and photons. Conversely, all particles having spin ½ are created and destroyed in *pairs*. This phenomenon has already been mentioned for the production of electron-positron pairs. Correspondingly, an antiproton can be produced only in combination with a proton or neutron. For example, the reactions

$$p + \pi^- \to p + n + \bar{n}$$
$$p + n \to p + n + \bar{p} + p \qquad (13\text{-}21)$$
$$p + \bar{n} \to \pi^0 + \pi^0 + \pi^+ + \pi^+ + \pi^-$$

are possible and are observed, but reactions such as

$$p + n \to p + n + n$$
$$n \to \pi^+ + e^- + \nu \qquad (13\text{-}22)$$
$$p + n \to n + \pi^+ + \pi^0$$

are not observed, although they do not violate the classical conservation laws of energy, momentum, angular momentum, or charge. This observation is important in connection with the following classification of interactions.

We now discuss the application of *conservation laws* to fundamental-particle interactions. Four conservation laws are taken directly from classical physics.   They are the conservation of energy, momentum, angular momentum, and electric charge.   Every process taking place within an isolated system, that is, a system that does not interact with its surroundings, takes place in accordance with these four conservation laws, no matter what kind of particles or interactions are involved; no exceptions to this general statement have been discovered experimentally.

Each of these four conservation principles is related to a *symmetry* of the physical system.   This is most readily seen for angular momentum.   The total angular momentum of an *isolated* system is constant because no external torques act on this system.   If there were such a torque, it would have to be associated with a particular direction in space. The absence of such a torque indicates that insofar as the system is concerned any orientation in space is equivalent to any other.   This fact is expressed succinctly by saying that the system and the mathematical language used to describe it are *invariant* with respect to rotations of the space coordinates.   If there were some external agency, such as an external magnetic field, which would give preference to some particular direction, all directions could no longer be said to be equivalent; correspondingly it would no longer be true that the total angular momentum is constant.   Thus the conservation of angular momentum for an isolated system is directly related to the symmetry property of invariance under space rotations.

In precisely the same way it can be shown that conservation of momentum for an isolated system is directly related to invariance of the system under translation from one point in space to another, or a transformation of coordinates involving a translation of the coordinate axes. Conservation of energy can be shown to be related similarly to invariance under a translation of the time scale, and conservation of electric charge to the property of the electromagnetic potentials called gauge invariance. So it is with all the other conservation laws to be mentioned; each is associated with a certain symmetry.   In some cases the description of this symmetry is somewhat more subtle than in the cases just mentioned, but there always is such a symmetry for every conservation law, and conversely.

There are two other universal conservation laws which have no analog in classical physics.   They are the conservation of the *baryon* number and the *lepton* number.   These two terms are generic names for two distinct classes of spin-½ particles.   The *baryons* all have masses equal to that of nucleons or larger; this class includes nucleons, Λ, Σ, and Ξ hyperons, and their corresponding antiparticles.   *Leptons* are the light particles with spin ½, including electrons, neutrinos, and μ mesons. These two conservation laws are direct consequences of the above observation that spin-½ particles are created and destroyed only in pairs.

The principle of conservation of baryon number states that in any interaction the number of baryons minus the number of antibaryons is constant. For example, the reactions

$$\Sigma^+ + \bar{p} \to \pi^+ + \pi^- + \pi^0$$
$$\Lambda^0 \to n + \pi^0$$

are permitted by this principle, but the reactions

$$n \to \pi^- + e^+ + \nu$$
$$\pi^- + p \to n + n$$

are forbidden. Similarly, the reactions

$$\mu^+ \to e^+ + \nu + \bar{\nu}$$
$$\pi^0 \to e^+ + e^-$$

obey the law of conservation of leptons, but the reactions

$$\pi^+ \to \pi^0 + e^+$$
$$p + \pi^- \to p + e^- + \gamma$$

do not, and they do not occur. Like the four classical conservation principles mentioned above, the principles of conservation of baryons and of leptons are believed to be *universal* conservation laws; no exceptions have been discovered.

We now come to a group of conservation laws which are different from those of classical physics, inasmuch as they are obeyed by some interactions and not by others. The first is *isotopic spin.* The concept of isotopic spin was originally devised to express the fact that the observed strong interactions between nucleons seem not to depend on the charges; the nuclear interaction between two protons is exactly the same as that between two neutrons. This observation is usually called the charge independence of nuclear forces. We cannot describe the isotopic-spin formalism in detail, but the basic idea is to introduce a fictitious three-dimensional space, not related to the actual physical space in which the particles move, and a vector quantity τ in this space, called isotopic spin, which is quantized according to the same rules as angular momentum. That is, the quantum number describing the total isotopic spin of a particle must be zero or an integer or half integer. Correspondingly, the z component of isotopic spin τ_z can take integer or half-integer values, respectively. Furthermore, we assert that τ_z for a particle is directly related to the *charge* of the particle.

Thus we describe the group of three π mesons as three states of a single particle, having total isotopic spin of one unit, with a component in the z direction of 1, 0, or -1, corresponding to the three possible charges, $+1$, 0, and -1, of the pion. Similarly, the nucleon has isotopic spin $\frac{1}{2}$, with the proton state represented by $\tau_z = +\frac{1}{2}$ and the neutron state by $\tau_z = -\frac{1}{2}$. Clearly, the conservation of the total z component of isotopic spin is equivalent to the conservation of electric charge. Conservation of the other components may not seem at first glance to have any direct physical significance. Somewhat surprisingly, it has been found that all the *strong interactions* between mesons and baryons occur in such a way that the *magnitude* of the total isotopic spin is also conserved. Thus the observed charge independence of nuclear forces is equivalent to the conservation of isotopic spin, which in turn is equivalent to the symmetry of the interaction with respect to rotations not in real physical space but in isotopic-spin space.

The remarkable feature of this new conservation principle is that it is *not* a universal principle. Conservation of isotopic spin is a property only of the strong interactions, not of the electromagnetic or weak interactions. Thus this is the first example of the use of a conservation principle to classify interactions.

Next we consider the principle of conservation of *strangeness*. This principle was born in an attempt to understand the properties of the strange particles, the heavy meson and hyperons. We recall that the associated production of these particles is characteristic of a strong-interaction process, while the decay of the individual particles seems more characteristic of a weak interaction. Perhaps there is a new conservation law that is obeyed in the production process but violated in the weaker decay process.

Attempts to state this new principle quantitatively led to the introduction of a new quantum number called, for the lack of a better term, *strangeness*. Values of this quantum number for all the known particles were assigned as follows: All particles except the K mesons and hyperons have a strangeness number of 0. The Λ and Σ hyperons have strangeness $+1$, and the mesons K^+ and K^0 have strangeness -1. The Ξ particles have strangeness $+2$. Correspondingly, the antihyperons $\overline{\Lambda}$ and $\overline{\Sigma}$ have strangeness -1, and $\overline{\overline{\Xi}}$ strangeness -2, and the mesons $\overline{K^-}$ and $\overline{K^0}$ strangeness $+1$.

With this scheme, the production and decay of the strange particles can be understood at least qualitatively on the assumption that the production process for strange particles is a strong interaction, of strength comparable to that of the pion-nucleon interaction, in which strangeness is conserved. For example, in the reaction

$$p + p \rightarrow K^+ + \Sigma^-$$

the *total* strangeness on each side is zero. Furthermore, according to this theory, the interactions by which these particles decay are not subject to this conservation law, so that in a decay process the total strangeness need not be conserved. An example is

$$\Sigma^- \rightarrow n + \pi^-$$

Finally, we mention the principle of conservation of *parity*. The basic idea is the following: Suppose for a given experiment we make two sets of apparatus, one of which is precisely the mirror image of the other. According to the principle of conservation of parity, the results of any experiment performed with one set of apparatus will be exactly the mirror image of the results with the other set of apparatus. This conservation law, clearly, is associated with symmetry with respect to *reflections* of the physical system, just as angular-momentum conservation is associated with symmetry with respect to rotations.

For many years this principle seemed so obvious and self-evident as not to require experimental testing; certainly there is no evidence in classical mechanics or electrodynamics to suggest a violation of it. Furthermore, none of the phenomena of atomic physics or even the strong interactions of nuclear particles suggest a violation of this principle. But by 1956 a number of phenomena had been observed in connection with the decay of heavy mesons which were difficult to understand within the framework of theories that included conservation of parity in their description of the weak interactions responsible for the decay of these particles. Thus it seemed desirable to design new experiments to test directly whether or not parity is conserved in the weak interactions.

Several possible experiments to test conservation of parity directly were suggested by T. D. Lee and C. N. Yang of Columbia University. The first such experiment was performed in 1956 at Columbia by C. S. Wu; it involved the angular distribution of β particles emitted by radioactive nuclei whose spins were aligned by a magnetic field. To everyone's surprise, this experiment revealed that in the weak β-decay interaction parity is *not* conserved. This discovery represented the overthrow of a seemingly obvious and long-cherished principle, and some physicists were at first reluctant to accept it. But the spirit of the scientific community is such that new ideas that make possible increased understanding of physical phenomena must be accepted even if they represent radical departures from established beliefs. The theory of the weak interactions is now reasonably well established, and it is recognized that parity is not conserved in any weak interactions, although it *is* conserved in strong and electromagnetic interactions.

We now summarize briefly the properties of the three classes of interactions discussed. A fundamental event in an electromagnetic interaction always involves three particles, one of which is a photon. Photons interact directly only with particles having electric charge. A Feynman diagram describing a fundamental electromagnetic interaction always contains three lines meeting at a point, as shown in Fig. 13-4b. One of these is a photon; the other two are charged particles. Electromagnetic interactions obey all the universal conservation laws discussed above and also conservation of parity and strangeness, but *not* conservation of isotopic spin. A fundamental strong interaction process always involves two baryons and one meson. These processes are believed to obey all the conservation laws discussed above, including isotopic spin, strangeness, and parity.

The weak interactions, as contrasted with the other two, always involve four different particles of spin ½. These are the interactions re-

Fig. 13-4 *Diagrammatic representation of strong, electromagnetic, and weak interactions. (a) Strong-interaction vertex, corresponding to the creation or destruction of a meson (broken line) by a baryon (solid line). (b) Electromagnetic interaction, corresponding to the creation or absorption of a photon (broken line) by a charged particle which may be a lepton, meson, or baryon. (c) Weak interaction, in which four spin-½ particles are involved.*

(a)

(b)

(c)

sponsible for β decay, the decay of the μ meson, and indirectly the decay of the π^0 meson. All these processes can be described in terms of a four-particle interaction. For example, the decay of the π^+ meson into a μ^+ meson and a neutrino can be understood as a two-stage process in which the π^+ meson first creates a virtual nucleon-antinucleon pair, which then undergoes a transition via the weak interaction to a μ^+ meson and a neutrino. This process is shown by the Feynman diagram of Fig. 13-5a. The weak interactions may or may not conserve strangeness and, in general, do *not* conserve parity.

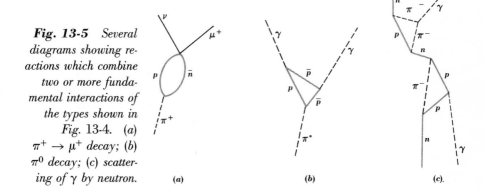

Fig. 13-5 *Several diagrams showing reactions which combine two or more fundamental interactions of the types shown in Fig. 13-4. (a)* $\pi^+ \rightarrow \mu^+$ *decay; (b)* π^0 *decay; (c) scattering of* γ *by neutron.*

(a)   (b)   (c).

The observed production and decay processes for all the fundamental particles can be understood on the basis of combinations of these three fundamental interactions. Several examples of processes involving combinations of two or more interactions are illustrated in Fig. 13-5. In all these examples, the concept of virtual intermediate states is a useful and important one.

An additional comment should be made concerning the weak interaction, which always involves at least one neutrino. In the past few years there has been increasingly strong evidence that there are really *two* kinds of neutrinos, one involved with electrons and the other with μ mesons. Thus the neutrino in the process

$$n \rightarrow p + e^- + \nu$$

is not the same particle as in

$$\pi^+ \rightarrow \mu^+ + \nu$$

The definitive test of the two-neutrino hypothesis was made at Brookhaven National Laboratory in 1963, and the existence of two kinds of neutrinos is now firmly established. Furthermore, there is an anti-neutrino corresponding to each kind. In the above discussion we have not distinguished between neutrino and antineutrino; in the usual convention, the particle on the right side of the neutron-decay reaction above is actually an antineutrino and should be denoted as $\bar{\nu}$.

The search for conservation laws and associated symmetry properties in the interactions of fundamental particles has led to a certain degree of understanding of the roles of these various processes in the structure of matter. Furthermore, the symmetry properties provide a very important guide in the formulation of detailed theories to describe the interactions. Just as the principle of relativistic invariance, together with the requirement of spin ½, led to the formulation of the Dirac equation, so the requirements of the various conservation laws and their associated symmetries lead directly to the possible forms of the mathematical formulations of the various fundamental-particle interactions. It has not yet been possible to use symmetry properties to predict uniquely what the form of the detailed theory should be; some choices still have to be made empirically. Some physicists hope that, with the discovery of new phenomena and new associated conservation laws, perhaps we shall eventually be led to a unique theory. This, however, is purely conjecture at the present time.

13-6   *Frontiers*

Lest the reader should receive the erroneous impression that the problems of fundamental-particle physics are now essentially solved, we bring this volume to a close with a brief mention of some of the unsolved fundamental problems.

In the years since 1955 still other particles have been discovered, including additional short-lived mesons more massive than the K mesons, as well as heavier hyperons. There is a growing tendency to describe these particles not as independent entities but rather as excited states of some other system. The situation may be compared with atomic physics. In the usual point of view, a hydrogen atom does not cease to be a hydrogen atom when it is excited by absorption of a photon to an energy level above the $n = 1$ ground state. But if the details of the atom's structure were not known, we might perfectly well call it a different atom; it certainly has different mechanical properties, including energy-mass and angular momentum, from the usual hydrogen atom, and it is *unstable,* decaying spontaneously into an ordinary hydrogen atom and a photon. Perhaps some of the new unstable particles have a similar status.   Indeed, the question "What is a particle?" is becoming more and more crucial and the answer less and less obvious.

A large amount of effort is being exerted on attempts to formulate a theory which would permit *predictions* of the masses of the fundamental particles, which up to now have been regarded as purely empirical. That is, we should like to have a theory that permits us to predict in advance the masses which new particles, not yet discovered, should have. There seems little doubt that, with the building of machines capable of higher and higher energies, still more new particles *will* be discovered. Correspondingly, there is no fundamental theory that permits the prediction of the strengths of the various interactions; these also must be regarded at the present time as empirical.

Several recent attempts to understand the relationships among the various particles have reverted to the scheme of describing all particles in terms of a few (perhaps three) fundamental entities.   In these attempts, the point of view is that the particles themselves have a sort of structure, in the sense that they have constituent parts.   In one such scheme, popular in 1965, there are three fundamental entities called *quarks,* having rather unusual properties including fractional electric charges.   Some of these theories have had a degree of success in correlating the observed properties of the various particles, but they are still in the speculative stage, and none has yet become really accepted. An even more fundamental question is whether the correct language is being used to describe elementary particles.   Most of the recent work describes particles in the terms of quantized fields, just as the Schrödinger equation describes the properties of the electron in terms of a field ψ and the Dirac equation provides a generalization of this, together with an extension to a many-particle field.   This language provides a very convenient mathematical description of particle interactions in terms of the interactions of the corresponding *fields,* regarded as the fundamental physical entities.   As one physicist remarked, Shakespeare's comment, "We are such stuff as dreams are made on . . . " might well be paraphrased in the case of quantum field theory, "Fields are the dreams that stuff is made of."   But is this the only possible language for describing particles?   We do not know; no one has yet devised a suitable alternative, but perhaps some day there *will* be a more suitable language.

We have hardly mentioned cosmological questions.   What is the origin of cosmic rays?   What events take place in remote regions of space to produce particles with a million times as much energy as have been produced in the laboratory?   What relevance do these processes have for the understanding of matter as we know it? What relation have they to gravitational effects, which seem to be of no importance for microscopic phenomena but which are clearly of primary importance in celestial and galactic mechanics? Theories of gravitational interactions are still on a somewhat speculative basis; they are much weaker than even the weak interactions described above, and it is exceedingly difficult to perform experiments that provide new empirical data on gravitational interactions. Currently accepted theories of gravitational interactions make use of supposed relationships between gravitational fields and the properties of a non-euclidean space. What implications these have for the structure of elementary particles, if any, we do not know.

In short, the legendary man who resigned his job in the U.S. Patent Office in 1875 because he thought all the important inventions had already been made has no counterpart among present-day physicists. The frontiers of physics are not disappearing; they are changing and expanding. For every phenomenon that is analyzed and understood, a dozen new ones clamor for analysis and understanding.

It does not seem likely that man will ever know everything there is to know about physics. Nevertheless, the quest for new knowledge and new understanding proceeds on an ever-expanding frontier. And this inquiry into the properties and behavior of the physical world, which we call physics, continues and will continue to be one of the most exciting adventures of the human mind.

PROBLEMS

13-1 In the energy-level scheme shown in Fig. 13-1, where would the energy levels for an electron in a hydrogen atom lie?

13-2 An electron and a positron annihilate, with the emission of two photons. Find the energy of each, in Mev, assuming the two particles were initially at rest. What is the photon wavelength?

13-3 An electron and a positron annihilate with the emission of three photons. Show that the photons can have various energies in various events, within a certain range. Find the minimum and maximum photon energies.

13-4 Find the energy threshold for electron-positron pair production in a proton-proton collision, with one proton initially at rest.

$$y' = y$$

$$z' = z$$

$$t' = \frac{t - ux/c^2}{\sqrt{1 - u^2/c^2}} \qquad \text{(B-1)}$$

The time interval Δt between two events occurring at the same space point in S is called a *proper time interval.* The time interval $\Delta t'$ between the same two events, as measured in S', is given by

$$\Delta t' = \frac{\Delta t}{\sqrt{1 - u^2/c^2}} \qquad \text{(B-2)}$$

The effect is sometimes called time dilation or dilatation. Similarly, the distance Δx between two space points at rest in S is called a *proper length* in S. The distance $\Delta x'$ between the same two points, measured simultaneously in S', is given by

$$\Delta x' = \Delta x \sqrt{1 - \frac{u^2}{c^2}} \qquad \text{(B-3)}$$

This relation is sometimes called the Lorentz contraction. Two events that are simultaneous when observed in S are, in general, not simultaneous when observed in S', and conversely. Two events that occur at the same space point in S occur, in general, at different space points in S'.

A particle whose x component of velocity in S' is v' has an x component of velocity v in S given by

$$v = \frac{u + v'}{1 + uv'/c^2} \qquad \text{(B-4)}$$

The momentum $\mathbf{p}$ of a particle is given in terms of its rest mass m and its velocity $\mathbf{v}$ not by the newtonian expression $\mathbf{p} = m\mathbf{v}$ but by

$$\mathbf{p} = \frac{m\mathbf{v}}{\sqrt{1 - v^2/c^2}} \qquad \text{(B-5)}$$

The kinetic energy T of a particle is given in terms of its rest mass and velocity by

$$T = \frac{mc^2}{\sqrt{1 - v^2/c^2}} - mc^2 \qquad \text{(B-6)}$$

This expression suggests the interpretation that mc^2 represents the energy equivalent of the rest mass. The total energy E is then the sum of rest energy and kinetic energy:

$$E = T + mc^2$$

$$= \frac{mc^2}{\sqrt{1 - v^2/c^2}} \tag{B-7}$$

Combining Eqs. (B-5) and (B-7) yields the additional useful relation

$$E^2 = (mc^2)^2 + (pc)^2 \tag{B-8}$$

For a particle having zero rest mass (photon or neutrino) this reduces to

$$E = pc \tag{B-9}$$

The motion of a charged particle with charge q and rest mass m moving in electric and magnetic fields $\mathbf{E}$ and $\mathbf{B}$ is governed by the equation of motion

$$q(\mathbf{E} + \mathbf{v} \times \mathbf{B}) = \frac{d}{dt} \frac{m\mathbf{v}}{\sqrt{1 - v^2/c^2}} \tag{B-10}$$

where $\mathbf{v}$, $\mathbf{E}$, and $\mathbf{B}$ are all measured in the same inertial frame of reference.

THE WAVE FUNCTION $\psi(x)$ corresponding to the wave-number distribution function $A(k) = Ae^{-a^2(k-k_0)^2}$ is given by the integral

$$\psi(x) = \int_{-\infty}^{\infty} Ae^{-a^2(k-k_0)^2}e^{ikx}\,dk \tag{C-1}$$

To evaluate this integral, we first introduce the change of variable $K = k - k_0$ to obtain

$$\psi(x) = \int_{-\infty}^{\infty} Ae^{-a^2K^2}e^{i(k_0+K)x}\,dK$$

$$= Ae^{ik_0x}\int_{-\infty}^{\infty} e^{-(a^2K^2-iKx)}\,dK \tag{C-2}$$

We now complete the square in the exponent in the integrand by adding and subtracting the quantity $x^2/4a^2$, as follows:

$$a^2K^2 - iKx = a^2K^2 - iKx - \frac{x^2}{4a^2} + \frac{x^2}{4a^2}$$

$$= \left(aK - i\frac{x}{2a}\right)^2 + \frac{x^2}{4a^2}$$

$$= a^2\left(K - i\frac{x}{2a^2}\right)^2 + \frac{x^2}{4a^2} \tag{C-3}$$

Introducing this expression into Eq. (C-2) yields

$$\psi(x) = Ae^{ik_0x}\int_{-\infty}^{\infty} e^{-a^2(K-ix/2a^2)^2}e^{-x^2/4a^2}\,dK$$

$$= Ae^{ik_0x}e^{-x^2/4a^2}\int_{-\infty}^{\infty} e^{-a^2(K-ix/2a^2)^2}\,dK \tag{C-4}$$

485

Equation (C-4) is simplified by the further substitution $y = K - ix/2a^2$, which puts it in the form

$$\psi(x) = Ae^{ik_0x}e^{-x^2/4a^2}\int_{-\infty}^{\infty}e^{-a^2y^2}\,dy \tag{C-5}$$

By a bit of mathematical trickery or by inspection of a table of definite integrals, it can be shown that this last integral has the value $\sqrt{\pi}/a$. Thus we finally obtain

$$\psi(x) = \frac{\sqrt{\pi}\,A}{a}e^{ik_0x}e^{-x^2/4a^2} \tag{C-6}$$

A WAVE PACKET is constructed from a superposition of sinusoidal waves of the form $e^{i(kx-\omega t)}$; the most general superposition is written

$$\Psi(x,t) = \int_{-\infty}^{\infty} A(k)e^{i(kx-\omega t)}\, dk \tag{D-1}$$

where the function $A(k)$ specifies the distribution of wave numbers to be used. We consider only wave packets formed by superposing sinusoidal waves with values of k in the vicinity of a central value k_0, in which case the function $A(k)$ is sharply peaked at $k = k_0$, dropping off toward zero on both sides. The angular frequency ω is a function of k. If all sinusoidal waves have the same wave speed u, then $\omega = uk$, and the speed of the wave packet is also u. In general, however, the ratio $\omega/k = u$ is different for different values of k, and so ω is a more complicated function of k. We now calculate the velocity of the envelope of the resulting wave packet, usually called the *group velocity* of the packet.

The key to the calculation is the observation that since $A(k)$ differs significantly from zero only near k_0 it is legitimate to expand the function $\omega(k)$ in a Taylor series about the point $k = k_0$, as follows:

$$\omega(k) = \omega(k_0) + \left(\frac{d\omega}{dk}\right)_{k_0} (k - k_0) + \frac{1}{2!}\left(\frac{d^2\omega}{dk^2}\right)_{k_0} (k - k_0)^2 + \cdots \tag{D-2}$$

In the spirit of this approximation, we retain only the first two terms of the series. Using the abbreviation $\omega(k_0) = \omega_0$, we obtain

$$\omega = \omega_0 + \left(\frac{d\omega}{dk}\right)_{k_0} (k - k_0) \tag{D-3}$$

We now introduce Eq. (D-3) into the exponent of Eq. (D-1) and make a series of rearrangements, adding and subtracting ik_0x, as follows:

$$kx - \omega t = kx - \omega_0 t - \left(\frac{d\omega}{dk}\right)_{k_0} (k - k_0)t$$

$$= (k - k_0)x + k_0x - \omega_0 t - \left(\frac{d\omega}{dk}\right)_{k_0} (k - k_0)t \qquad \text{(D-4)}$$

$$= k_0x - \omega_0 t + (k - k_0)\left[x - \left(\frac{d\omega}{dk}\right)_{k_0} t\right]$$

The exponential function in Eq. (D-1) can now be written

$$e^{i(kx-\omega t)} = e^{i(k_0x-\omega_0 t)}e^{i(k-k_0)[x-(d\omega/dk)_{k_0}t]} \qquad \text{(D-5)}$$

The first factor is independent of k and may be taken outside the integral. Equation (D-1) then becomes

$$\Psi(x,t) = e^{i(k_0x-\omega_0 t)}\int_{-\infty}^{\infty}A(k)e^{i(k-k_0)[x-(d\omega/dt)_{k_0}t]}dk \qquad \text{(D-6)}$$

The factor preceding the integral is a sinusoidal wave with the central wave number k_0 and corresponding frequency ω_0. The integral represents the envelope function, whose speed of propagation is to be identified with the group velocity of the wave packet. The form of Eq. (D-6) shows that the envelope is a superposition of waves each of which contains x and t in the combination

$$x - \left(\frac{d\omega}{dk}\right)_{k_0} t$$

Thus each of these waves, and therefore their superposition, moves with a speed v given by

$$v = \left(\frac{d\omega}{dk}\right)_{k_0} \qquad \text{(D-7)}$$

which establishes this expression as the group velocity of the wave packet.

APPENDIX E *Periodic Table of the Elements*

The number above the symbol of each element is its atomic mass, and that below is its atomic number. The elements whose atomic masses are given in parentheses do not occur in nature, but have been prepared artificially in nuclear reactions. The atomic mass in such a case is the mass number of the most long-lived radioactive isotope of the element.

Period	Group I	Group II											Group III	Group IV	Group V	Group VI	Group VII	Group VIII
1	1.00 H 1																	4.00 He 2
2	6.94 Li 3	9.01 Be 4											10.81 B 5	12.01 C 6	14.01 N 7	16.00 O 8	19.00 F 9	20.18 Ne 10
3	22.99 Na 11	24.31 Mg 12											26.98 Al 13	28.09 Si 14	30.98 P 15	32.07 S 16	35.46 Cl 17	39.94 Ar 18
4	39.10 K 19	40.08 Ca 20	44.96 Sc 21	47.90 Ti 22	50.94 V 23	52.00 Cr 24	54.94 Mn 25	55.85 Fe 26	58.93 Co 27	58.71 Ni 28	63.54 Cu 29	65.37 Zn 30	69.72 Ga 31	72.59 Ge 32	74.92 As 33	78.96 Se 34	79.91 Br 35	83.8 Kr 36
5	85.47 Rb 37	87.66 Sr 38	88.91 Y 39	91.22 Zr 40	92.91 Nb 41	95.94 Mo 42	(99) Tc 43	101.1 Ru 44	102.91 Rh 45	106.4 Pd 46	107.87 Ag 47	112.40 Cd 48	114.82 In 49	118.69 Sn 50	121.75 Sb 51	127.60 Te 52	126.90 I 53	131.30 Xe 54
6	132.91 Cs 55	137.34 Ba 56	* 57–71	178.49 Hf 72	180.95 Ta 73	183.85 W 74	186.2 Re 75	190.2 Os 76	192.2 Ir 77	195.09 Pt 78	197.0 Au 79	200.59 Hg 80	204.37 Tl 81	207.19 Pb 82	208.98 Bi 83	(210) Po 84	(210) At 85	222 Rn 86
7	(223) Fr 87	226.05 Ra 88	† 89–103															

* Rare earths

138.91 La 57	140.12 Ce 58	140.91 Pr 59	144.24 Nd 60	(145) Pm 61	150.35 Sm 62	152.0 Eu 63	157.25 Gd 64	158.92 Tb 65	162.50 Dy 66	164.92 Ho 67	167.26 Er 68	168.93 Tm 69	173.04 Yb 70	174.97 Lu 71

† Actinides

227 Ac 89	232.04 Th 90	231 Pa 91	238.03 U 92	(237) Np 93	(242) Pu 94	(243) Am 95	(247) Cm 96	(249) Bk 97	(251) Cf 98	(254) Es 99	(253) Fm 100	(256) Md 101	(254) No 102	(257) Lw 103

	K	L		M			N				O				P			Q
	1s	2s	2p	3s	3p	3d	4s	4p	4d	4f	5s	5p	5d	5f	6s	6p	6d	7s
1 H	1																	
2 He	2																	
3 Li	2	1																
4 Be	2	2																
5 B	2	2	1															
6 C	2	2	2															
7 N	2	2	3															
8 O	2	2	4															
9 F	2	2	5															
10 Ne	2	2	6															
11 Na	2	2	6	1														
12 Mg	2	2	6	2														
13 Al	2	2	6	2	1													
14 Si	2	2	6	2	2													
15 P	2	2	6	2	3													
16 S	2	2	6	2	4													
17 Cl	2	2	6	2	5													
18 Ar	2	2	6	2	6													
19 K	2	2	6	2	6		1											
20 Ca	2	2	6	2	6		2											
21 Sc	2	2	6	2	6	1	2											
22 Ti	2	2	6	2	6	2	2											
23 V	2	2	6	2	6	3	2											
24 Cr	2	2	6	2	6	5	1											
25 Mn	2	2	6	2	6	5	2											
26 Fe	2	2	6	2	6	6	2											
27 Co	2	2	6	2	6	7	2											
28 Ni	2	2	6	2	6	8	2											
29 Cu	2	2	6	2	6	10	1											
30 Zn	2	2	6	2	6	10	2											
31 Ga	2	2	6	2	6	10	2	1										
32 Ge	2	2	6	2	6	10	2	2										
33 As	2	2	6	2	6	10	2	3										
34 Se	2	2	6	2	6	10	2	4										
35 Br	2	2	6	2	6	10	2	5										
36 Kr	2	2	6	2	6	10	2	6										
37 Rb	2	2	6	2	6	10	2	6			1							
38 Sr	2	2	6	2	6	10	2	6			2							
39 Y	2	2	6	2	6	10	2	6	1		2							
40 Zr	2	2	6	2	6	10	2	6	2		2							
41 Nb	2	2	6	2	6	10	2	6	4		1							
42 Mo	2	2	6	2	6	10	2	6	5		1							
43 Tc	2	2	6	2	6	10	2	6	5		2							
44 Ru	2	2	6	2	6	10	2	6	7		1							
45 Rh	2	2	6	2	6	10	2	6	8		1							
46 Pd	2	2	6	2	6	10	2	6	10									
47 Ag	2	2	6	2	6	10	2	6	10		1							
48 Cd	2	2	6	2	6	10	2	6	10		2							
49 In	2	2	6	2	6	10	2	6	10		2	1						
50 Sn	2	2	6	2	6	10	2	6	10		2	2						
51 Sb	2	2	6	2	6	10	2	6	10		2	3						
52 Te	2	2	6	2	6	10	2	6	10		2	4						

	K	L		M			N				O				P			Q
	1s	2s	2p	3s	3p	3d	4s	4p	4d	4f	5s	5p	5d	5f	6s	6p	6d	7s
53 I	2	2	6	2	6	10	2	6	10		2	5						
54 Xe	2	2	6	2	6	10	2	6	10		2	6						
55 Cs	2	2	6	2	6	10	2	6	10		2	6			1			
56 Ba	2	2	6	2	6	10	2	6	10		2	6			2			
57 La	2	2	6	2	6	10	2	6	10		2	6	1		2			
58 Ce	2	2	6	2	6	10	2	6	10	2	2	6			2			
59 Pr	2	2	6	2	6	10	2	6	10	3	2	6			2			
60 Nd	2	2	6	2	6	10	2	6	10	4	2	6			2			
61 Pm	2	2	6	2	6	10	2	6	10	5	2	6			2			
62 Sm	2	2	6	2	6	10	2	6	10	6	2	6			2			
63 Eu	2	2	6	2	6	10	2	6	10	7	2	6			2			
64 Gd	2	2	6	2	6	10	2	6	10	7	2	6	1		2			
65 Tb	2	2	6	2	6	10	2	6	10	9	2	6			2			
66 Dy	2	2	6	2	6	10	2	6	10	10	2	6			2			
67 Ho	2	2	6	2	6	10	2	6	10	11	2	6			2			
68 Er	2	2	6	2	6	10	2	6	10	12	2	6			2			
69 Tm	2	2	6	2	6	10	2	6	10	13	2	6			2			
70 Yb	2	2	6	2	6	10	2	6	10	14	2	6			2			
71 Lu	2	2	6	2	6	10	2	6	10	14	2	6	1		2			
72 Hf	2	2	6	2	6	10	2	6	10	14	2	6	2		2			
73 Ta	2	2	6	2	6	10	2	6	10	14	2	6	3		2			
74 W	2	2	6	2	6	10	2	6	10	14	2	6	4		2			
75 Re	2	2	6	2	6	10	2	6	10	14	2	6	5		2			
76 Os	2	2	6	2	6	10	2	6	10	14	2	6	6		2			
77 Ir	2	2	6	2	6	10	2	6	10	14	2	6	7		2			
78 Pt	2	2	6	2	6	10	2	6	10	14	2	6	9		1			
79 Au	2	2	6	2	6	10	2	6	10	14	2	6	10		1			
80 Hg	2	2	6	2	6	10	2	6	10	14	2	6	10		2			
81 Tl	2	2	6	2	6	10	2	6	10	14	2	6	10		2	1		
82 Pb	2	2	6	2	6	10	2	6	10	14	2	6	10		2	2		
83 Bi	2	2	6	2	6	10	2	6	10	14	2	6	10		2	3		
84 Po	2	2	6	2	6	10	2	6	10	14	2	6	10		2	4		
85 At	2	2	6	2	6	10	2	6	10	14	2	6	10		2	5		
86 Rn	2	2	6	2	6	10	2	6	10	14	2	6	10		2	6		
87 Fr	2	2	6	2	6	10	2	6	10	14	2	6	10		2	6		1
88 Ra	2	2	6	2	6	10	2	6	10	14	2	6	10		2	6		2
89 Ac	2	2	6	2	6	10	2	6	10	14	2	6	10		2	6	1	2
90 Th	2	2	6	2	6	10	2	6	10	14	2	6	10		2	6	2	2
91 Pa	2	2	6	2	6	10	2	6	10	14	2	6	10	2	2	6	1	2
92 U	2	2	6	2	6	10	2	6	10	14	2	6	10	3	2	6	1	2
93 Np	2	2	6	2	6	10	2	6	10	14	2	6	10	4	2	6	1	2
94 Pu	2	2	6	2	6	10	2	6	10	14	2	6	10	5	2	6	1	2
95 Am	2	2	6	2	6	10	2	6	10	14	2	6	10	6	2	6	1	2
96 Cm	2	2	6	2	6	10	2	6	10	14	2	6	10	7	2	6	1	2
97 Bk	2	2	6	2	6	10	2	6	10	14	2	6	10	8	2	6	1	2
98 Cf	2	2	6	2	6	10	2	6	10	14	2	6	10	10	2	6		2
99 Es	2	2	6	2	6	10	2	6	10	14	2	6	10	11	2	6		2
100 Fm	2	2	6	2	6	10	2	6	10	14	2	6	10	12	2	6		2
101 Md	2	2	6	2	6	10	2	6	10	14	2	6	10	13	2	6		2
102 No	2	2	6	2	6	10	2	6	10	14	2	6	10	14	2	6		2
103 Lw	2	2	6	2	6	10	2	6	10	14	2	6	10	14	2	6	1	2

FOLLOWING IS A demonstration of Stirling's formula, valid for large integers N:

$$\ln N! \cong N \ln N - N \tag{G-1}$$

By definition

$$N! = N(N - 1)(N - 2) \cdots (3)(2)(1) \tag{G-2}$$

and so

$$\ln N! = \ln 1 + \ln 2 + \ln 3 + \cdots \\ + \ln (N - 2) + \ln (N - 1) + \ln N \tag{G-3}$$

Figure G-1 is a plot of $\ln x$ as a function of x. In the figure, $\ln 2$ is simply the rectangular area shown between $x = 1$ and $x = 2$, $\ln 3$ that between $x = 2$ and $x = 3$, and so on. Of course, $\ln 1 = 0$. Thus $\ln 3!$ is the sum of the rectangular areas between $x = 1$ and $x = 3$, and in general $\ln N!$ is the sum of the rectangular areas between $x = 1$ and $x = N$.

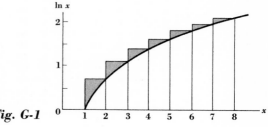

Fig. G-1

This area may be approximated as

$$\int_1^N \ln x \, dx$$

which is less than $\ln N!$ because it does not include the shaded three-cornered areas between the curve and the top of each rectangle. But for very large N this omitted area becomes negligibly small compared with the *total* area, and the *fractional error* in the approximation becomes very small. Thus we have

$$\ln N! \simeq \int_1^N \ln x \, dx$$

$$= \left[x \ln x - x \right]_1^N = N \ln N - N - 1 \tag{G-4}$$

Since the three-cornered areas have a magnitude of the order of unity, omitting the term -1 improves the approximation somewhat, and we obtain

$$\ln N! \cong N \ln N - N \tag{G-5}$$

which is the form of Stirling's approximation used in Chap. 10.

A somewhat more precise approximation[1] is given by

$$\ln N! = (N + \tfrac{1}{2}) \ln N - N + \ln (2\pi)^{1/2} \tag{G-6}$$

This added precision is never needed in statistical mechanics, for which Eq. (G-5) is always sufficient.

---

[1] See, for example, R. Courant, "Differential and Integral Calculus," vol. I, p. 361, Interscience Publishers, Inc., New York, 1937.

THE BASIC PRINCIPLE of magnetic resonance is exactly the same as that of a toy gyroscope such as is shown in Fig. H-1. The action of the gyroscope is familiar; when the flywheel is set into motion with angular momentum $\mathbf{J}$, and the gyroscope is placed in the position shown, it precesses about the vertical axis as shown[1] because of the torque τ exerted on the system by gravity and the upward reaction at the point of support. The direction of this torque is shown in the figure. As newtonian mechanics shows, this torque is equal to the time rate of change of angular momentum, associated with the change in *direction* of the angular-momentum vector $\mathbf{J}$. As the gyroscope precesses, the vector $\mathbf{J}$ describes a circle, as shown in the figure. The angular velocity ω with which the axis changes direction is called the *precession angular velocity*.

To compute ω, we note that in a small time interval Δt the angular momentum changes by an amount given by

$$\Delta \mathbf{J} = \tau \, \Delta t \tag{H-1}$$

This change is associated solely with the component of $\mathbf{J}$ perpendicular to the vertical axis about which the gyroscope precesses, as shown in Fig. H-1b, since the component parallel to this axis is constant. In terms of the angle θ shown in the figure, this component is $\mathbf{J} \sin \theta$. In the interval Δt, the angle $\Delta \phi$ through which the axis direction turns is

---

[1] H. D. Young, "Fundamentals of Mechanics and Heat," sec. 13-4, McGraw-Hill Book Company, New York, 1964.

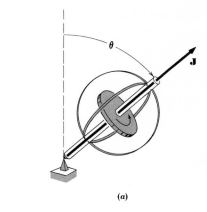

(a)

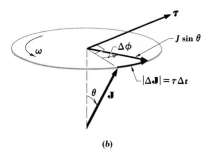

Fig. H-1   (b)

approximately

$$\Delta\phi = \frac{\Delta J}{J \sin \theta} = \frac{\tau \, \Delta t}{J \sin \theta} \tag{H-2}$$

and so the precession angular velocity is given by

$$\omega = \frac{d\phi}{dt} = \frac{\tau}{J \sin \theta} \tag{H-3}$$

where we have taken the limit as $\Delta t \to 0$. In the case of the gyroscope, the torque is proportional to $\sin \theta$, and so the angular velocity is independent of the orientation of the gyroscope.

It may not be obvious what this discussion has to do with nuclear spins. The point is that we may regard a nucleus as a gyroscope. In particular, suppose we impose a magnetic field **B** in the vertical direction; then the field exerts a torque τ on the magnetic moment μ of the nucleus:

$$\tau = \mu \times \mathbf{B} \tag{H-4}$$

The direction of τ is perpendicular to the plane containing μ and **B**, just as the torque on the gyroscope is perpendicular to the plane containing the vertical direction and the gyroscope axis. Under the action of this torque, the direction of the angular momentum (and thus of the magnetic moment) of the nucleus *precesses* around the direction of the magnetic field, just like a gyroscope; again the precession angular velocity is given by Eq. (H-3).

The magnitude of the torque τ is given by

$$\tau = \mu B \sin \theta \tag{H-5}$$

and so the precession angular velocity is

$$\omega = \frac{\mu B}{J} = \gamma B \tag{H-6}$$

which is just the product of the gyromagnetic ratio $\gamma = \mu/J$ of the nucleus and the magnetic field.

This precessional motion cannot be readily observed directly but is made visible by an additional refinement in the experiment. Suppose in addition to the constant vertical magnetic field B we impose an additional field which lies in the horizontal plane and which *rotates* with constant angular velocity. Such a magnetic field can be produced in principle by a rotating permanent magnet, but the same effect can be produced more easily by two coils with perpendicular axes, with currents that are 90° out of phase. If the angular velocity of this rotating field is not the same as that of the precession angular velocity, the relative orientations of the additional torque and the angular momentum will be such as to tend during part of a cycle to tip the axis further up, and at

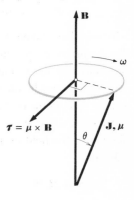

Fig. H-2

other times to tip it further down.   If, however, the angular velocity of
the rotating field is *synchronized* with that of the precession, the result
is a steady torque which tends always to turn the direction of the angular
momentum toward the direction of the magnetic field, or always away
from it, depending on the relative phase of the rotating field and the
precessing angular momentum.   In terms of energy, since the orientation of the magnetic moment with respect to the field is changing, the
associated potential energy changes as work is done by the rotating
magnetic field.   This absorption of energy can be measured as a loss of
energy in the circuits supplying current to the coils that produce the
rotating magnetic field.

Thus one possible procedure is to vary the frequency of the rotating
magnetic field until one observes a strong absorption of energy from
the power supply, indicating that the precession frequency is the same as
that of the rotating field, or, to use the more usual term, the two frequencies are in *resonance*.   Both the frequency and the magnetic field
can be measured very precisely, and so the result is a direct measurement of the gyromagnetic ratio $\gamma = \mu/J$ of the nucleus, from Eq. (H-6).
If the angular momentum, always an integer or half-integer multiple of $\hbar$,
is also known, as from observations of hyperfine splitting of spectrum
lines, the magnetic moment of the nucleus can be obtained.

Nuclear-magnetic-resonance experiments have been the principal
experimental technique for making precise measurements of magnetic
moments of nuclei, which in turn are very important in understanding
nuclear structure.   Conversely, when used with nuclei whose magnetic
moments are known, the method of nuclear magnetic resonance provides
a very precise method of measuring magnetic fields.   This is the basis
of operation of nuclear-magnetic-resonance flux meters.

Although we have used classical mechanics in the analysis of the
precession of the nuclear angular momentum, a correct quantum-
mechanical calculation yields the same result.   The energy associated
with the interaction of the magnetic moment and the magnetic field can
be expressed as

$$E = -\boldsymbol{\mu} \cdot \mathbf{B} \tag{H-7}$$

as already pointed out.   Furthermore, $\boldsymbol{\mu}$ is proportional to the angular
momentum, which has a component $m\hbar$ in the direction of the field,
where m is an integer or a half integer.   Thus the energy levels associated
with the interaction with the field are given by

$$E = -\mu B = -m\gamma\hbar B \tag{H-8}$$

In the quantum-mechanical description of the change in orientation of the angular-momentum axis as a result of the interaction with the rotating field, the component of **J** in the direction of **B** changes in discrete steps $\hbar$, with corresponding discrete energy changes of magnitude

$$\Delta E = \gamma \hbar B \tag{H-9}$$

This energy change is accomplished by the emission or absorption of a quantum of electromagnetic energy of angular frequency $\omega = \gamma B$, which agrees with the frequency of the rotating field given by Eq. (H-6).

Chapter 1

1-1 (b) 5 m/sec in $+x$ direction

(c) $y(x,t) = \dfrac{0.10}{4 + (2x + 10t)^2}$

1-3 (a) $-ukA \cos k(x - ut)$

(b) $kA \cos k(x - ut)$

1-5 (b) 1.0 m

1-7 100 m/sec

1-9 $y(x,t) = 0.1 \sin 2\pi(\frac{1}{2}x - 5t)$

(x, y in meters, t in seconds)

10 m/sec

1-11 $\lambda = 10$ m; $u = 20$ m/sec; $A = 0.05$ m

1-13 0.157 m/sec; 0.0314

1-15 (b) $\dfrac{1 - k}{1 + k}$

1-17 Simple harmonic motion with amplitude $A\sqrt{2}$; uniform circular motion with radius A and angular velocity ω

1-21 $\pm 1, \pm\frac{1}{2} \pm i \dfrac{\sqrt{3}}{2}$

Chapter 2

2-1 (a) 300 m

(b) 3 m

2-3 $B = \frac{1}{2}\mu_0\epsilon_0 r\omega\, E_0 \sin \omega t$

2-5 $\omega = 6.65 \times 10^{18}$ sec^{-1}; displacement current $90°$ ahead

2-7 (a) 3.33×10^{-12} weber/m^2

(b) Much weaker (by the order of 10^{-8})

2-11 1.73×10^{-2} volt/m; 0.577×10^{-10} weber/m^2

2-15 3.33×10^{-6} nt; no

2-17 The order of 4×10^4 volts/m

2-21 1.58

2-23 (a) Plane-polarized in plane of filter; plane-polarized in plane of second filter

(b) $\left(\dfrac{\mu_0}{\epsilon_0}\right)^{1/4} I_0^{1/2}, \frac{1}{2}I_0$

$\left(\dfrac{\mu_0}{\epsilon_0}\right)^{1/4} \left(\dfrac{I_0}{2}\right)^{1/2}, \frac{1}{4}I_0$

2-25 Plane-polarized, perpendicular to wires

2-29 Quarter-wave plate with axes at $45°$ to desired direction of plane polarization; two quarter-wave plates with corresponding axes aligned, or one half-wave plate

2-31 $B_y = \dfrac{E_0}{c} \sin (kx - \omega t)$

$B_z = \dfrac{E_0}{c} \cos (kx - \omega t)$

2-33 (a) 102.8 sec^{-1}

(b) 97.2 sec^{-1}

2-37 $f' = \dfrac{u - v}{u - v'}f$

2-39 $f' = \dfrac{u - v_0}{u - v_s}f;$ when $v_0 = v_s, f' = f$

Chapter 3

3-1 x axis: amplitude $\sqrt{2} \times$ amplitude from either dipole individually; plane-polarized at $45°$ to $x - y$ and $x - z$ planes

y axis: only the dipole along z axis contributes.

z axis: only the dipole along y axis contributes.

3-3 1.74×10^{-5} watt

3-5 (b) $I = 2I_0[1 + \cos (\pi + \pi \sin \theta)]$

3-7 No interference pattern because of perpendicular polarizations

3-9 3.76×10^{-5} m

3-11 $I = I_0 \dfrac{\sin^2 (2\pi \sin \theta)}{\sin^2 (\frac{1}{2}\pi \sin \theta)}$

3-13 $\lambda = 10^{-6}$ m/n $n = 1, 2, 3, \ldots$

$= 10{,}000$ Å, $5{,}000$ Å, $3{,}333$ Å, $\ldots$

3-15 $I = I_0 \dfrac{\sin^2 [N\pi(1 + \sin \theta)/4]}{\sin^2 [\pi(1 + \sin \theta)/4]}$

at $\theta = -\pi/2$, $I = N^2 I_0$

3-17 1,620 Å

3-19 1.88×10^{-4} m; dark

3-21 (a) Dark

(b) Dark: $r_n = R\left[1 - \left(1 - \dfrac{n\lambda}{R}\right)^2\right]^{1/2}$

$\simeq \sqrt{2n\lambda R}$

Bright:

$r_n = R\left\{1 - \left[1 - \dfrac{(n - \frac{1}{2})\lambda}{R}\right]^2\right\}^{1/2}$

$\simeq \sqrt{2(n - \frac{1}{2})\lambda R}$

$R = 30$ cm; $\lambda = 6{,}000$ Å

3-23 (100) planes: $14.5°$, $30°$, $48.6°$

(110) planes: $20.7°$, $45.1°$

(111) planes: $25.7°$, $60°$

3-25 1 cm

3-29 Yes; rotation of polar molecules becomes insignificant at optical frequencies.

3-33 $\dfrac{\omega^4}{(\omega_0{}^2 - \omega^2)^2} \dfrac{e^4 E_0{}^2}{12\pi\epsilon_0 m^2 c^3}$

$\dfrac{e^4 E_0{}^2}{12\pi\epsilon_0 m^2 c^3}$

3-35 10^{-4} mho/m

Chapter 4

4-1 3.75 ft

4-5 36 in. high; bottom edge 33 in. from floor

4-9 (a) 10 cm from mirror; 1 cm; inverted, real

(b) 20 cm behind mirror, 5 cm; erect, virtual

4-13 (a) 30 cm to right; 1.5 cm; inverted, real

(b) 15 cm to left; 3.0 cm; erect, virtual

4-15 Object appears with actual size and location.

4-17 Beam is focused into a line parallel to cylinder axis.

4-21 (a) 3.50 in.

(b) 3.60 in.

4-27 (a) 6 cm

(b) $5X$

Chapter 5

5-1 3×10^{20}; 5×10^6 m

5-3 1.24×10^{-12} m, 2.42×10^{20} sec^{-1}; 1,000 times larger

5-5 (a) 7.09×10^3 m/sec

(b) No

5-7 1 ev, 4×10^{-15} ev sec

($= 6.4 \times 10^{-34}$ joule sec)

5-9 $\Delta\lambda$ is too small compared with λ to be easily observable.

5-11 7.10×10^{-13} m $= 0.00710$ Å; gamma ray

5-13 Because $V(r)$ is zero at infinity, negative for finite r

5-15 1.03 ev, 3.11 ev (in either order)

5-17 10.2 ev; about 0.05% correction

5-19 3.87 m/sec

5-21 $r = 0.529 \times 10^{-10}$ m

$v = 2.19 \times 10^6$ m/sec

$\omega = 4.13 \times 10^{16}$ sec^{-1}

$L = 1.06 \times 10^{-34}$ kg m^2/sec

5-23 Energy levels larger by factor of 4, radii smaller by factor of 2

5-27 (a) 6,130 watts/m^2

(b) 6.13×10^7 watts/m^2

($= 61.3$ watts/mm^2)

5-29 1.63 mm^2; yes

5-31 4,830 Å; blue-green part of visible spectrum

Chapter 6

6-1 (a) 0.0388 ev

(b) 4.6 Å

6-3 4.4×10^{-34} m; no!

6-7 The order of 0.1 ev

6-9 $u = c\sqrt{1 + \dfrac{\mu^2}{k^2}}$

$v = \dfrac{c}{\sqrt{1 + \mu^2/k^2}}$

6-11 $\Psi(x,0) = \dfrac{2A \sin ax}{x} e^{ik_0 x}$

Envelope $= \dfrac{2A \sin ax}{x}$; width $\simeq \dfrac{1}{a}$

6-15 About 5 Å; no

6-17 $\Delta p \simeq 6 \times 10^{-23}$ kg m/sec

6-21 $f(x) = (\text{const})\, e^{\pm i(2ima/h)^{1/2}}$; no

Chapter 7

7-1 0.136

7-3 $\dfrac{1}{2} + \dfrac{1}{\pi} \simeq 0.818$

7-5 8.2 Mev

7-13 $\dfrac{\hbar^{1/2}}{(mk)^{1/4}}$

7-15 $\dfrac{1}{2^{1/2}\pi^{1/4}}$

7-21 0.927×10^{-23} joule m^2/weber; 5.8×10^{-5} ev; three, above, equal to, and below original level

Chapter 8

8-1 41.2 Mev

8-3 $\dfrac{1}{(2a)^{3/2}\pi^{1/2}}$

8-11 Same functional form, with $a = \dfrac{4\pi\epsilon_0 \hbar^2}{2me^2}$

8-15 (a) Adjacent levels separated by 1.16×10^{-4} ev; $4p$ level split into three levels, $3d$ into five
(b) $\Delta E = 0, \pm 1.16 \times 10^{-4}$ ev
(c) $\Delta\lambda = 0, \pm 33.1$ Å

8-21 It is true!

Chapter 9

9-5 Terms in the sums represent numbers of electrons in successive filled subshells.

9-7 Cesium; different degrees of shielding by electrons in inner shells

9-9 Xenon, because it has the smallest ionization potential

9-11 21,800 ev, 4,160 ev; 0.71 Å

9-13 9,920 ev

9-15 < 1.44 Å

9-19 $r_n = \dfrac{4\pi\epsilon_0 n^2 \hbar^2}{(3\sqrt{3}-1)me^2}$

$E_n = -\left(\dfrac{3\sqrt{3}-1}{2}\right)^2 \left(\dfrac{e^2}{4\pi\epsilon_0}\right)^2 \dfrac{m}{n^2\hbar^2}$

9-21 (a) 3.48
(b) 484 nt/m

9-23 Levels for O^{16} larger by factor $(9/8)^{1/2}$

9-25 $\frac{4}{88} \times 10^{-21}$ joule or 0.0304 ev; 4.07×10^{-5} m; wavelength for D_2 double that for H_2

Chapter 10

10-1 $\left(\dfrac{2\,kT}{m}\right)^{1/2}$

10-3 No; the order of 10^{11} °K for hydrogen; yes; higher for more massive atoms

10-7 About 25,000°K

10-11 (a) 5.4×10^{-46} kg m^2
(b) 20

10-15 $2 \rightarrow 1$ line about ⅓ as strong

10-19 $C = \frac{5}{2}R + $ Eq. (10-68)

Chapter 11

11-13 17,000 Å; near infrared; yes

11-15 $T = \dfrac{V}{20k}$ (about 400°K for Ge)

Chapter 12

12-1 2.3×10^{17} kg/m^3; larger by 10^{14}

12-3 2.21×10^{-2} weber/m^2

12-5 $f = 21.2 \times 10^6$ sec^{-1}

12-7 17.8 Mev

12-9 (a) 8.25 Mev
(b) 34.9692 amu

12-11 12.7 Mev

12-13 12,900 years

12-15 In β decay the electron must share energy with a ν.

12-17 2 Mev

12-19 (a) 10 Mev
(b) $f = 15.2 \times 10^6$ sec^{-1}

12-21 0.475×10^{-2} m; yes; energy is greater than mc^2

12-23 7.35×10^{16}

12-25 17.7 Mev; 1.88×10^{14} joules/kg

Chapter 13

13-1 Slightly below $E = mc^2$

13-3 Zero; 0.255 Mev

13-7 4.8 Mev

13-9 2.00 Bev

13-11 108 Mev

13-13 67.5 Mev

13-15 No; impossible to conserve both energy and momentum

Index